MW00635291
NO SMOKING
Robinson
Ransbottom
Pottery
CROWN BRAND
company
Wilson

Additional SanfordS Guides

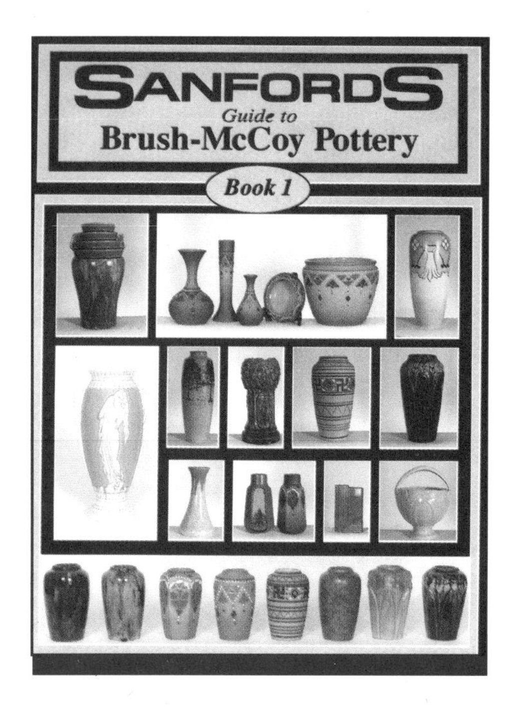

Sanfords Guide to Brush-McCoy Pottery,Book 1
Copyright 1992. Second Printing 1996
$40.00 plus $4.00 postage and handling.
California residents add 8.25% sales tax
ISBN 0-9633531-1-X

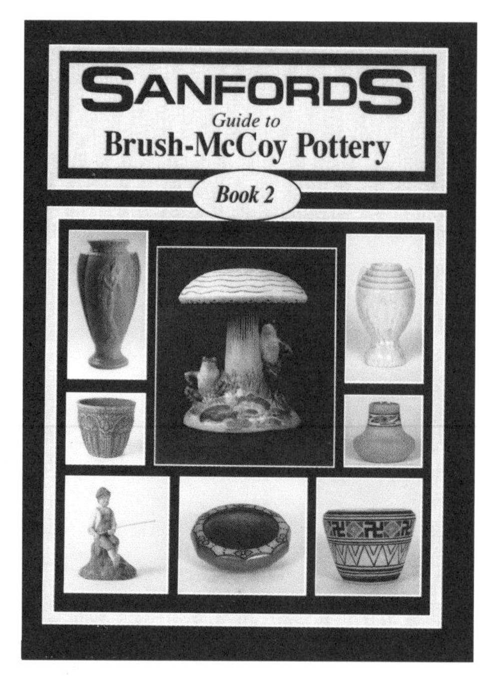

Sanfords Guide to Brush-McCoy Pottery,Book 2
Copyright 1996
$29.95 plus $4.00 postage and handling.
California residents add 8.25% sales tax
ISBN 0-9633531-2-8

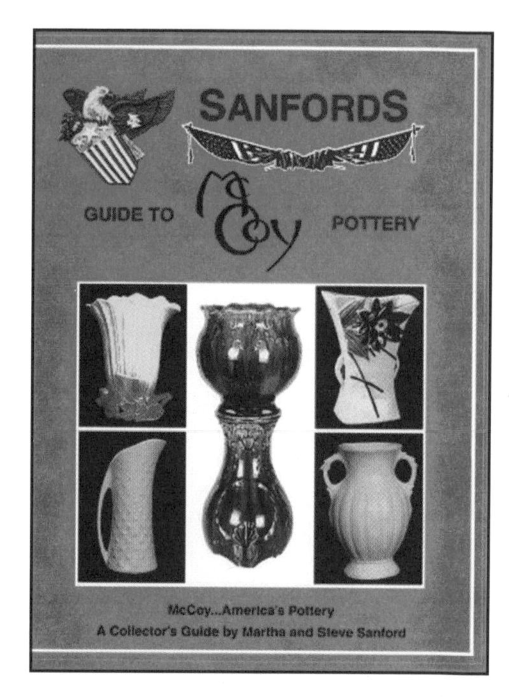

Sanfords Guide to McCoy Pottery
Copyright 1997
$40.00 plus $4.00 postage and handling.
California residents add 8.25% sales tax
ISBN 0-9633531-3-6

Sanfords Guide to Garden City Pottery
Copyright 1999
$25.00 plus $4.00 postage and handling.
California residents add 8.25% sales tax
ISBN 0-9633531-5-2

Sanfords Guide to Nicodemus
Copyright 1998
$25.00 plus $4.00 postage and handling.
California residents add 8.25% sales tax
ISBN 0-9633531-4-4

Sanfords Guide to Peters and Reed Pottery
Copyright 2000
$45.00 plus $4.00 postage and handling.
California residents add 8.25% sales tax
ISBN 0-9633531-6-0

Published by Adelmore Press
Printed in the United States of America

Additional copies of these books may be purchased from your favorite book source or may be ordered from:

Martha and Steve Sanford
230 Harrison Ave.
Campbell, CA 95008
Dealers and clubs should write for quantity discounts

Sanfords Guide to the Robinson-Ransbottom Pottery Company

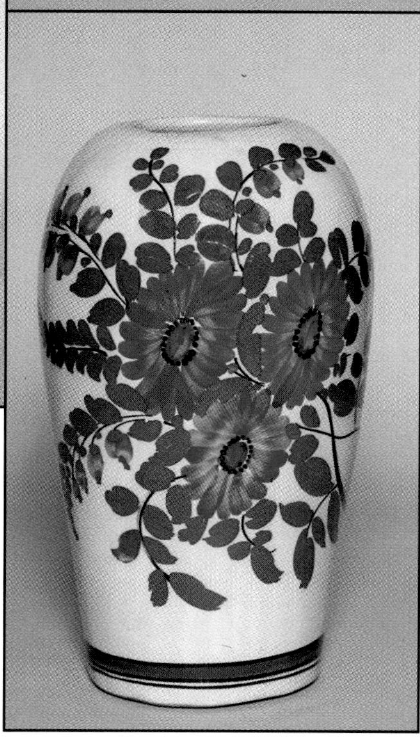

Book by Sharon and Larry Skillman

Production
Steve Sanford
Martha Sanford
Vivian Sanford
Maryann Terhune

Book Design by Diane Senif

About the Authors

The Skillmans

Sharon and Larry Skillman are long-time Robinson Ransbottom Pottery collectors. Larry is Executive Vice President of Robinson Ransbottom Pottery Company and Sharon recently retired after thirty-three years of teaching Ohio school children. Larry has always been a collector, starting with baseball cards, coins and records. He moved to cookie jars, many of which were made by Robinson Ransbottom. He had accumulated over one hundred cookie jars when he met and married Sharon. Together they expanded their collection but with very little information available and only a few catalog sheets to help them, they have identified and acquired a sample of most of the ware produced by the Robinson Ransbottom Pottery Company. They saw the need to share this information; to tell the history of a one-hundred year old company and identify pottery from a company that is known for its crocks and birdbaths but also produced a wide variety of pottery including art pottery.

The Ransbottom Bros. Pottery Co. Plant, Roseville, Ohio.

Table of Contents

Advertising Novelties 9
Animal Feeders 10
Ash Trays 12
Centennial Collection 14
Cookie Jars 16
Crocks and Jugs 24
Figurals 28
Garden Ware • Birdbaths and Pots 30
Garden Ware • Garden Ornaments 32
Garden Ware • Pots and Jars 35
Jardinieres and Pedestals 37
Jars for Umbrellas, Sand & Strawberries 44
Kitchen Ware • Bowls 48
Kitchen Ware • Gala 53
Kitchen Ware • Hot Caramel 54
Kitchen Ware • Kitchenette 55
Kitchen Ware • Modern Apple 56
Kitchen Ware • Pitchers 57
Kitchen Ware • Plymouth Colony 65
Kitchen Ware • Rustic 66
Kitchen Ware • Suburban (AKA Spongeware) 69
Kitchen Ware • Tea Pots 71
Kitchen Ware • Terra 72
Kitchen Ware • Wheat 73
Kitchen Ware • Williamsburg Pioneer 74
Kitchen Ware 75
Lamp Bases 82
Miscellaneous • Desert Dwellers 83
Miscellaneous Pottery 84
Planters • Dish Gardens 86
Planters • Flower Pots 88
Planters • Novelty 90
Rio 95
Vases 96
Vases • Hand painted 104
Vases • Old Colony 120
Vases • Tionesta Art Ware 122
Vases • Victoria 123
1915 Catalog 124
1926 Catalog 130
1931 Catalog 132
Birdbath Catalog 136
Ransbottom Photo Gallery 138
Index 140
Bibliography 142
Contributors 142

The four Ransbottom brothers.

Manufacturing Department.

"Wanna play cards with the Weller Boys tonight."

More historical photos on pages 138-139.

Robinson Ransbottom

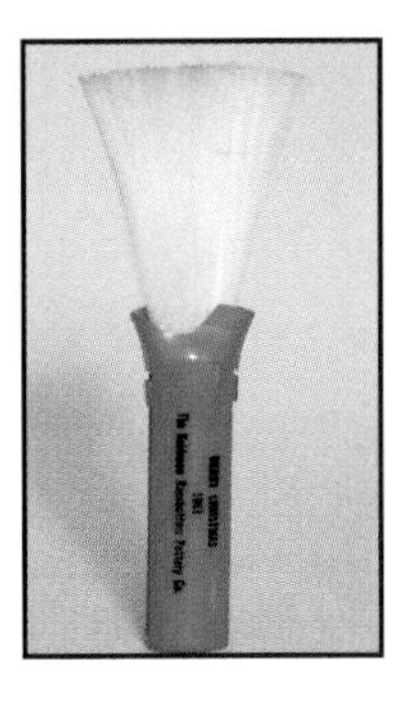
Advertising Novelties
9

Animal Feeders
10

Ashtrays
12

Bird Baths
15, 30

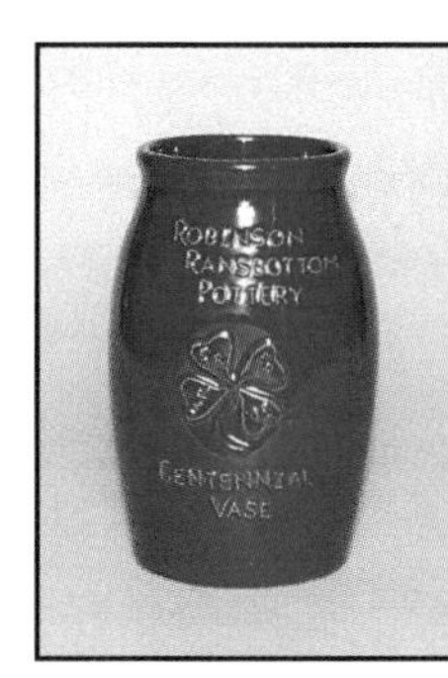

Centennial Collection
14

Cookie Jars
24

Crocks & Jugs
24

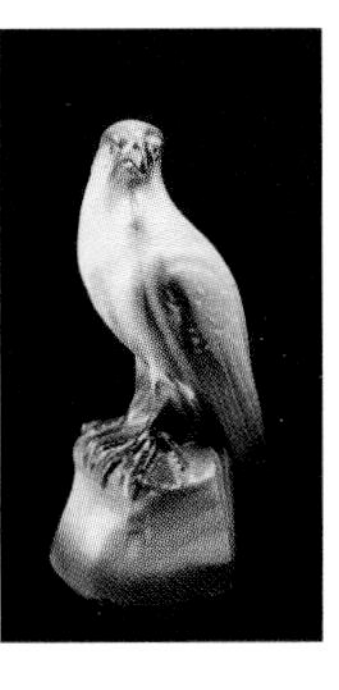
Figurals
28

Garden Ornaments
32

Garden Ware
35

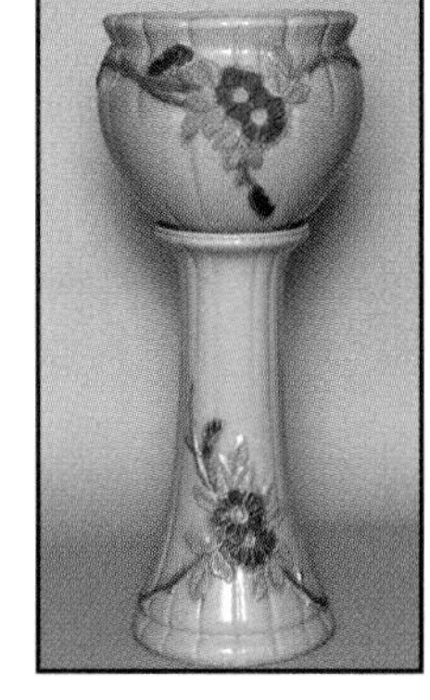
Jardinieres & Pedestals
37

Jardinieres
39, 42

Kitchen Ware Bow
48

Kitchen Ware Brown-Drip
61, 81

Kitchen Ware Confetti
52

Kitchen Ware Early American
76

Kitchen Ware Gala
53

Kitchen Ware Hand Painted
75

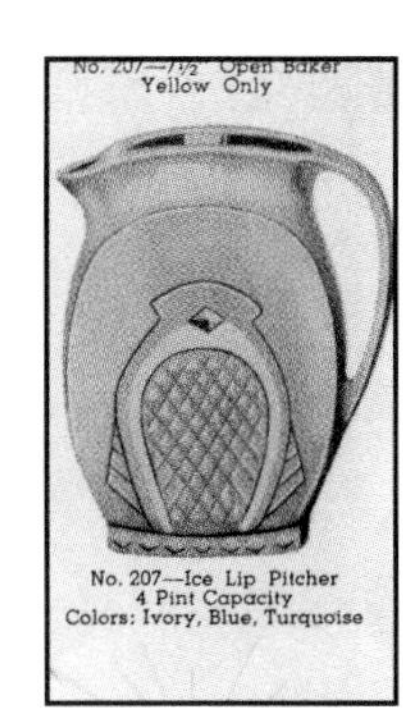

Kitchen Ware Hobnail
57, 61

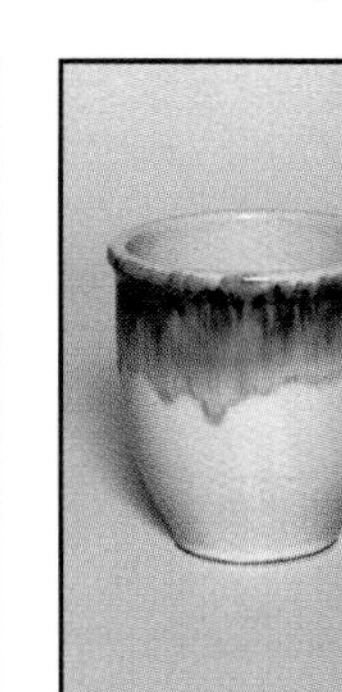
Kitchen War Hot Carame
54

Kitchen Ware Kitchenette
55

Kitchen Ware Modern Apple
56, 82

Kitchen Ware Pitchers
57

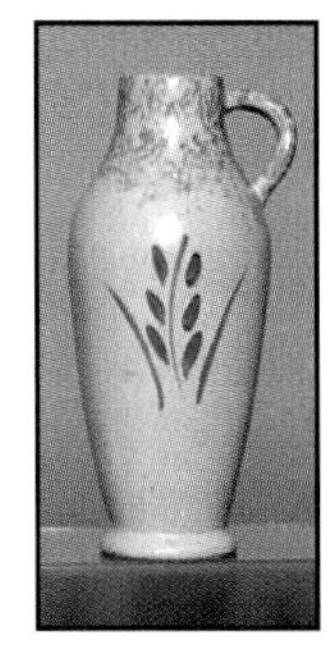
Kitchen Ware Plymouth Colony
65

Kitchen Ware Rustic
67

Kitchen Ware Suburban-Sponge
69

Kitchen Ware Tea Pots
71

Line Finder

Kitchen Ware
Wheat
73

Kitchen Ware
Williamsburg-
Pioneer
74

Lamp Bases
82

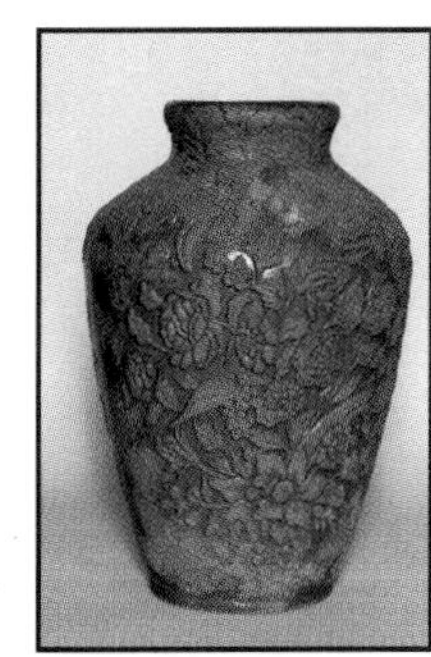

Lucia Jar
107, 117

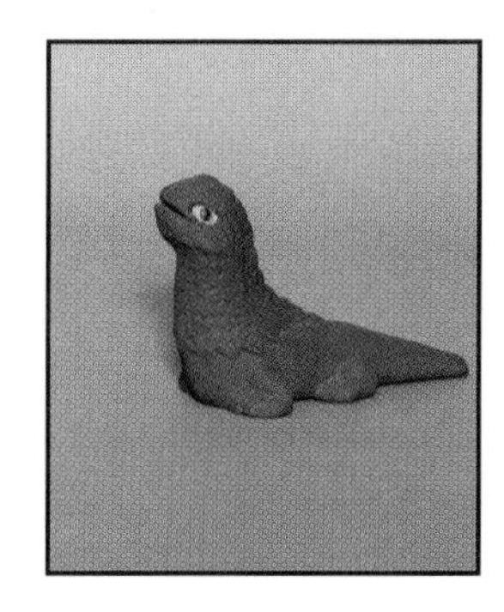

Miscellaneous
Desert Dwellers
83

Miscellaneous
Pottery
84

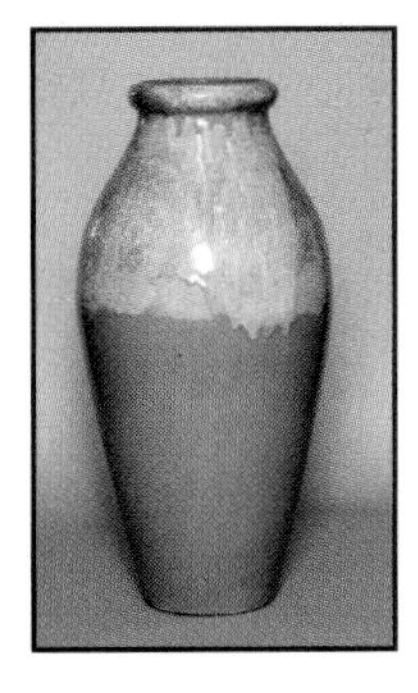

Oil Jars
115

Personalized
Stone Ware
75

Planters
Dish Gardens
86

Planters
Flower Pots
35, 88, 90

Planters
Novelty
90

Rio
95

Sand Jars
44

Snowman
77

Strawberry
Jars
47

Swirl
57

Terra
72

Tionesta
Art Ware
122

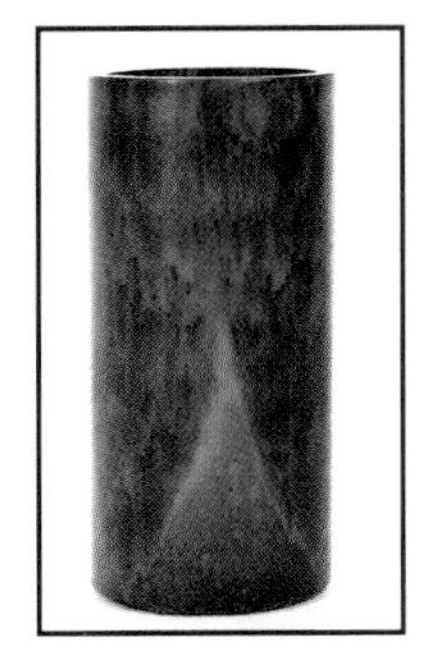

Umbrella Jars
44

Vases
96

Vases
Floor Vases
116

Vases
Hand Painted
104

Vases
Old Colony
120

Victoria
123

Robinson Ransbottom Pottery Company History

The Robinson-Ransbottom Pottery Company represents a pottery dynasty that started before 1900. This pottery dynasty started with a man named Alfred Ransbottom. Alfred was born in 1831 in Delaware County, Ohio. He learned his pottery making skills from John Horr, a farmer who also made pottery. In April of 1858 Alfred married a niece of John Horr's wife, Ruth Goldsmith Wickham. The couple had eight children: William, Almeda (who married William Watt), Jane, Edwin M., Charles W., Francis M., James C. and Morton C. In 1861 or 1862 Alfred enlisted in the Ninety-seventh Regiment, Ohio Volunteer Infantry, and served during the Civil War. For his bravery at the battle of Franklin Tennessee, on November 30, 1864, he was awarded the Congressional Medal of Honor. During his service years, Alfred was injured and became ill. After the war, Alfred returned to Ohio near the town of Nashport. Later the family moved to McLuney, a small town in Perry County, Ohio. Alfred operated Bluebird Potteries on farms in both Perry and Muskingum counties. These two counties were to become the center of the pottery industry in the United States.

Alfred was a master of the art of pottery making and trained all of his sons in this trade. The family moved again to Roseville, Ohio, but Alfred's health continued to decline. He died April 14, 1893.

Francis M. Ransbottom (known as Frank in the pottery business) was born on June 19, 1873 near Roseville, Ohio. Frank was working with his father in the pottery business at the age of fifteen. He learned the trade and worked with his father until he was nineteen years old when he became a salesman for Crooksville Pottery Company. In 1894, Frank married Lizzie May Kackley and they had three children: Ruth, Clare Louise and Esther Mae. By the late 1890's Frank had become one of best jobbers of stoneware and pottery that was produced in the Roseville and Crooksville area, but he lacked the control to produce the type of ware he felt the general public would purchase. He started working toward having his own pottery plant. In 1900 an opportunity that Frank wanted came his way. A brick plant, The Oval Ware and Brick Company, owned by John H. Beem, located in Beem City, was for sale. Frank wasted no time contacting three of his brothers, Edwin (Ed), Charles (Johnie) and Morton (Mort) and persuaded them to join him in owning their own pottery company.

Ed was born in 1868 and married Phoebe Etta Bash in 1889. They had three children: Edna, John Alfred and Mary Kathleen. Johnie was born in 1871 and married Ida M. Smith. They had three children: Charles A., Lawton Edward and Fay. Johnie had turned and jiggered ware in many of the local plants including The Weller Pottery Company. Sam Weller said he considered Johnie Ransbottom the finest ware maker that he had ever seen in his or any other pottery plant. Mort was the youngest of the eight children. He was born in 1878 and married Rose Cunningham in 1899. They had six children: William, Pauline, Paul, Margaret, Frances and James Alfred plus an infant son who died in 1908. Both Mort and Ed had held positions at the Roseville Pottery Company.

After acquiring the Oval Ware and Brick Company in 1900, the Ransbottom brothers had to remodel and repair the building and purchase new equipment. When everything was completed a new business known as The Ransbottom Brothers Pottery was ready. Mort was elected president. Production did not begin until 1901. The company from the beginning used local clays to produce their stoneware body.

Around 1905, the Beem family had sold most of their assets and holdings so a name change was proposed for the community. Bricks had been produced in this area for many years and the bricks contained iron. During the firing process, dark spots would appear in the bricks. These spots were called "ironspots" and this was the name chosen for the community, Ironspot. Roseville, Ohio is the name used for the location of the pottery. Ironspot was too small to be a village by itself so it was considered a suburb of Roseville.

The Ransbottom Brothers Pottery became an instant success. Demand for their products was so great that for a period of about four years, pottery was also produced at the Buckeye Pottery in Saltillo, Ohio that had an additional thirty five workers. Early production consisted of stoneware crocks, preserve jars, churns, milk pans or bowls, flower pots, cuspidors and jardinieres. Stoneware production is measured by the amount of liquid the crocks and jugs can hold and in 1906 this production was 12,000 gallons a day. The plant in Ironspot employed over 100 workers and had a monthly payroll in excess of $6,000.

On January 30, 1907, the four Ransbottom Brothers decided to incorporate the company. At the first meeting, held on February 6, 1907, the name of the company was changed to The Ransbottom Brothers Pottery Company. Mort was elected President, Frank was Secretary and Sales Manager, Ed was General Manager and Johnie was Vice President. The first Board of Directors included J. Walter Ransbottom, the son of William H. Ransbottom, the oldest brother who had died in 1888. Each brother received 24¾ shares of The Ransbottom Brothers Pottery Company stock and J. Walter Ransbottom received one share.

By 1916, production of stoneware jars reached an all time high. The company was producing a (box) carload per working hour. The Ransbottom Brothers Pottery Company had now become the world's largest manufacturer of stoneware jars, a position it still holds today. By 1917 The Ransbottom Brothers Pottery Company added poultry and chicken fountains, fire clay meat roasters, pie plates, stew kettles, salt boxes with covers and a variety of pitchers to their production lines.

In 1917, the first of the four brothers, Charles W. Ransbottom, passed away. On January 6, 1919, at the annual meeting of the board of directors, a discussion was held to consider a proposal by The American Clay Products Company to purchase all of the output of the company for five years with an option for an additional five years. The American Clay Products Company was created to decrease the sales and marketing expenses for each participating company. There would be one catalog that would feature products from all member pottery companies. This created a monopoly in the pottery industry with many local potteries participating. Frank Ransbottom was the President and A.E. Hull was the first Vice President. Other officers were: C.L. Adcock, Second Vice President, Floyd F. Hull, Treasurer, J.G. Burley, Assistant Treasurer and Nelson McCoy, Secretary.

In June of 1919, a newspaper article reported that an interest in The Ransbottom Brothers Pottery Company would be sold to The Robinson Clay Products Company of Akron, Ohio. The entire production of the Roseville and the Akron plants would be sold through The American Clay Products Company. The Ransbottom Brothers Pottery Company was still the largest stoneware plant in the world and The Robinson Clay Products Company of Akron ranked second. This combined affiliation was to continue until 1965.

In 1981 ownership in Robinson-Ransbottom changed hands. The company was purchased by the Brittany Corporation of Cleveland, Ohio.

In the late teens, demand for stoneware jars had started to decline and the company wanted to take steps toward product diversification. The production was shifted from stoneware to gardenware. New items produced were: birdbaths with pedestals, large vases, urns and strawberry jars. In 1920, two new names were added to the Board of Directors for The Ransbottom Brothers Pottery Company: H.B. Manton and John J. Starr. J. Walter Ransbottom was elected Secretary of the company. He held this position until his death in 1936. Edwin M. Ransbottom died in 1923 and his son, John A. Ransbottom succeeded him on the Board of Directors from 1923 until his death in 1955. John also served as Chief Engineer for many years.

At a meeting of the Board of Directors held on June 22, 1923 a motion was made to change the name of the firm to The Ransbottom-Robinson Pottery Company. No action was taken on this motion but on January 14, 1924 at the annual stockholders meeting a motion was made by Frank M. Ransbotton to change the company name to The Robinson-Ransbottom Pottery Company. This name change was approved. The newly elected officers were: Mort C. Ransbottom (President and General Superintendent), John J. Starr (Vice President), Frank M. Ransbottom (Treasurer), J.W. Ransbottom (Secretary). H.B. Manton, Thomas Rockwell and W.E. Robinson were elected as directors.

In 1926 the end came for The American Clay Products Company. There had been many problems over the years and on December 16, 1926 at a special meeting of the Board of Directors of The Robinson-Ransbottom Pottery Company, The American Clay Products Company's liquidation was approved.

In the late 1920's, Robinson-Ransbottom produced their best lines of art ware. The company hired Francesco (Frank) DeDonatis and Sam Celli to hand decorate pottery. These pieces were a complete break from Robinson-Ransbottom's normal production. The pieces were

THE PRESIDENTS

MORT RANSBOTTOM
1900-1942

BILL RANSBOTTOM
1942-1965

J. ALFRED RANSBOTTOM
1965-1977

JACK WOODWARD
1978-1985

PETE PETRATSAS
1985-PRESENT

both jiggered and hand thrown and had large showy flowers hand painted on them, often times covering the piece. Since Frank and Sam had come directly from Castelli, Italy in the Province of Teramo, the pieces they decorated were decidedly Italian. Frank DeDonatis and Sam Celli only worked at Robinson-Ransbottom for a few years. They went on to work for The Weller Pottery Company between 1930 and 1932 where they were asked to create a new line for the Pottery. They designed a number of glossy white pots with underglaze decoration, sometimes called "DeDonatis Wares". This information is contained in the book All About Weller, by Ann Gilbert McDonald. Examples of DeDonatis Wares by Weller can be seen on page 146 of her book and the signature used on page 188. Only one piece produced at Robinson-Ransbottom has been found that bears his signature or mark. Frank DeDonatis worked at Franciscan Ceramics (Gladding-McBean) after leaving Weller.

During those years Robinson-Ransbottom was firing ware in periodic or "beehive" kilns. At one time the pottery had twelve of those kilns in use. Today none remain. The last one was replaced in 2000 with a shuttle kiln. The "beehive" kilns took three days to load, three days to fire and one day to draw or unload. Temperatures in the kiln rose to over 2000 degrees. Each kiln held over 6,000 pieces of ware.

In the late 1920's and early 1930's, Robinson-Ransbottom was producing a line of stoneware animals that included dogs, cats and rabbits. The larger pug dog was for many years thought to be a piece of Weller Pottery, but Robinson-Ransbottom catalogs clearly indicate their ownership of this design.

The depression that began in 1929 affected all of the pottery companies. Robinson-Ransbottom ceased production of all art pottery. The remaining undecorated DeDonatis pieces were finished with a combination of green over either orchid glaze or blue glaze. This stock of pieces consisted of vases, pitchers, jardinieres and pedestals, and floor vases. This production was limited and short lived but produced another unusual line for Robinson-Ransbottom, one that is unmarked and often mis-identified. During the depression, sales fell dramatically but the company did not lay off their workers. Instead, they continued to produce pottery and stockpile it, waiting for better days to come. Most of the stock bins in the plant were filled with ware from the floor to the ceiling. An unrelated industry stepped in with an order that would help the company come through the depression. A leading lead oxide manufacturer asked Robinson-Ransbottom to produce "lead pots□". These were bisque pots with holes in them that were used to produce lead oxide. Production began immediately and many boxcars were filled with lead pots and shipped day after day.

By 1935 Robinson-Ransbottom had installed a tunnel kiln. This kiln was almost 200 feet long and gas fired at temperatures in excess of 2,000 degrees. Each hour a car filled with ware entered the kiln and twenty five hours later it was removed at the other end of the kiln. The first car of ware went through the tunnel kiln on August 24, 1935. The addition of the tunnel kiln allowed Robinson-Ransbottom to broaden its product line.

In 1937 the company began offering "crown"□ ovenware that featured an ovenproof whiteware body. Robinson-Ransbottom could now produce bowls, casseroles, refrigerator jars and custard cups. Many of the bowls were impressed with the Robinson-Ransbottom crown trademark on the bottom of the piece. The crown logo had been used since the 1920's on stoneware jars, jugs and churns. Early pieces made at Robinson-Ransbottom and Ransbottom Brothers were not marked, with the exception of the four leaf clover logo. Some pitchers and water kegs were stamped in blue lettering on the front of the piece: Ransbottom Brothers Pottery Company-Roseville, Ohio.

Frank Ransbottom also died in 1937. The pottery industry had lost one of its true pioneers. Frank had been a close personal and political friend of President Warren G. Harding and had been a guest at the White House. He was also a delegate to the Republican National Convention in 1924. In 1912 President Taft gave a speech at Frank Ransbottom's home in Roseville, Ohio. Frank's dream of having his own pottery business had been fulfilled. He created a company that grew to be the largest stoneware producer in the world and continued a pottery dynasty.

New lines were added in the late thirties. In 1938 the "Rio" and "Kitchenette" lines were first produced. Rio had a "south of the border" look with hand decorating against red or black background. Kitchenette was fired in soft colors with spoons, tea pots and cups in relief design and often carried a foil-covered paper label marked Kitchenette, Pantry Ware, Robinson-Ransbottom, Roseville, Ohio. In 1939 the "Victoria" line was added. At the end of the 1930's and into the 1940's, items were again hand decorated when the company hired Willard Pace and he created "Old Colony" and "Rustic" lines. Willard Pace, along with his father, Luther C. Pace, his cousin, David Pace and David's son Jewett Pace had formed and managed the Pace and Sons Pottery Company in Roseville, Ohio. This company was newly formed when the economics of the depression put it out of business. Willard then joined the J.L. Weaver Pottery Company before coming to Robinson-Ransbottom to manage the artware department, where he stayed until shortly before his death in 1955. Willard Pace developed many art ware lines and decorating patterns for Robinson-Ransbottom. A large number of examples are pictured in this book. He often custom-made pieces and hand decorated dinner ware for friends and relatives. His son, Donald Pace was a sales manager for Robinson-Ransbottom.

The "Old Colony" line was introduced in 1941 and featured vases, console bowls, pitchers, jardinieres and flower pots with attached saucers. Each piece in this line was hand decorated under the glaze. The demand for the "Old Colony" line was so great that the company was unable to keep up with the orders and discontinued the line in 1942.

At the end of 1942 Mort Ransbottom decided to step-down as the President of Robinson-Ransbottom and his oldest son, William (Bill) Ransbottom took over as president of the company. Bill would continue in this position until 1965. When Mort died in 1959, he had served as president of Robinson-Ransbottom for forty-two years and was the last surviving brother of the four founders.

In 1943 in honor of the military men serving in the war, Robinson-Ransbottom produced two new cookie jars: "Jack" the sailor and "Bud" the soldier. A few years earlier the company made two grass-growing heads that they named "Barnacle Bill" the sailor and "Elmer" the doughboy. In 1947 Robinson-Ransbottom introduced the "Zephyrus"□ kitchenware line and pro-

Robinson Ransbottom Pottery Company History

duced it in a rainbow of colors. In 1948 The Weller Pottery Company ceased operations and Robinson-Ransbottom purchased a number of their molds. The two most recognized items are the No. 67 sand jar that was in the Ivory line at Weller Pottery and was originally designed by Rudolph Lorber in 1910 and the No. 421 jardiniere and pedestal that came from one of the lines produced in the late 1930's by Weller. Some of the Weller garden ware planters continue to be produced at Robinson-Ransbottom today. In 1949, to keep up with the pottery market and competition from other pottery companies, Robinson-Ransbottom produced smaller vases and planters, baby planters and love bird planters all in a variety of colors. During the 1950's the company continued to produce sand jars, umbrella jars, oil jars, bird baths and pedestals, feeders and stoneware jars and added some new kitchenware items. The figural cookie jars were produced during this time. Except for the "Bud", "Jack" and "Oscar" cookie jars, all of the cookie jars had been cylinder or ball style. The new figural jars produced were: Hi Diddle Diddle, Hootie Owl, Sheriff Pig, The Chef, The Dutch Boy and Girl, The Chicken, The Whale and Peter, Peter Pumpkin Eater. The last of the figural cookie jars was produced in 1960 with one carry-over to 1961, but that production had come to an end. Figural garden pieces were introduced as were a number of figural bird bath inserts. The "Rustic" line designed by Willard Pace was introduced in 1954, the outer space planter series in 1955 and other novelty planters were added in the 1950's. In 1961 Robinson-Ransbottom began producing kitchen ware items in brown with white overdrip. These pieces are often confused with Hull's "Mirror Brown" or McCoy's "Brown Drip".

In 1962 Robinson-Ransbottom, in an effort to cut production costs, discontinued using the white clay body they had used for twenty-five years on their small planters and kitchen ware items. They started using the stoneware body for all of their production. Stoneware clay has more sand in the mix and results in a heavier, coarser body.

A new glaze treatment was introduced in 1963 in honor of an Ohio hero, John H. Glenn, and his historic space flight in 1962. The glaze was called "Astroglo".

In 1965, The Robinson Clay Product Company sold their interest in Robinson-Ransbottom but remained a distributor for the Ransbottom products. At the end of 1965, Bill Ransbottom decided to retire, his brother James A. Ransbottom replaced him as President.

In 1970, the company introduced the "Plymouth Colony" line of kitchen items. These pieces were hand decorated in blue on a white background, but were only produced one year. The company's first retail shop opened in 1973 near the production plant. The store was named "The Pot Shop" and is still open today. Many new lines were introduced in the 1970's. They included: "Pewter" in 1973, "Pioneer Ware" and "Williamsburg" in 1974, "Apple Ware" in 1978, the "Sponge" line in 1979 and a popular line of hand decorated pitchers, mugs, tall jars, temple jars, Aladdin jars and Lucia jars. Dorothy Archer decorated many of these pieces. Many of these pieces are signed and sometimes numbered. Dorothy was first a decorator at Mary Art (pottery, owned by Mary Ungamah) in Roseville in 1946. She then went to Brush Pottery in 1948, Trevewood Pottery (owned by Ruth Prindle) in 1951 and then to Robinson-Ransbottom where she worked until she retired. Dorothy did not want to sign her work and only did because Alfred Ransbottom insisted she do so. Dorothy also trained another decorator, Sally Guy Henderson. Sally decorated during the 1970's. The signatures found on these hand-decorated pieces can be D.A., D. Archer, Dorothy Archer, or S. G.

In 1977, James A. Ransbottom stepped down as president and was followed by Jack C. Woodward. He remained as president until 1985 when Peter Petratsas was elected to this position. Peter remains president as the Robinson-Ransbottom Pottery Company moves into the twenty-first century. In 100 years of operation, the company has only had five presidents: Mort C. Ransbottom 1900-1942, William Ransbottom 1942-1965, James A. Ransbottom 1965-1977, Jack C. Woodward 1978-1985 and Peter Petratsas 1985-present.

A RAM press was purchased in the late 1980's to improve the production process. Until this date all pieces had been jiggered, cast or made on the spindle press, often referred to as a pot press. The company had discontinued production of red clay pots some years earlier and was purchasing them from other sources. The spindle press was used to produce high and low jars, bowls and animal feeders.

In 1990, the company introduced the "Wheat" line, a hand decorated line that has been very popular and is still produced today. More items sold by the company were being out-sourced: red clay pots and saucers, window boxes, strawberry jars and glazed cylinder pots. The company was still producing stoneware jars, with the fifteen-gallon size the largest. The twenty, thirty and fifty gallon sizes were discontinued about 1972. At the end of the 1990's the eight, ten and fifteen gallons jars were discontinued with five gallon the largest size available.

In 1997, Robinson Ransbottom merged with the Burley Clay Products Company and Roseville Stoneware, manufacturers of stoneware garden accessories that include birdbaths, garden pots and planters, and decorative birds and animals.

Today The Robinson-Ransbottom Pottery Company still uses local clays mined five to ten miles from the plant in Ironspot. Glazes used at Robinson-Ransbottom are lead and cadmium free. The company recycles 100% of the glazes and 90% of the clay they use.

As The Robinson-Ransbottom Pottery Company enters into the twenty-first century and begins the next one-hundred years, the commitment to the vision of the founders remains strong. That vision was for quality, design, workmanship and service. The company is proud of the past and excited about the future.

Ransbottom Party House

The house in this picture just looks like a small cottage, but in the 1930's and 40's this house was the unofficial party house for the owners of Robinson Ransbottom and was a grand house. The house is located adjacent to the plant, was owned by John Ransbottom and was used to entertain visiting VIP's, friends and family. It was beautifully furnished and had a piano, an organ, a full kitchen and a basement. Many wonderful events were held there with lots of singing, piano playing and special meals. Turtle soup was one specialty that was served often. After John's death, the house was rented and was no longer used by the Ransbottoms.

Note the three tiles inset above the door, they are probably AE Tiles.

Advertising Novelties

Robinson Ransbottom hats given to employees for no missed days of work. $5-10 each

RRPC Lighters, 1958. $35-50 each

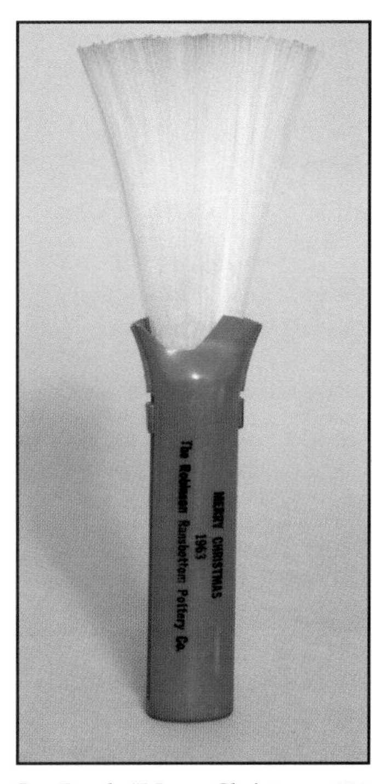

Car Brush "Merry Christmas, 1963, The Robinson Ransbottom Pottery Co." $15-20

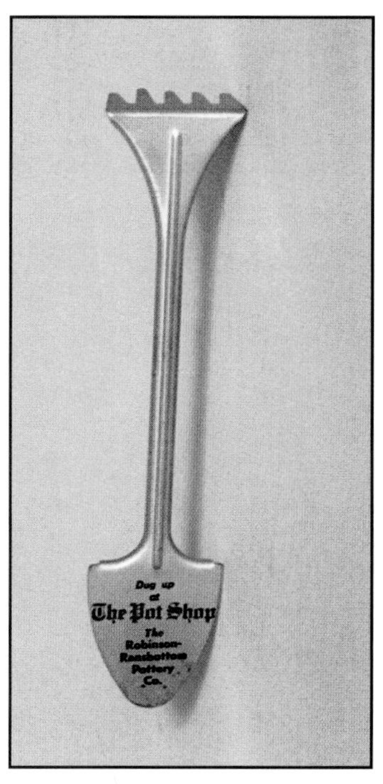

Rake, "Dug up at The Pot Shop. The Robinson Ransbottom Pottery Co." $20-25

Paper weight showing 4 brothers. "The Ransbottom Brothers Pottery Co. The largest manufacturer of Stoneware in the world." 1900-1920. $100-150

"Merry Christmas, 1967. Robinson Ransbottom Pottery Co." $10-15

Knife/Manicure Set, "Merry Christmas, 1974, Robinson Ransbottom." Gift to employees. $15-20

Purple Pennant, 28½" long. Late teens/early 20's. Made by Brown and Co., St. Paul, Minn. $200-225

Spaniel Feeder (water dish), 3½" x 4½", blue, also available in ivory, tan, and light blue glazes. 1949-1950.
$40-50

Chicken Feeder, 10", dish not attached, glazed bottom. 1931-1955.
$40-50

1937 Catalog page

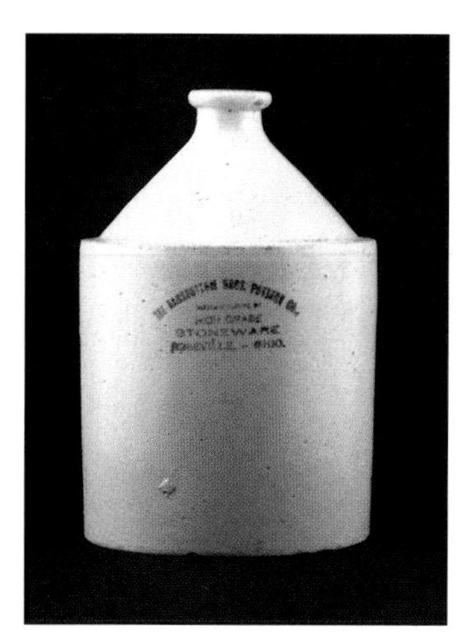

Poultry Water Fountain, "The Ransbottom Brothers Pottery Company, manufacturers of stoneware, Roseville, Ohio. 1908-1920."
$125-150

11" Stoneware Chicken Feeder, detail of ink stamp.

Stoneware Chicken Feeder, 11", detail of back.

Robinson Ransbottom Pottery Co. Roseville, O., Poultry Fountain. Eureka Poultry Fountain and Feeder, "patent app'd for", stamp.
$75-100 each

1943 Catalog page

Detail of above feeders. Late 1920's-1930's.

Animal Feeders

Pet Feeders

Decorated Feeders Packs - 6

30315 5½"
70005 5½"
80005 5½"
30305 5½"
70009 9½"
70007 7½"
30307 7½"
30309 9½"
80009 9½"
80007 7½"

02516 6½"
00346 3½"
02047 7½"
02007 7½"
02015 5½"
02507 7½"
02009 9½"
02505 5½"

24

2000 Catalog page

CROWN POTTERY

Pigeon Nest
Heavy bottom. Unglazed.
8½" and 9" diameter

Spaniel Feeder
4½" and 5¼" top diameter

Rabbit Feeder
Glazed Top.
Sizes 5½" and 7½" diameter

Rabbit Water Jar
Heavy Bottom. Rounded Inside.
6½" diameter

"Kitty" Feeder
5½" diameter

No. 193 Cuspidor
7¼" diameter

Poultry Water Fountain
(With Saucer)
Capacity 1 gallon

Dog Feeder
Sizes 5½" and 7½" diameter

Stone Acid Pitcher
For Factory or Laboratory Use.
Sizes ½ and 1 gallon

Ice Cube or Butter Tub
9½" diameter, 6" tall

Low Ice or Butter Tub
White Glazed, Blue Banded
9½" diameter, 5¾" tall
Capacity 1 gallon

THE ROBINSON-RANSBOTTOM POTTERY CO., MAIN OFFICE AND PLANT, ROSEVILLE, OHIO
AFFILIATED WITH
THE ROBINSON CLAY PRODUCT CO., AKRON, OHIO

R-100

1950 Catalog page

Dog Dishes:

Top Row:	2½" x 7", aqua, glazed bottom, dry foot, no mark.
	2¾" x 7", green, RRPCo USA Roseville O.
	3" x 5½", green, RRPCo USA Roseville O.
Bottom Row:	3" x 6", yellow, glazed bottom, big dry foot, no mark.
	3¾" x 9½", yellow, RRPCo USA Roseville O. 1965-1971.

7" $20-25 5" $15-20 9" $30-35

Pet Feeders, Kitty, Rabbit, unmarked and Dog, various sizes. "Contemporary"

Row 1: $4, $5 Row 2: $5-6, $5 Row 3: $5, $4
Row 4: $6-7, $5-6 Row 5: $7-8, $7-8

No. 406 Cocker Spaniel Ashtrays, $5^{1}/_{2}$" tall, glazed bottoms, 1954.
Left to right: Brown and tan, no mark.
Irridesent and black, RRPCo Roseville, OH, No 406.
Brown and green, RRPCo Roseville, OH, No 406.
These were not pictured in catalogs, referenced only on price sheets.
$65-70 each

Season's Greetings Ashtrays:
2 are $4^{1}/_{4}$"
1 is $4^{3}/_{4}$". 1940's.
$50-60 each

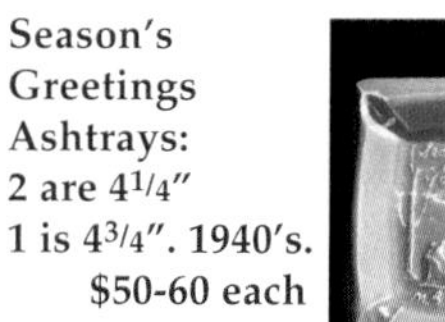
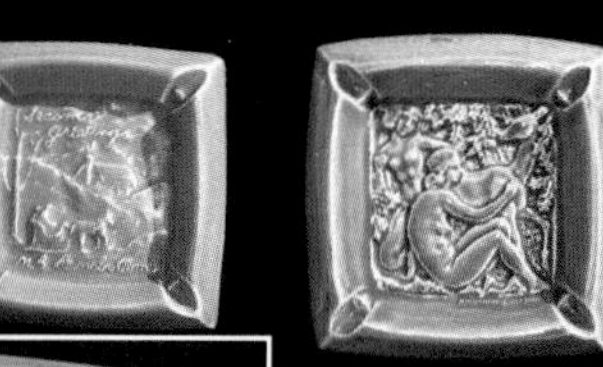

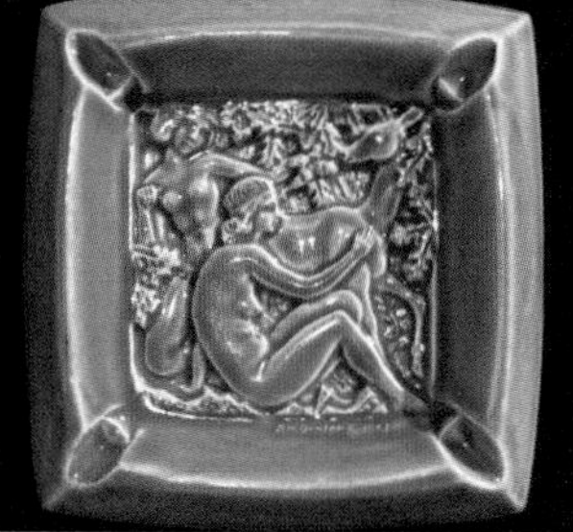

No. 290 Ashtrays, $4^{1}/_{2}$", Made for Robinson Clay Products, Akron. 1950's. $10-15 each

No. 406 Dog Ashtray, brown glazed bottom, 2 holes, RRPCo Roseville, OH, No 406. $5^{1}/_{2}$" tall x $6^{1}/_{2}$". 1954.
$65-70

No. 406 Ashtray with Dog, glazed bottom, RRPCo Roseville, OH, No 406. $5^{1}/_{2}$" tall x 7". Mid 50's.
$65-70

No. 329 Lily Pad Ashtray, $6^{1}/_{2}$" x 6", glazed all over, wiped feet, RRPCo Roseville, Ohio, No 329 impressed. 1941.
$30-35

Top and bottom of $4^{1}/_{2}$" ashtray. 1969. $25-30

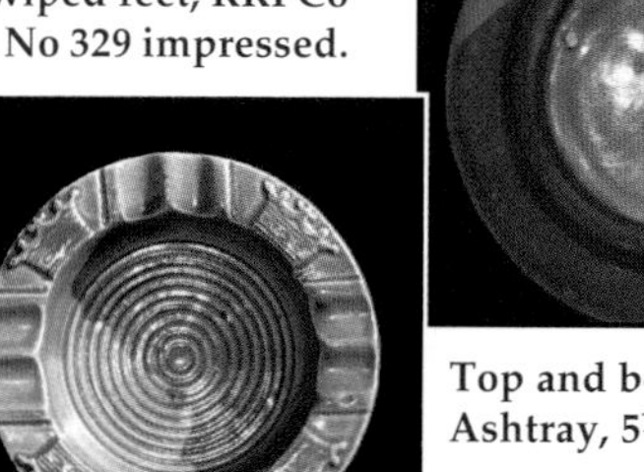
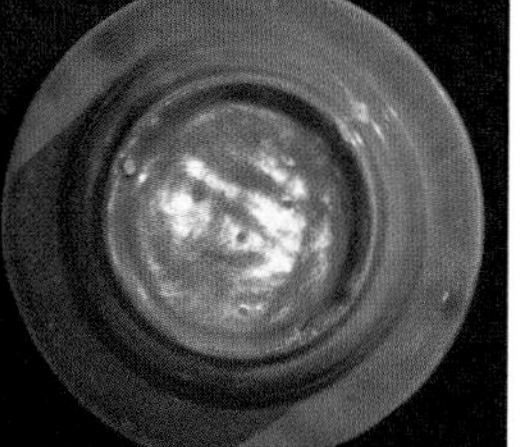

Top and bottom of Crown Ashtray, $5^{1}/_{2}$". $10-15

"Cardette Set" No. 281 Coaster/ash-tray/snack sets, RRPCo Roseville, OH, Pat. Pend., No 281. 1950-1952.
$20-25

#7 Ashtray, $7^{3}/_{4}$" x $5^{3}/_{4}$", RRPCo Roseville, O USA. Early 60's.
$7-10

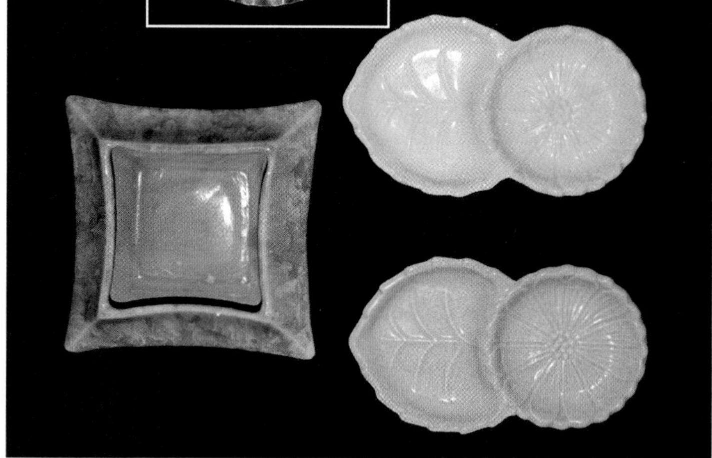

Coasters and ashtrays. 1950's. $15-20 each

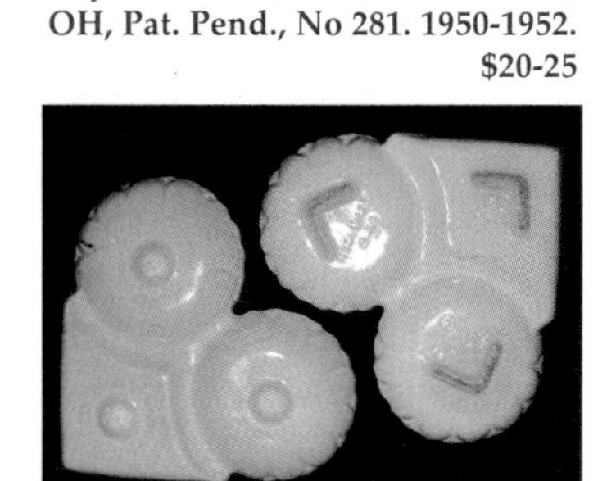

Back of "Cardette Set"

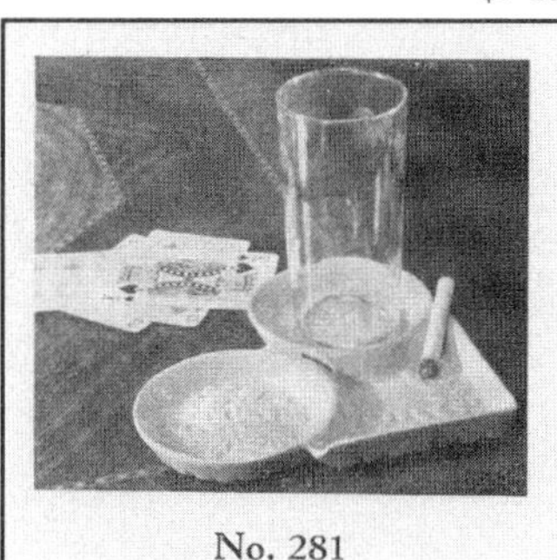

No. 281
Cardette Set
Combination Twin Coasters and Ash Tray. Set consists of two pieces packed in attractive gift box.

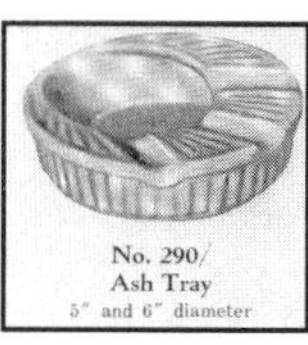

No. 290/
Ash Tray
5" and 6" diameter

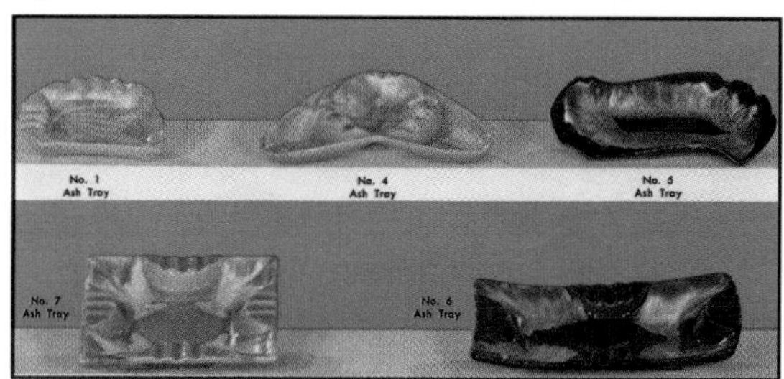

1950 Catalogs left and above. 1961 Catalog right.

Ashtrays

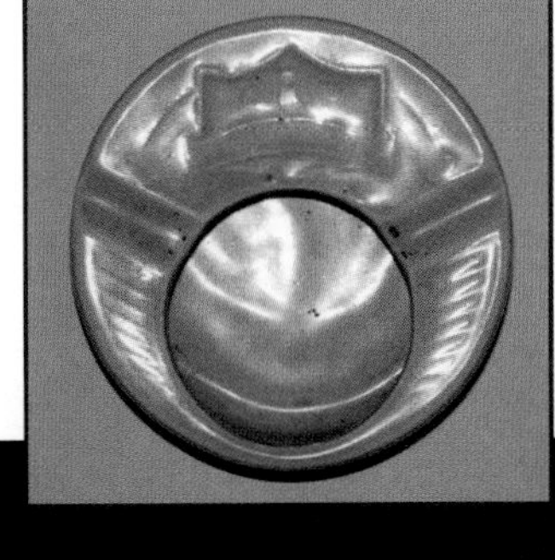

Ashtray, 4$^{1}/_{2}$".
$20-25

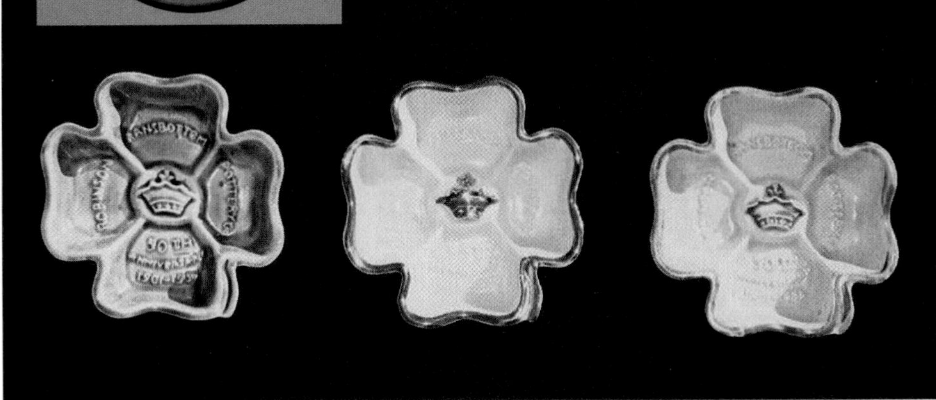

50th year Anniversary pieces: Clover ash trays, 4 feet, glazed bottom, no mark. 1901-1951.
$25-35 each

No. 1

No. 2

No. 3

No. 4

No. 1 No. 5

1960 Catalog page.

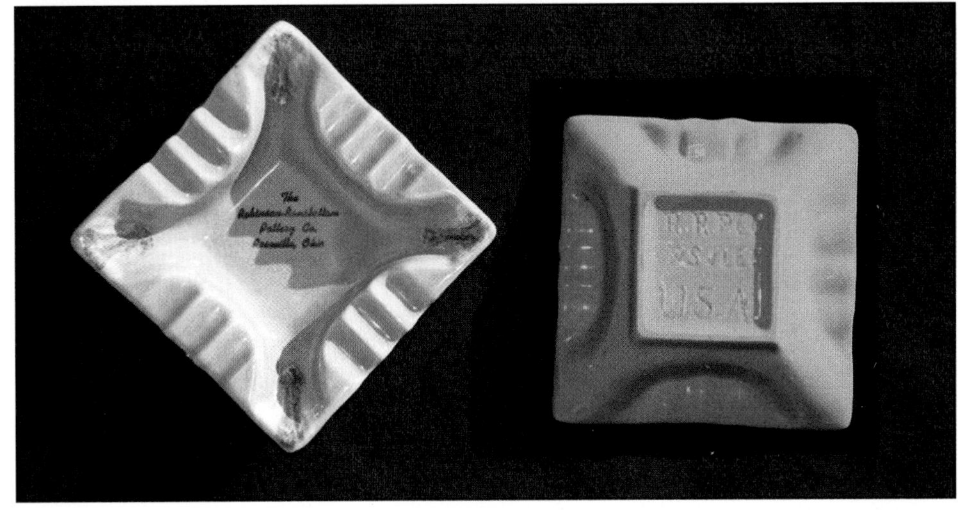

Ashtrays, 5$^{1}/_{4}$", green and yellow. Inside of the green is shown, back of yellow is shown. 1960's.
$20-25 each

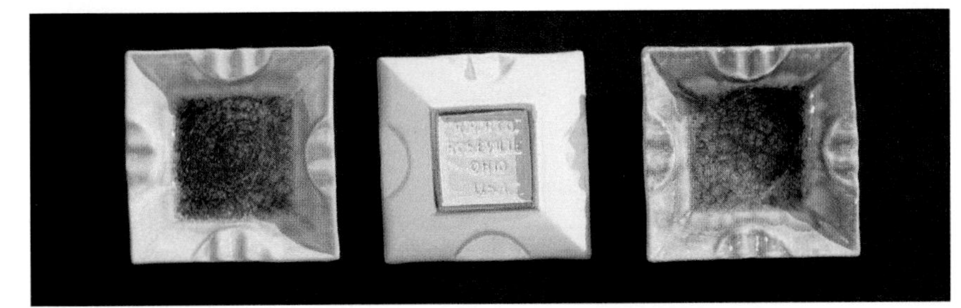

Ashtrays, 6$^{1}/_{2}$". Powdered glass placed in the center before firing. 1960's-1970's.
$10-15 each

Ashtrays, 5$^{1}/_{2}$" . 1950's. $25-35 each

Ashtray, 5$^{1}/_{2}$". Made by RRPCo for Robinson Clay. 1940's.
$20-25 each

2000 Catalog page

Hanging Birdbath, (chain included) with crown in center, Centennial-1900-2000, Ransbottom Pottery, 14" USA Roseville, O. 2000. $27-32

Roseville-Crooksville Pottery Festival Commemorative plate. #7 of 10 made. Four Ransbottom brothers on pie plate. $250-300

Centennial Spirit Jug. $45-50

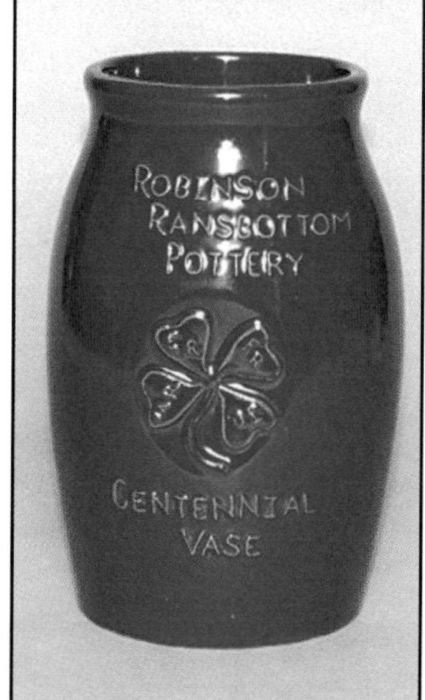

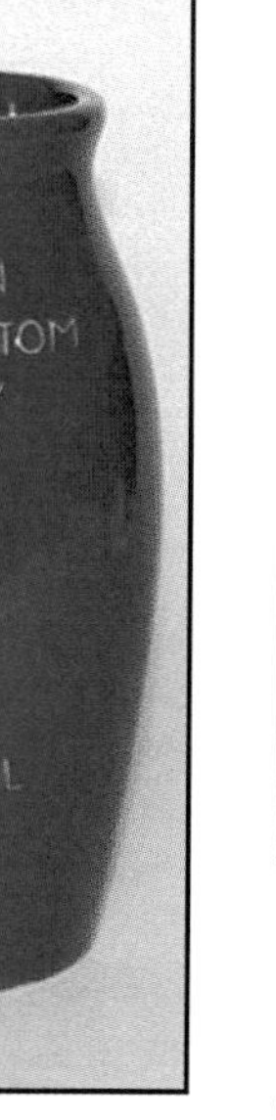

Robinson Ransbottom Pottery Centennial Vase. 2000. $30-35

No. 700 Centennial Ball Cookie Jar, sponge. $35-40

Robinson Ransbottom Pottery Centennial Vase. 2000. $30-35

No. 600 Centennial Ball Cookie Jar, Wheat pattern. $35-40

No. 303 Centennial Ball Cookie Jar, blue stripe. $35-40

Centennial Collection

Centennial Crown Paperweights, $5^{3/4}$" x $3^{1/2}$" $10-15 each
Centennial Crown Plates, 7". 2000. $15-20 each

BAY AREA POTTERY SHOW

TRADE MARK
Robinson - Ransbottom
Pottery Company
Roseville, Ohio

2000 COMMEMORATIVE VASE

Smooth	Ribbed
❑ Green	❑
❑ Midnight Blue	❑
❑ Morning Blue	
❑ Sunset Russet	
❑ Blue Spongeware	
❑ Green Spongeware	
❑ White	
❑ Williamsburg	

Commemorative pieces for The Bay Area Pottery Show, 2000, with box, 3" tall, marked with ink stamp: RRPCO., Roseville, Ohio, BAPS 2000. Flat, unglazed bottom, 30-50 of each color made. Made from the molds used for salesman's samples from 1970's. $25-35 each
Above: box label.

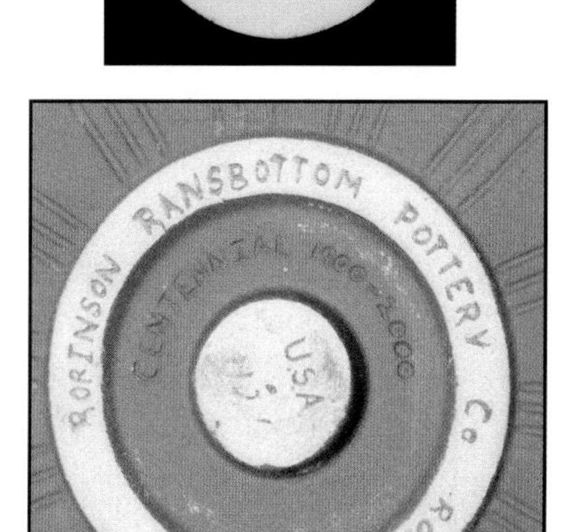

Bottom of Luxor Centennial Bird Bath.

Centennial Bird Bath, $24^{1/2}$", 1946 mold, Nutone. 2000. $40-45

Centennial Bird Bath, $24^{1/2}$", 1946 mold, Luxor finish. 2000. $40-45

Cookie Jar, 9", round with special palm tree decoration by Pace, #350, RRP Roseville, Ohio. Early 1950's. $150-200

Cookie Jar, 9", round with special blue and floral decoration by Pace, no mark, glazed, dry foot. Early 1950's. $150-200

Cookie Jar, 9", round, yellow and red stripes, no mark, glazed, dry foot. 1950's. $25-35

Cookie Jar, 9", round, yellow and brown stripes, no mark, glazed, dry foot. 1950's. $25-35

Cookie Jar, 8", round, footed, with stripes, USA RRPCo Roseville O. 1950's. $25-35

Cookie Jar, 8½", blue and brown sponge with clear glazed bottom, dry foot. 1920-1930's. $100-125

Cookie Jar, 8½", stoneware, with DeDonatis decoration, glazed bottom and dry foot. Late 1920's. $125-150

Cookie Jar, 8½", dark red speckled, unglazed footed bottom. Late 1930's. $30-50

Pair of Stoneware Cookie Jars, Morning Glory decoration: 8½" and 6¾". Late 1920's. Large $125-150 Small $100-125

Cookie Jar, 8", orchid, glazed bottom, dry foot. 1930's. $75-100.

Cookie Jar, 8", stoneware, glazed bottom, no mark. 1928-1929. $125-150.

Cookie Jar, 8", with morning glories painted on front and DANDY-KAKE COOKIES, Krispy-Krust on lid. 1930's. $150-175

Cookie Jar, 9", stoneware with DeDonatis decoration and advertising under the lid: "Star Baking Company. Refill with Happy Home cookies.", glazed bottom with dry foot, 1928-1929. $150-200

1959 Catalog page

Cookie Jars, 12", Hootie (top with gold trim), RRPCo Roseville Ohio, #354. 1954-1959.
With gold trim $150-175
Without $100-125

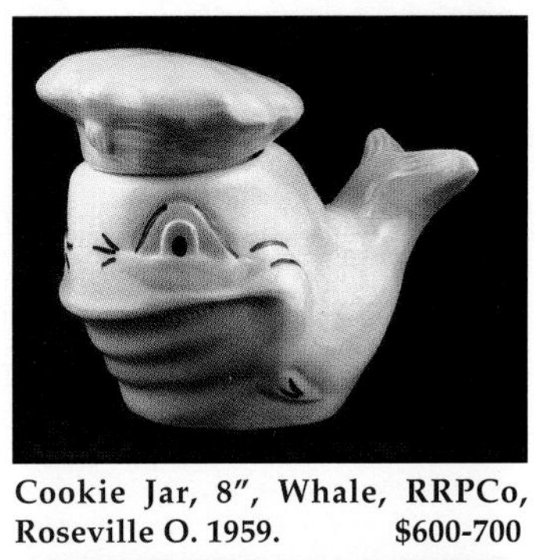

Cookie Jar, 8", Whale, RRPCo, Roseville O. 1959. $600-700

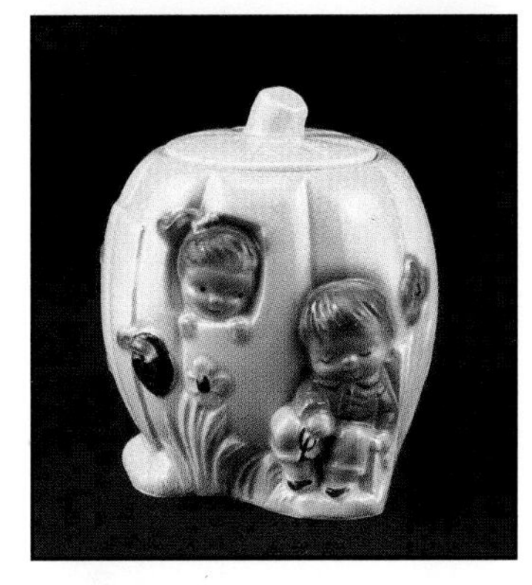

Cookie Jar, 8½", "Peter, Peter, Pumkin Eater", RRPCo Roseville Ohio, No. 1502, USA (raised). 1957-1959. $175-200

Cookie Jar, 8½", stoneware, with DeDonatis decoration, glazed bottom, dry foot. 1928-1929. $150-175

Cookie Jar, 12", Dutch Girl, RRPCo, Roseville Ohio. 1956. $175-200
With gold trim. $250-300

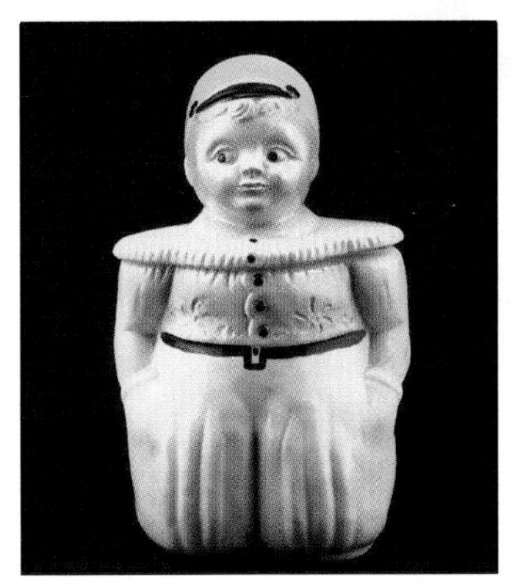

Cookie Jar, 13", Dutch Boy, RRPCo Roseville, Ohio, No. 423. 1956. $175-200
With gold trim. $250-300

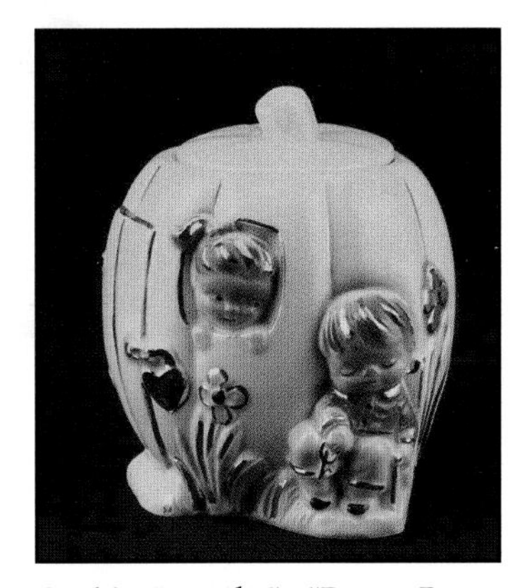

Cookie Jar, 8½", "Peter, Peter, Pumkin Eater", with gold trim. 1957-1959. $225-250

No. 186 Embossed Cookie Jar, 1937-38. $50-60

Cookie Jar, 11", white chicken, RRPCo Roseville O USA. 1958. $125-135

Brown Chicken Cookie Jar. 1958. $100-125

Cookie Jar, 12", "Jocko the Monkey", RRPCo, Roseville O. 1960-1961. $200-250

Sheriff Pig Cookie Jar, 12", no mark, glazed bottom. 1954-1959. $100-125

Pig Bank, same mold as cookie jar, slot on top. 1954. $200-225

Sheriff Pig, showing hat with slot on back. 1954. $200-225

Sheriff Pig Cookie Jar, 12", no mark, glazed bottom. 1954-1959. $100-125

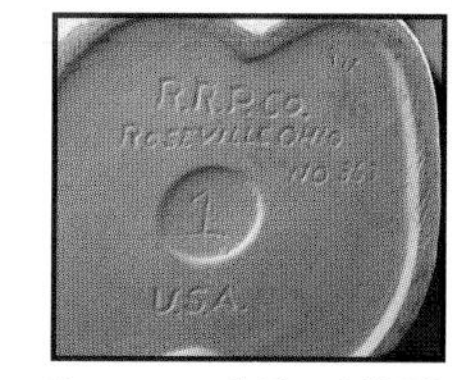

Bottom of Sheriff Pig.

Sheriff Pig Bank, $11^{1/2}$", hand decorated, Kay and Bill on back. 1955. $300-325

Sheriff Pig Bank, $11^{1/2}$", hand decorated, Kay and Bill on back. 1955. $300-325

Sheriff Pig in Stoneware, 10", no hat, RRPCo Roseville, Ohio, No. 363, U.S.A. Circle with 1 inside indent, test piece. $200-225

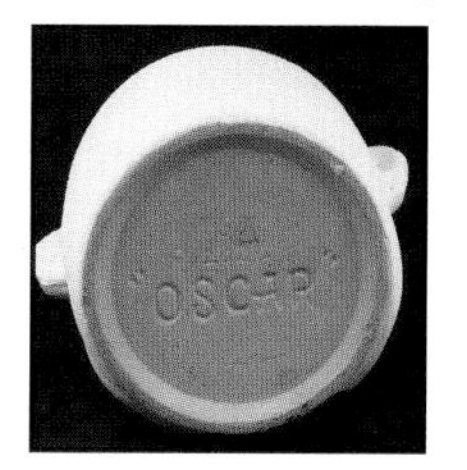

Bottom of Oscar Cookie Jar, 1943-1950, 1955-1957.

"Jack" War Time Cookie Jar, 12", flat unglazed bottom. 1942-1943. $175-200

"Bud" War Time Cookie Jar, 12", flat unglazed bottom. 1942-1943. $150-175

CROWN POTTERY

COOKIE JARS

. . Gay and colorful. There is a wide range of glazed and lacquer background colors from which to choose. Hand decorated of course, and only a few of the decorations are illustrated.

No. 104 Cookie Jar
Assorted Backgrounds and Decorations.
8 Pint Capacity

No. 194 Cookie Jar
Assorted Backgrounds and Decorations.
7 Pint Capacity

No. 203 Cookie Jar
Assorted Backgrounds and Decorations.
7 Pint Capacity

Meet—
"THE BOYS"
Our Newest Cookie Jar Sensation

"BUD"

"JACK"

No. 106 Cookie Jar
Assorted Backgrounds and Decorations.
8 Pint Capacity

"OSCAR"
Children Can't Resist Him
9 Pint Capacity

No. 209 Cookie Jar
Assorted Backgrounds and Decorations.
7 Pint Capacity

● *Please refer to Information Sheet for complete details* ●

1943 Catalog page

Snowman Cookie Jar, 14", R.R.P.Co. Roseville, Ohio, No. 363 USA. 1960. $400-500

Snowman Cookie Jar, 10", stoneware cylinder, stamped Robinson-Ransbottom Roseville, O. 1999. $25-30

Ol' King Cole Cookie Jar, 10½", with red coat, RRPCo Roseville, Ohio. $350-400

Ol' King Cole Cookie Jar, 10½", with yellow coat. $200-225

Cow Jumped Over the Moon Cookie Jar, 11", no mark. 1949, 1957-1959. $125-150

Cow Jumped Over the Moon Cookie Jar, 11", gold trim, no mark. 1949, 1957-1959. $175-200

Chef Cookie Jar, 11", with gold trim, RRPCo Roseville, Ohio, No. 411. $150-175

Chef Cookie Jar, 11", RRPCo Roseville, Ohio, No. 411. 1955-1957. $100-125

Oscar Cookie Jar, 10", green hat, Oscar on bottom. $65-75

Oscar Cookie Jar, 10", red hat, Oscar on bottom. $65-75

Oscar also came with a blue hat. He was made from 1943-1950 and again from 1955-1957.

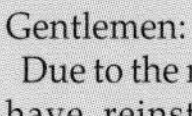

August 20, 1946

Gentlemen:

Due to the renewed heavy demand we have reinstated our No. 202 Oscar Cookie Jar in our production schedule.

This cookie jar of 9 pt. capacity is, as you know, lacquered and decorated and is available with red or green hat. The jar weighs 6 pounds, the list price is $12.00 per dozen less your regular discount. In as much as no cartons are available the Oscar Cookie Jar will be bulk packed, tissue wrapped.

We are now in production and shipment can be made reasonable prompt after receipt of order.

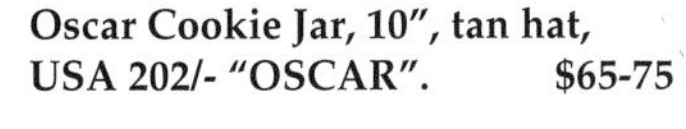

Oscar Cookie Jar, 10", tan hat, USA 202/- "OSCAR". $65-75

CROWN BRAND WARE

LOIS POTS and SAUCERS

DECORATION "U"

DECORATION "T"

HAND DECORATED POTS & SAUCERS

No. 103 COOKIE JAR

No. 104 COOKIE JAR

No. 105 COOKIE JAR

No. 106 COOKIE JAR

No. 108 COOKIE JAR

SNACK JARS

WATER JUGS

No. 841 JARDINIERE

1937 Catalog page

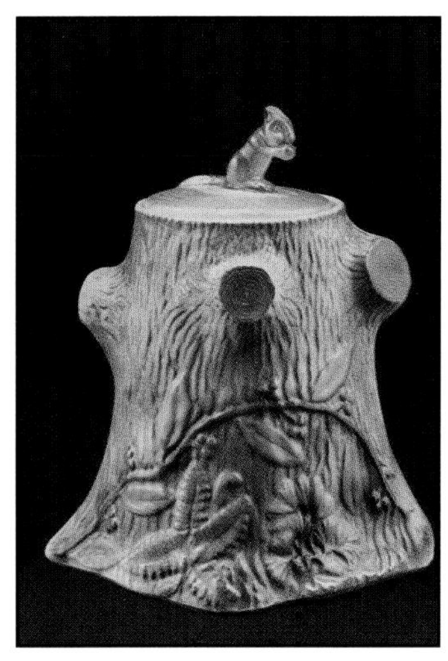
Cookie Jar, 12″ log with squirrel, RRPCo Roseville O. $250-300

"Sample, Take to Bill's Office" bottom of Apple Cookie Jar below.

R.R.P.Co. Roseville U.S.A. Crown impressed.

Cookie Jar, 8½″, crock, (Early American Stoneware). 1965-1972. $25-30

Ball Cookie Jar, 9″, blue and white sponge, RRPCo Roseville O. 1960. $25-30

Apple Cookie Jar, 8½″, with black trim, RRPCo, Roseville Ohio #312. 1949 and 1954-1956. $50-60

Plymouth Colony Cookie Jar, 8″, plain bottom. 1970. $50-60

Cookie Jar, 7½″, cylinder with flower decoration, USA mark. 1940's. $40-50

Old Colony Cookie Jar, 7″ eared cylinder with flowers, hand decorated, glazed bottom, incised PACE (decorator). 1930's-1940's. $60-75

Apple Cookie Jar, 8½″ with gold trim, RRPCo Roseville Ohio, #312. 1949, 1954-1956. $60-70

Cookie Jar, 10″, blue sponge, RRPCo Roseville O. 1960. $30-40

Cookie Jar, 7½″, cylinder, decorated and signed Pace '67, dry bottom. $50-75

Cookie Jar, 10″, circus tigers, RRPCo Roseville Ohio, #386. 1955. $75-100

Apple Cookie Jar, 8½″, RRPCo Roseville Ohio, #312. 1949, 1954-1956. $40-50

Apple Cookie Jar, 8½″ with clear tan glaze. 1970's. $25-30

Cookie Jar, 8″ orange with apples, orange glazed bottom, RRPCo Roseville Ohio, 312. 1970's. $100-125

Cookie Jar, 8½", yellow flowers, signed Pace '67, USA impressed on dry bottom. 1930's. $50-75

Cookie Jar, 8½", red speckled, unglazed footed bottom. Late 30's. $30-40

Cookie Jar, 7½", red ball, USA 512, dry bottom, 1937-1940. $40-50

Cookie Jar, 7½", red speckled 2 handled, plain stoneware bottom, 1930's. $30-40

Cookie Jar, 8½", Santa Claus, with "Merry Christmas to All" in red around top, USA, impressed on dry unglazed bottom. (Special one-of - a kind, hand painted jar for company Christmas parties during the 1960's.) $150-200

Cookie Jar, 9½", red, Mexican decoration, flat, unglazed bottom, USA impressed. 1937-1940. $60-70

Cookie Jar, 8½", red speckled, unglazed footed bottom. Late 1930's. $30-40

Victoria glaze Cookie Jar, 7", red ball, USA, RRPCo Roseville O. 1938-1939. $60-75

Cookie Jar, 7½", no lid, blue speckled, 209/ and (crown impressed). 1941-1948. $25-30

Rio Cookie Jar, 9", with lid, crock bottom, unglazed, cold paint lacquered, glazed inside. 1939. $50-60

Cookie Jar, 10", DeDonatis, blue flower, plain, flat unglazed bottom. 1928-1929. $100-125

Cookie Jar, 10", DeDonatis, blue and orange flowers, plain, flat unglazed bottom. 1928-1929. $100-125

No. 207 Blue Hobnail Cookie Jar. 1941. $65-75

Cookie Jar, 9½", red, plain stoneware bottom. Late 1930's. $40-50

Cookie Jar, 9½", stoneware cylinder with DeDonatis decoration, flat, dry bottom. 1928-1929. $75-100

Cookie Jar, 10", DeDonatis with orange flower, plain, flat unglazed bottom. 1928-1929. $75-100

Cookie Jar, 7", cylinder with flower decoration, "Crown with RRPCo Roseville O, USA" 1950's. $25-30

Cookie Jar, 9½" stoneware with wheat design and sponged top, flat bottom, blue and white. Sample made in 1990's. $30-35

Cookie Jar, 9", Caramel, square ink stamp RRPCo, Roseville, O USA. 1980's. $30-35

Cylinder Cookie Jar, 8½", red speckled with concave dry bottom. Late 1930's. $30-40

Stoneware Cookie Jar, 10", with 'Cookie', blue and white sponge. $35-40

Stoneware Cookie Jar with 'Cookie', tan and blue sponge, rubber stamp on bottom, glazed with dry foot. $25-30

Stoneware Cookie Jar, 9½", hand decorated by Dorothy Archer, clear glazed bottom, dry foot. 1977. $150-200

Green Canister Cookie Jar, 7" with hand painted flowers, crown impressed on plain unglazed bottom, RRPCo Roseville Oh. 1940's-1950's. $25-30

1937 Catalog

1951 Catalog

1950 Catalog

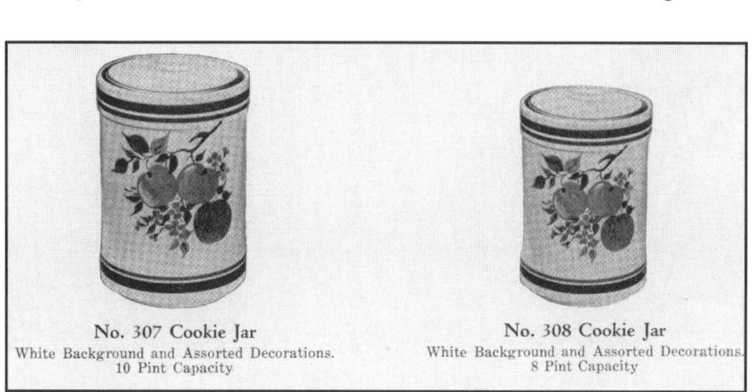

1947 Catalog detail above.

CROWN POTTERY

No. 120
Yellow Bowl
Sizes 5¾", 6¾", 7¾", 8¾", 9½", 12", 14¼" and 15½".

No. 305 Shoulder Bowls
Brown Banded.
Sizes 5", 6", 7", 8", 9", 12" and 14".

No. 194 Cookie Jar
Assorted Backgrounds and Decorations.
7 Pint Capacity

No. 306
Octagon Teapot
Sizes 2, 4 and 6 Cups

Boston Bean Pot
Brown and White Glaze.

No. 307 Cookie Jar
10 Pint Capacity.
Assorted Backgrounds and Decorations.

Steam Table Jars
Solid White Glaze.
Sizes 6½", 8½" and 10½"

"OSCAR"
Children Can't Resist Him
9 Pint Capacity

No. 104 Cookie Jar
Assorted Backgrounds and Decorations.
8 Pint Capacity

THE ROBINSON-RANSBOTTOM POTTERY CO., MAIN OFFICE AND PLANT, ROSEVILLE, OHIO
AFFILIATED WITH
THE ROBINSON CLAY PRODUCT CO., AKRON, OHIO

1949 Catalog page right.

Coffee Jar, 8", blue with yellow bands, decal added, crock bottom, USA impressed. Front and back views. $25-30

No. 386 Cylinder Cookie Jar, 7", with flower decoration, 386 RRPCo, Roseville O, (Rustic). 1954. $60-70

No. 386 Cylinder Cookie Jar, 7", with flower decoration and gold trim, marked 386 RRPCo, Roseville O (Rustic). 1954. $90-110

CROWN POTTERY

No. 103 Cookie Jar
Assorted Decorations
See Price List for Details
1 Gallon Capacity

No. 104 Cookie Jar
Assorted Decorations
See Price List for Details
1 Gallon Capacity

No. 105 Cookie Jar
Assorted Decorations
See Price List for Details
1 Gallon Capacity

No. 106 Cookie Jar
Assorted Decorations
See Price List for Details
1 Gallon Capacity

No. 107 Snack Jar
Lacquered Backgrounds in Solid Colors
Assorted Hand Decorations

No. 108 Cookie Jar
Assorted Decorations
See Price List for Details
1 Gallon Capacity

No. 172-A Ball Cookie Jar
Mexican Decoration
Solid Color Lacquer Backgrounds
Capacity 5 and 8 pints

No. 104-A Cookie Jar
Mexican Decoration
Solid Color Lacquer Backgrounds
Capacity 1 Gallon

No. 172-B Cookie Jar
Sleeping Peon Design
Solid Color Lacquer Backgrounds
Capacity 5 and 8 pint

1937 Catalog page above, 1956 below.

CROWN POTTERY

COOKIE JARS . . . Gay and colorful. There is a wide range of glazed and lacquer background colors from which to choose. Hand decorated of course, and only a few of the decorations are illustrated.

No. 104 Cookie Jar
Assorted Backgrounds and Decorations.
8 Pint Capacity

No. 194 Cookie Jar
Assorted Backgrounds and Decorations.
7 Pint Capacity

No. 203 Cookie Jar
Assorted Backgrounds and Decorations.
7 Pint Capacity

No. 207 Hobnail Cookie Jar
Solid Glaze Colors.
7 Pint Capacity.
(See also Pages 13 and 14 for Other Hobnail Items)

"OSCAR"
Children Can't Resist Him
9 Pint Capacity

No. 209 Cookie Jar
Assorted Backgrounds and Decorations.
7 Pint Capacity

No. 106 Cookie Jar
Assorted Backgrounds and Decorations.
8 Pint Capacity

No. 194 Dutch Boy Cookie Jar
Processed Decoration.
Assorted Colors.
7 Pint Capacity

No. 104-A Cookie Jar
Indian Motif.
Solid Color Lacquer Backgrounds.
8 Pint Capacity

1941 Catalog page

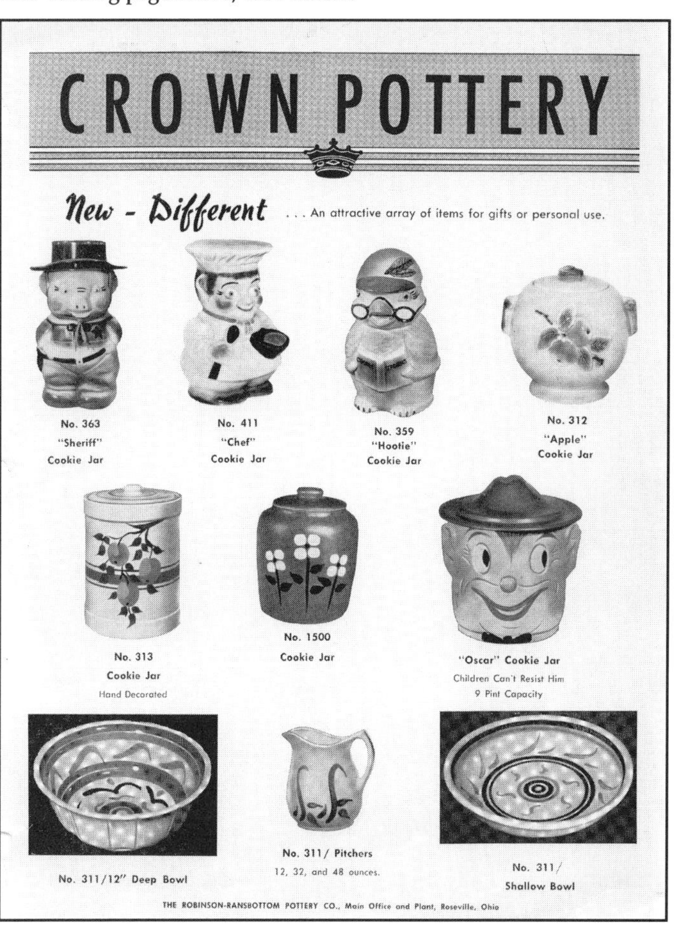

CROWN POTTERY

New - Different . . . An attractive array of items for gifts or personal use.

No. 363
"Sheriff"
Cookie Jar

No. 411
"Chef"
Cookie Jar

No. 359
"Hootie"
Cookie Jar

No. 312
"Apple"
Cookie Jar

No. 313
Cookie Jar
Hand Decorated

No. 1500
Cookie Jar

"Oscar" Cookie Jar
Children Can't Resist Him
9 Pint Capacity

No. 311/12" Deep Bowl

No. 311/ Pitchers
12, 32, and 48 ounces.

No. 311/
Shallow Bowl

THE ROBINSON-RANSBOTTOM POTTERY CO., Main Office and Plant, Roseville, Ohio

Shoulder Jug. $90-100

Crock, 14", 2 gal, with clover, circa 1908-1912. $80-100

Crown Shoulder Jug, 21", 5 gal. 1930's-1940's. $70-80

Shoulder Jug, 12", with advertising. $75-80

Shoulder Jug, 14", 2 gal., crown mark, "Phil Seiden". 1931-1946. $70-80

Jug, 16", clover leaf with a three (gallon). Circa 1908-1912. $100-110

Miniature Jugs, 6". Late 1920's-1930's. "His masters breath" $100-125
Middle, $125-150 "She ain't what she used to be" $100-125

Top Row: Bean Pot, 6", 2 qt. $25-30
Shoulder Jug, 9", 1/2 gallon, marked: R-CP Co Akron, Ohio. (Robinson Clay Products before the merger). $30-40
Bottom Row: Shoulder Jug, 13", 2 gal. $80-100
Shoulder Jug, 14", 2 gal. 1930's. $90-100

Advertising Shoulder Jug, 14", 2 gal. $70-80
Plain Shoulder jug, 16", 3 gal. $40-50
Covered crock, 10 1/2", 2 gal. 1930's. $35-40

The term "Shoulder" was used on bowls and jugs when there was a dry, flat area (no glaze) on the upper area of the piece to allow stacking in the kiln. Thus the name "Shoulder Jugs or Shoulder Bowls."

Advertising Jugs, 14" shoulder jugs, 2 gal 1930's-1940's. Left: $70-80 Right $75-80

Crocks and Jugs

Advertising Jugs:
Top Row: 9", ½ gal. $40-60, $20-40, $40-60
Bottom Row: 11", 2 gal. 1930's-1940's. each $90-100

CROWN POTTERY

Churns and Covers
(White Glazed Inside and Out)
Sizes 2, 3, 4, 5, 6, 8 and 10 gallon.
8 and 10 gallon sizes have ear type handles.
Wooden Dashers shipped if ordered.

Standard High Stoneware Jars
Sold With or Without Covers or Handles
White Glazed Inside and Out
(Sizes 12 to 50 gallons, brown lined)
(Outside Dimensions)

Sizes	High	Diam.	Sizes	High	Diam.
¼ gal.	5"	4⅝"	8 gal.	17½"	13½"
½ gal.	6"	4⅞"	10 gal.	17¾"	15⅓"
1 gal.	7½"	7⅝"	12 gal.	19½"	15½"
1½ gal.	9¾"	7⅝"	15 gal.	21"	18½"
2 gal.	9"	9½"	20 gal.	23"	19"
3 gal.	11"	10½"	25 gal.	22"	21¾"
4 gal.	12¾"	11¼"	30 gal.	24½"	21¾"
5 gal.	13½"	12"	35 gal.	24"	25"
6 gal.	14¾"	13"	40 gal.	26"	25"
			50 gal.	31"	25"

Water Keg and Cover
(With or Without Faucet)
White Glazed, Blue Bands.
Sizes 2, 3, 4, 5, 6, 8, 10 and 12 gallons.

Refrigerator Jar
White Glazed
Enameled Cover.
Sizes 5, 8 and 10 pounds.

Iced Tea or Coffee Keg
(With or Without Faucet)
2¼ gallon capacity.

Standard Low Stoneware Jars
Sold With or Without Covers
White Glazed Inside and Out
(Sizes 12 to 30 gallons, brown lined)
(Outside Dimensions)

Sizes		High	Diam.	Sizes	High	Diam.
¼ gal.	1 lb.	3"	4½"	5 gal.	11½"	13½"
⅓ gal.	2 lb.	3¾"	5¾"	6 gal.	11¾"	15½"
⅜ gal.	3 lb.	4¾"	5¾"	8 gal.	12¾"	15½"
½ gal.	5 lb.	4½"	7¾"	10 gal.	13¾"	16½"
1 gal.	10 lb.	5½"	9½"	12 gal.	13¼"	19"
1½ gal.	15 lb.	7"	9½"	15 gal.	13¾"	21¾"
2 gal.	20 lb.	7¼"	10½"	20 gal.	17½"	21¾"
3 gal.	30 lb.	8¾"	11¼"	25 gal.	16½"	25"
4 gal.		10"	13½"	30 gal.	20½"	25"

Handy Handled Preserve Jar and Cover
Sizes ¼, ½, 1 and 1½ gallon have no handles.
Sizes 2, 3, 4, 5 and 6 gallon have bailed handles.

JARS WITH FAUCET HOLES:
Sizes 6 gallons and upwards, are stocked with 1¼" holes. Any size and type of jar can be made up to individual specification.

Shoulder Jugs
Sizes ¼, ½, 1, 2, 3, 4, 5, 6 gallons.

● *Please refer to Information Sheet for complete details* ●

1940 Catalog page

Water Jug, 10" $35-40
Mug 4" $5-10

Both marked RRPCo, Roseville O. 1960's.

Jug, 20", with "4" in crown. 1930's. $60-70

Jug, 8½", brown, RRPCo USA, Roseville, O, Pioneerware. 1970's. $15-20

Water Keg, 13½", marked Ransbottom Bros, flat crock bottom. 1910. $200-250

Early Robinson Clay Products Water Jar, 14". $250-300

Advertising Crocks: Top: 9¾" Pickle Crock. $45-55
Shoulder Jug, 12", 1 gal. $50-75

Bottom: Jugs, 12", 1 gal. 1930's-1940's. Plain $30-35
With advertising $50-75

Water Keg, 13½", older style lid, crown with 2, no mark, flat unglazed bottom. 1960's-1970's. $65-75

Water Keg, 20" x 12½". "Crown", flat unglazed bottom. $125-175

THE ROBINSON-RANSBOTTOM POTTERY COMPANY — Roseville, Ohio, U.S.A.

LOW BUTTERS

HANDY HANDLED AND STANDARD JAR

PRESERVE JARS

SHOULDER JUGS

CHURNS

MILK PANS

RAGLAZE WATER JARS

FRENCH PANS

WATER KEGS

DUTCH POTS

1931 Catalog page

Old Stoneware: All 1930's.
Top Row: Butter Crock, 4". $125-150
Casserole, 3$^{3/4}$", green bottom with crown. $75-85
Butter Crock, 4", raglaze. $175-200

Bottom Row: Butter Crock, 5". $175-200
Crock, 6". $125-130
Butter Crock, 5", raglaze. Knobs have clover leaf on dome. $225-250

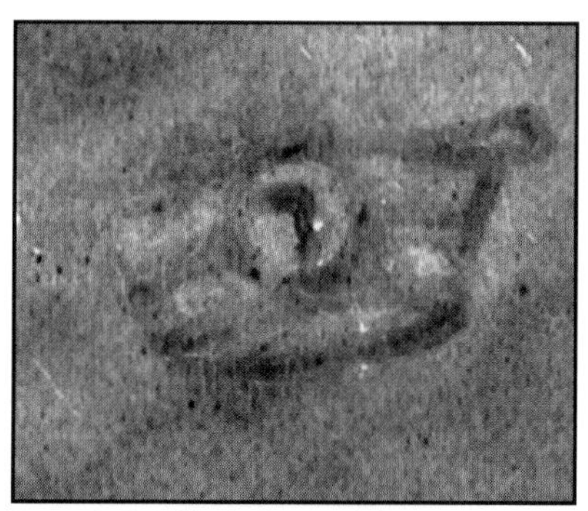

Bottom detail of top row center.

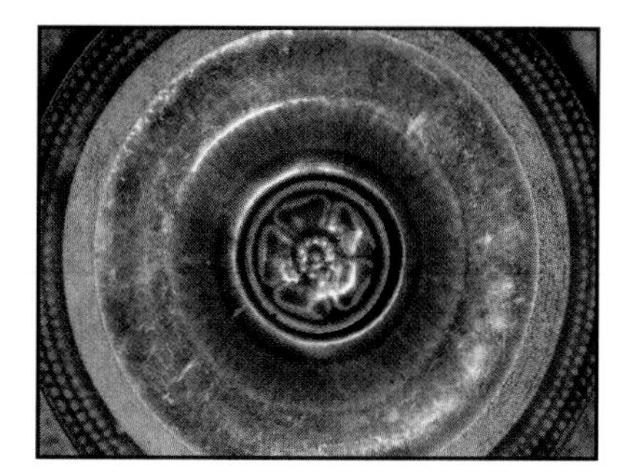

Top view of lid, bottom row center.

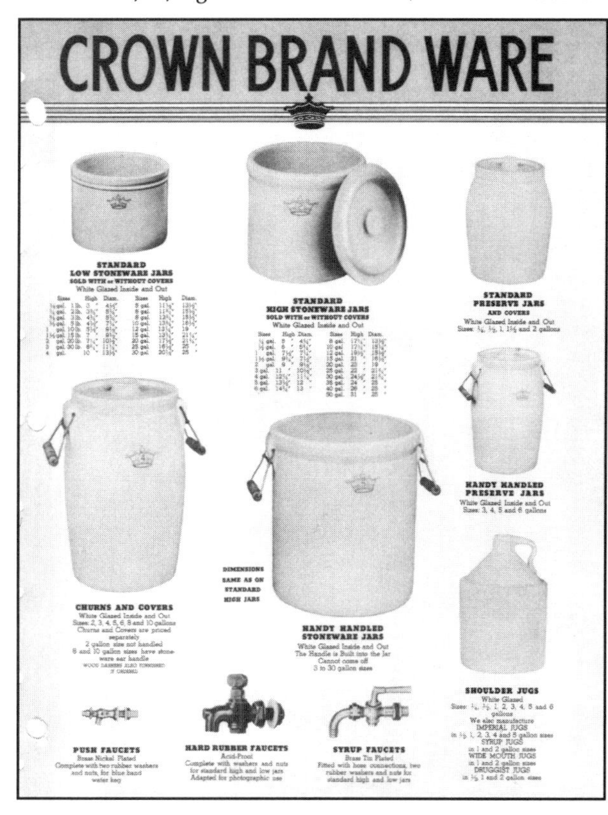

1937 Catalog

1947 Catalog

Water Jar with lid, 13$^{1/2}$", ivory with green, with stag, fawn and pine trees decoration, flat bottom. 1930's. $800-1,000

Iced Tea or Coffee Jar, 13", blue glazed bottom, dry foot, no mark. (Also made with ivory glaze). 1938-1953. $125-150

Crock, 11" with 5$^{1/2}$" opening. Raglaze. $30-35

Bread Jar, 10" orchid glaze. 1930's. $800-900

Crocks: 1 gal, 8", no mark. $25-30
3 gal, 11", marked USA 3 GAL. $40-50
2 gal crock, 9", no mark, late 1990's. $35-40

Churn, 4 gal, 15 1/2" with wooden handle, clover mark. Circa 1910. $125-150

Advertising Crock, 6" crock, plain unglazed bottom. $50-75

Blue and white crock. Ransbottom Brothers Pottery, Teens. $75-100

Decorated Crock, 20", square ink stamp, RRPCo Roseville O USA, "Honey". 1980's. $30-35

Crock, 5 1/2", Crown refrigerator jar, mauve, flat stoneware bottom, tin lid with crown trademark. 1928-1931, 1945. $75-100

Crock with lid, 32" x 25", 50 gal., crown mark on outside. $250-300

Crown mark detail from 20 gal. crock.

RAGLAZE Bread Jar, 10", with lid, flat crock bottom. 1928-1931. $1,000-1,200

Crock, 20 1/2", clover ink stamp with a 4 (gallon). Circa 1908-1912. $100-120

Meat Tubs: Clover, 9", 2 gal. Circa 1908-1912. $65-75
Crown, 10", 3 gal. 1920's-1930's. $50-60
Clover, 13", 6 gal. Circa 1908-1912. $125-150

Lion, 14"x 5½", blue and green (pewter) glaze, appeared on cover of 1973 catalog, no mark. $30-40
Elephants, 11" x 9" tall, one with "Nixon 72" on back, gray and pewter, 1972-1973. $30-35

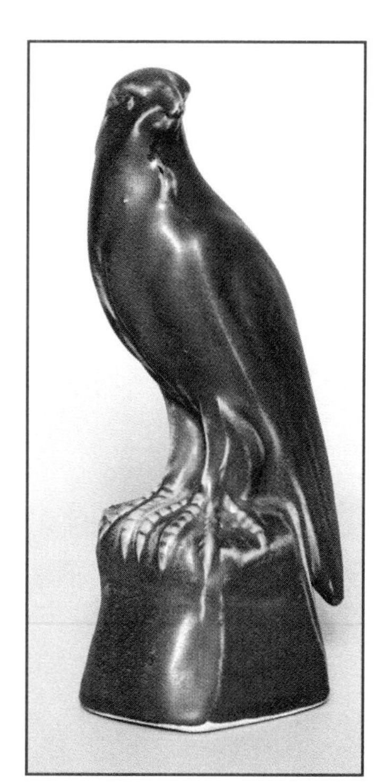

Brown Eagle, 11". 1931. $100-150
Green Eagle, 10", no marks, open bottoms. 1970's. $50-60
Green is smaller because company had to make new molds from the brown one.

Left: Eagle, 10½", green with black over, open bottom, no mark. 1931. $100-150

Duck, 9½", rare, open bottom, no mark. 1931. $250-300

Pieces of 'The Cow Jumped Over the Moon', 4" moon, 6" cow, 5½" cat. 3 piece set: $150-200

Elephants, 11" x 9" tall, light blue and bronze, 1972-1973. $30-35

Airdale, 6½", grey and brown with good detail. 1931. $175-200

Pekinese, 6¾", in green gloss glaze, large hole, no glaze on bottom. 1931. $150-175

Top Row: Dachsund, 5" $125-150
Black and cream Pekinese, 7" $150-175
Rust and cream Pekinese, 7" $150-175

Bottom Row: Bulldogs, 6½", rust and cream with diamond and stripe on head. $100-125 each

All gloss glazed (also came in matt finish), flat unglazed bottoms with large circular opening. 1931.

Glazed Pug dog, 14" x 12" tall, unusual glaze, original eyes puttied in. 1931. $2,000-2,500

Dog. $1,500-2,000

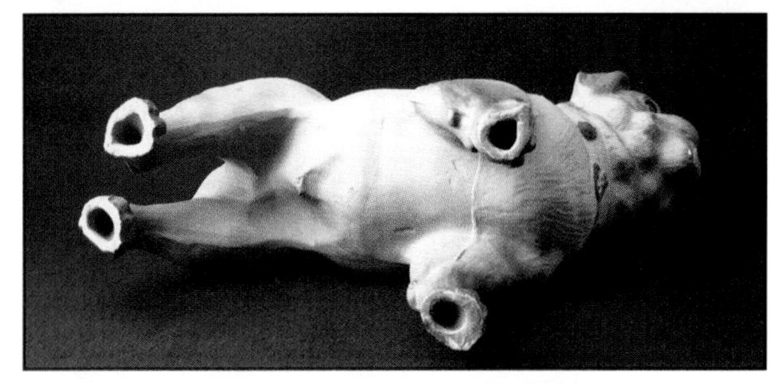

Top Row: Airdale, 3¾" (1945-1946), completely open on bottom. $35-40
Cats, 6", brown, rust, (note how detail makes appearance different), green. $150-175 each
Bottom Row: Airdales, cream, rust and green with drip glaze on chin. 1931. $175-200 each

Various glazes, 12" $1,500-2,000 each

CROWN BRAND WARE

No. 104 MIXING BOWL
Ivory Glaze
With three blue bands
Size 5" to 10"

No. 154 HANGING BASKET
WITH CHAIN
Jade, Maroon and White
8" diameter

No. 149 BULB BOWL
Maroon, Green and White
6½" diameter

No. 103 MIXING BOWL
Solid colors Ivory and Green
Special order colors
Blue, Yellow and Rose

No. 153 JARDINIERE AND PEDESTAL
Blend of Brown and Green
Blend of Rose and Green
Solid colors White and Green
Jardiniere diameter 9½"
Total height 21"

No. 9 BIRD BATH
Finishes Natural, Nutone and Luxor
Bath diameter 17½"—total height 24"

No. 153 JARDINIERE AND PEDESTAL
Blue, Green and White
Jardiniere diameter 13"
Total height 31"

1938 Catalog page

Bird Bath tops, 17", Pedestals, one 20", one 20½", all bisque fired bird bath top marked: RRPCo 18 USA, Tantone. 1964-2000. $30-35 set

Brown Garden Stump, 17¼", 9¼" across top, a garden seat. NEW. $35-40

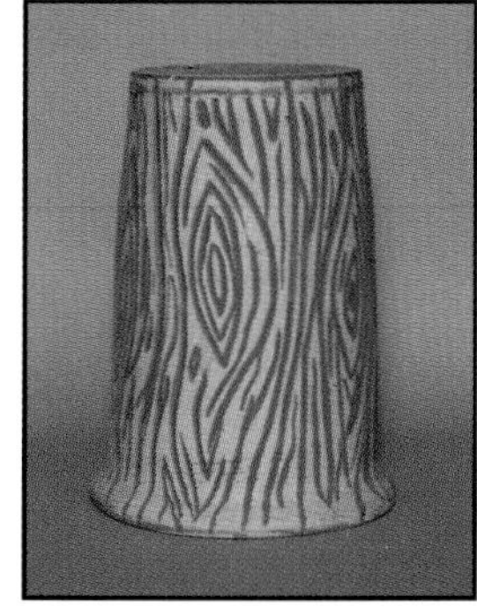

Garden Stump, 17¼" tall, 9¼" across top. Luxor glaze, a garden seat. NEW. $35-40

Footed Planter, 18¾" across, 8" tall, Luxor. Robinson Ransbottom Pottery, Roseville, Ohio USA. NEW. $35-40

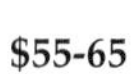

Bird Bath, 27", dark blue with lily pads; White Bird Bath bottom, Green Bird Bath top. No 14. NEW. 1990's. (Glaze on mold used 1941 to present.) $55-65

Bird Bath, 23", blue sponge with birds around rim and bottom, 2 pieces. NEW. 1995. $70-75

Decorated Luxor Pots: 7¾" (light green inside). $40-50
6" (dark green inside) green with pink and white flowers, no marks, plain unglazed bottoms. 1931. $30-40

Right: Footed Planters, green wiped glaze, drain holes, unglazed bottoms, no mark. 1930's on. No. 15/15", $40-45
No. 15/11", $25-30

Garden Ware
Bird Baths and Pots

CROWN BRAND WARE

CEMETERY VASE
Luxor

Diameter	Height
5"	8½"
6"	10"

No. 25 PORCH JAR
Can also be used inverted as base for Garden Urn
Ivory or Green Glazes
Luxor or Nutone
13" diameter — 10" high

GAZING GLOBE BASE
Nutone or Bisque
7" diameter

LUXOR PORCH POT AND SAUCER
Sizes: 8", 10", 12", 14" and 16"

GARDEN URN
Ivory or Green Glazes
Luxor or Nutone
15" diameter — 15" high

ROMAN JAR
Ivory, Green or Blue Glazes and Nutone
12¼" diameter — 10¼" high

IVY JAR
Ivory, Metallic Green or Blue
8" high

GARDEN STUMP
Luxor
17½" high

IVY HANGING BASKET WITH CHAIN
Green Glazed
7¼" diameter

1938 Catalog page

Aladdin Oil Jar with Lion heads on sides, 26", Rufftone. 1931-1938. $1,000-1,200 each

Bird Bath, 28" Rufftone, 2 pieces, 22" across top, no mark. 1931. $1,000-1,200

Bird Bath, 31", Rufftone, 2 pieces, 22" across top, no mark. 1931. $1,000-1,200

Wren Houses, 7", one green, one rust. Green with 4 holes in bottom and a slight foot. Rust with 3 holes in bottom, Luxor finish. 1931. $75-100 each

Rufftone Ware is made on a stoneware body, matt green inside, outside finished rough with matt green in the low parts, natural Terra Cotta finish on the high parts.

Elf Garden Ornament, "The Smithy", 16 1/2", with removable tools and 4 1/4" anvil, open bottom, no marks. 1954. $200-250

Elf Garden Ornament, "The Gardener" (wheelbarrow missing), 16" open bottom, no mark. 1954. $200-225

Gnome Garden Ornaments
"The Thinker", No. 395, 12" x 7", air-brushed, large open hole in bottom, no glaze inside. 1954. $100-125
Gnome "Happy Man", No. 390, airbrushed, U.S.A. ink stamp mark. 1954. $35-45

Seated Gnome Garden Ornament, 12", flat bottom, round hole. 1931 or before. $200-250
Standing Gnome, 11", airbrushed, open bottom. 1970's. $30-35

No. 333 "Huck" Bird Bath Inserts, 10 1/2" with metal rod, and 12 1/2". Both: corn cob pipes missing, ink stamp inside, USA, open bottoms, no marks. 1951-1969. $30-35 and $45-50

Chicken Lawn Ornament, 12", white, open bottom, no mark. 1958-1959. $80-100

1954 Catalog detail

Green Gnome Garden Ornament, 14" x 9 1/2", green glazed bottom, with green glaze inside, not marked, not in catalog, but looks like large airbrushed one from the 1970's. $125-150

No. 331 Bird Bath Insert, 12", air-brushed Mallard, open bottom. 1951. $50-75

Turtle, 12" x 6", air-brushed, completely open, #1104/G4 Turtle. 1956. Also came in smaller sizes. $75-90

Turtle, 7", Bird Bath Insert or Garden Ornament, light green glazed inside, dry foot, no mark, No 346. 1952. $65-75

Owl (to fit over tree limbs), 11 1/2", no mark, glazed inside
Green, from 1970's. $40-50
Brown, from 1950's or 1960's. $70-80

Garden Ware Ornaments

Frog, $9^{1/4}$" x 12", no hole for hardware, No. 1100/G2 Large Frog. $150-175

Frog Lawn Sprinkler, $9^{1/4}$" x 12", No. 1100/G2 Large Frog. 1956. $150-175

Hootie Owl, $11^{1/2}$", red clay, unglazed. 1970's. $35-45

Four Frogs, 12", open bottom, no mark, No. 1100/G6 Singing Frogs. 1958. $175-200

Frog on Base, 11", open bottom, hose opening, no mark. 1931. $150-175

Garden Frog, 9". 1931. $1,100-1,300

Frog, $6^{1/2}$", nose to tail, $3^{1/2}$" tall, No. 103. 1931. $250-300

Garden Frog, 9" x 12" from front to back, 8" across. Came with sprinkler for lawns. 1928-1937. $1,200-1,500

Garden Frog, 9" x $12^{1/2}$", with Turning Sprinkler. 1931. $1200-1500

Frog, 10", airbrushed, open bottom, no mark. No. 1100/G3 Standing Frog. 1956. $100-125

Red clay Frog, 11", open bottom, no mark, #1100/G3, Standing Frog. 1956. $40-50

No. 501 Bird Bath Insert, 8", open bottom. $25-30
No. 502 Bird Bath Insert, yard ornament. 1957. $35-45
No, 501 Bird Bath Insert, 8", pink, open bottom with some ridge. 1956. $25-30

No. 392 Fish Bird Bath 8" insert, air-brushed. $75-85

Frog, 10", standing, sponged, open bottom, no mark, No. 1100/G3. 1956. $150-175

Boy Riding Fish Bird Bath Inserts, No. 329, open bottom with lip, no mark. 11", cream, no glaze inside; 12" aqua, aqua glaze inside; 12" white, white glaze inside; 12" lime green, lime green glaze inside. 1952-1972. $40-60 each

Boy on a Fish Fountain Top; 12½", air-brushed, glazed inside, no mark. $75-100

Boy Riding Fish, 12", powder blue, no mark. 1948. $40-60

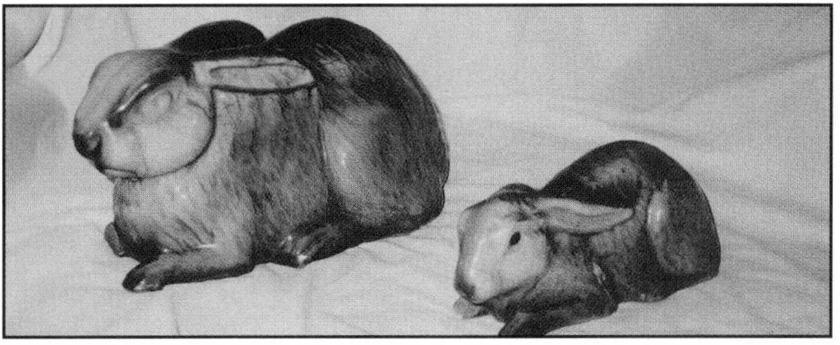

Glazed Rabbits, circa 1930's. Available with open or closed backs. $200-250 and $125-150

No. 503 Bird Bath Insert, 15", Girl with Goose, yellow, open bottom with lip, no mark. 1957. $60-75

Japanese Lady, 15", open bottom, big lip, no mark, air-brushed, No. 1136 (Sayonara Maiden). 1959. $30-40

Rabbit Planter, 5" x 10", tan with flat bottom. $150-175

Brown rabbit, 3" x 7", with flat bottom and large round opening. 1931. $125-150

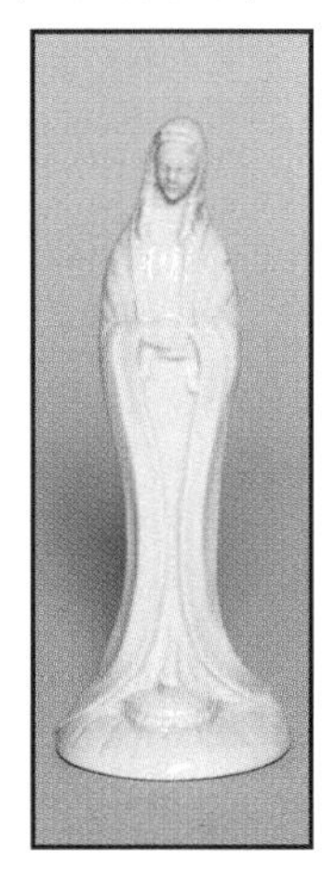

Madonna, 12", open bottom, no mark, M-100. 1964. $50-60

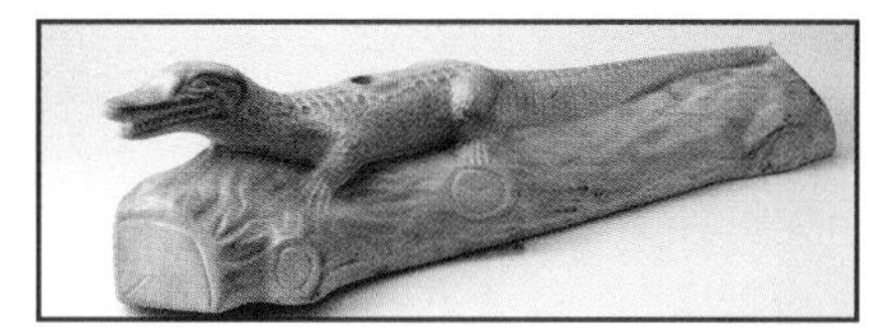

Alligator Sprinkler, 19½", hole in top, rectangular opening in bottom. 1931. $600-750.

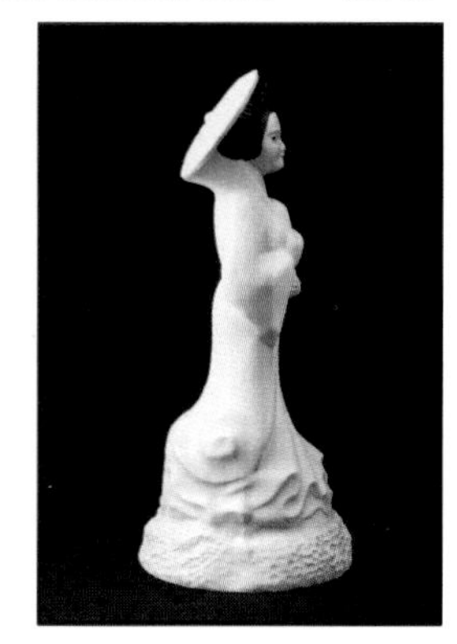

Side view of "Sayonara Maiden". $30-40

Sundials, 10", aqua and yellow, made to go into a pedestal, no marks. "I count none but sunny hours." 1965-1966. $50-60 each

St. Francis, 14½", glazed inside, open bottom, dry foot, no mark. $30-40

St. Francis, 15", open bottom, ink stamp, USA, No 1135. 1959. $30-40

1952 Catalog detail

"Pan" $75-100

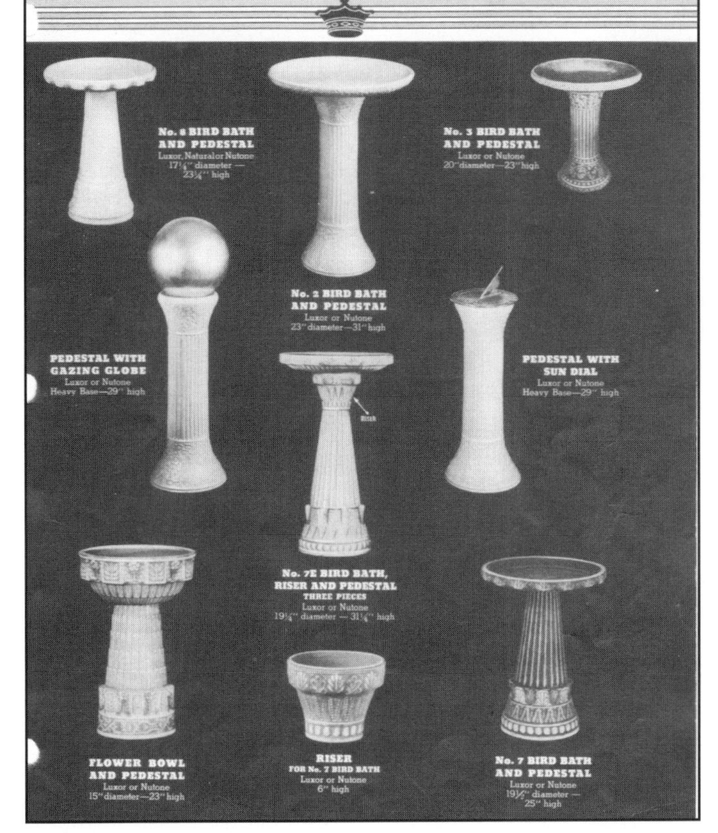

1938 Catalog

No. 38 Palm Leaves Porch Pot, 16"x13½", with saucer, white, Ransbottom Roseville, O USA, New. $60-65

Palm Leaves Porch Pot, 16" x 13½", with saucer, in Luxor glaze, Ransbottom Roseville, O USA. New. $55-60

Footed Planter, 10¼", drain-hole, flat unglazed bottom, No. 15. Garden or cemetary urn. New, Mold used since 1930's. $25-30

Porch Pot No. 125, 10" x 13", white, drainhole, flat unglazed bottom. New, 1930's and 1983-1990's. $28-32

Medallion or Villa Pot, 12¾" x 17½", Luxor glaze. New. $35-40

Grecian Urn, 11½", Tantone, wiped planter, drainhole, flat unglazed bottom. New, 1931-1990's. $38-42

Decorator Pot, 13½" x 17", RRPCo, with drainhole. New. $40-45

Medallion or Villa Pot, 12¾" x 17½", Tantone. New. $35-40

Imperial Tub, 16" x 16", planting pot, red clay, RRPCo USA, Roseville, O. Adobe Glaze. 1973. $35-45

No. 440 Luxor Glaze, 12½" x 15", bottom section to a bird bath pedestal or a Jardiniere, no mark. 1931. $75-100

Garden Ware
Pots and Jars

Grecian Jardiniere, 10" x 11", RRPCo, Roseville, O. No. 350. Bronzetone from the 1980's. $40-45

Red Clay Porch Jars, 17", made for Frank Ransbottom's Summer house, three twisted handles, incised on the jars, "Suit's Me." $800-1,000 each

Decorator Pot, 13½" x 17", blue, RRPCo, drainhole. New. $40-45

Porch Planter, #192, 10" x 8½", white. New. $18-22

Roman Jar, 10" x 12" across, no mark, drain hole. Mold used since 1930's. $30-35

Pair of Rufftone Porch Jars, 26", no mark. Late 1920's. $1,200-1,400 each

Jardiniers and Pedestals

Three Jardinieres and Pedestals, 21", brown and green of various drips.
No. 352, Fern Leaves, RRPCo Roseville, Ohio, 153 mark. 1952. $175-200
No. 153, Cat Tails, no mark on Jardiniere, 153 on Pedestal. 1937-1940. $200-225
No. 421, Flowers, Weller mold, RRPCo Roseville, Ohio, No 421. 1950's-1980's. $100-125

Jardiniere and Pedestal. Green Rufftone glaze.
$1,500-1,800

Yellow Tweed Jardiniere, $10^{1/2}$", glazed bottom, dry foot, impressed mark: RRPCo Roseville, O. No. 412-11 USA; Pedestal, 19", glazed inside, dry foot, no mark. 1955-1968. $75-100

No. 131 Jardiniere and Pedestal. $200-250
Jardiniere, $9^{1/2}$" x $7^{1/4}$" and Pedestal, $13^{3/4}$"
Jardiniere marked 131/-, impressed.

Green Porch Pot, 6", glazed bottom, dry foot, USA.
$20-25

No. 144 Jardiniere and Pedestal, 27¼" in turquoise. Pedestal marked on top 144/; Jardiniere marked 144/, punched holes for drainage.
1937-1945. $300-350

No. 131 Jardiniere, 9½" x 7¼"; Pedestal, 13¾".
1937-1940. $200-250

Jardiniere and Pedestal, green glaze over orchid glaze, 31", plain unglazed bottom, no mark.
1930's. $1,200-1,500

1982 Catalog detail

Pedestal, 21½", open top for gazing ball (also). Jardiniere, 10", slight foot, bottom unglazed, no marks. $1,200-1,500

Hand decorated DeDonati Jardiniere and Pedestal, 30". 1930. $1,500-2,000

Jardiniers and Pedestals

This mold purchased from Weller Pottery when they went out of business was used by RRPCo off and on in the 1950's-1980's in various colors and sizes.

Old Weller mold.
Jardiniere 10½", Pedestal 21", RRPCo Roseville, O #421. $300-350

No. 421/9 Jardiniere and Pedestal, 21", 4 holes in bottom of Jardiniere, white glazed bottom, dry foot. $225-250

Old Weller molds. Jardiniere 8", Persimmon with white drip, RRPCo Roseville, O, NO 421 USA. Pedestal 13¾", Persimmon with white drip, no mark. (Blend, green-brown, was made 1960's-1980's.) 1984. $100-125

No. 421/13 Jardiniere and Pedestal, 31½", white with blue flowers, marked RRPCo Roseville, Ohio 421. $300-350

No. 421/13 Jardiniere 8" and Pedestal 13¾", green with rose and yellow flowers, marked RRPCo Roseville, Ohio #421 USA. Also came in pink, blue and yellow and in a larger size. $225-250

Jardiniere and Pedestal, 30", Tweed design. Jardiniere marked USA in an oval (ink stamp). Pedestal marked RRPCo Roseville, Ohio No 412-18. 1955-1968. $125-150

"Colorful Jardinieres, fully glazed, suitable for indoor or outdoor use."

Flower pots, 1980's all. No. 1400 Flower Pot, 5", no mark. $15-20
Flower Pot, 5", RANSBOTTOM 1420 USA, 6" ROSEVILLE, O. $15-20
Crock with black duck, 3", oval ink stamp. $10-15

Jardiniere, 6", blend glazed bottom, dry foot, no mark. $25-30

No. 39 Palm Pot or Patio Tub, 9¾" x 11½" across, marked RRPCo 12" Roseville, O. USA. $25-30

Jardiniere and Pedestal, 20", all one piece. Few produced. $100-125

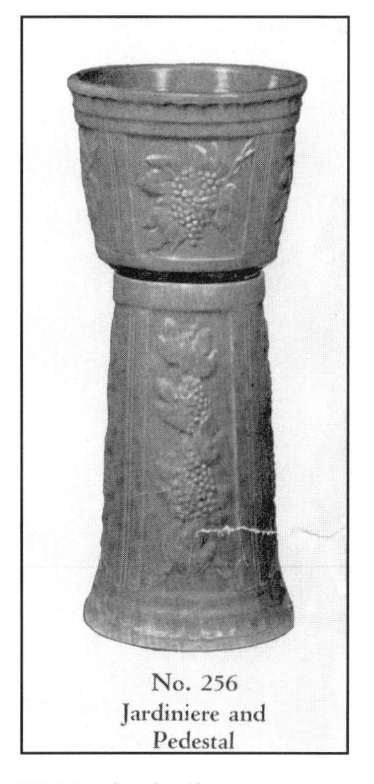

1947 Catalog detail

Tweed Jardiniere, 7¾". Pedestal, 15¼" Mandarin, marked 412/15" Roseville, Ohio. 1970's-1980's. $100-125

No. 412 Tweed Vase $40-50
No. 412 Tweed Jardiniere and Pedestal. 1955-1968. $125-150

White Jardiniere and Pedestal, 21½", Test sample, Weller mold, very rough clay and dull finish. RRP Co, Roseville, OH. No. 421 USA. $100-125

CROWN POTTERY

No. 144
Jardiniere and Pedestal
Jardiniere 10½" diameter
Pedestal 18" high
Total height 27¼"

No. 131
Jardiniere and Pedestal
Jardiniere 9¼" diameter
Pedestal 14" high
Total height 21"

No. 153
Jardiniere and Pedestal
Jardiniere 9¼" diameter
Pedestal 14" high
Total height 21"

No. 153 Jardiniere and Pedestal
Jardiniere 13" diameter
Pedestal 20" high
Total height 31"

No. 163 Jardiniere
5½", 8", 9¼" and 10¼" diameter

No. 112 Jardiniere
5", 6", 7", 8", 9¼" and 10¼" diameter

No. 149 Bulb Bowl
6½" diameter

No. 121 Jardiniere
(Victoria Finish Illustrated)
5¾", 6¾", 7¾" and 8¾" diameter

No. 157 Jardiniere
7", 8½", 9½" and 10½" diameter

1939 Catalog page

No. 8 Decorated Luxor Jardiniere and Pedestal, 30", no mark. 1931. $250-300

Jardiniere and Pedestal, 26", looks like crumpled cardboard with grapes on top and fern leaves on bottom. (Not a match). Rufftone Grecian Jardiniere and Pedestal. 1931. $175-200

First Jar and Pedestal below No. 421 Blend is most common. $100-125

1984 Catalog page

1979 Catalog page

CROWN BRAND WARE

FLOWER POTS
With Attached Saucers
STYLE NO. 121

HOLES FOR DRAINAGE
Colors: Jade, White, Yellow, or Blue

5½" 6½" 7½" 8½"

Made in sizes 5½", 6½", 7½", 8½"

POT and SAUCER
STYLE NO. 128
Colors: Jade, White, Yellow, or Blue

Saucers Detached

8½" 7½"

Made in sizes 7½", 8½"

TULIP POT and SAUCER
STYLE NO. 118
Colors: White, Green, and Blue

6½" 5½"

Made in sizes 6½" and 5½"

JARDINIERES
STYLE NO. 112
Colors: Metallic Green, White, Gloss Blend of Brown and Green

6" 7" 8" 9½" 10¼"

Made in sizes 6", 7", 8", 9½", 10¼"

JARDINIERES
STYLE NO. 113

9½" 8½" 7½"

Made in sizes 7½", 8½", 9½"

HANGING BASKET
SPRAYED PAINT FINISH
Colors: White or Green, Green Lustre Blend

1937 Catalog page

Jardiniere, 9½", 157/- with a large 3 incised.
Pedestal, 17¾", 157/-USA 3.
$275-300

Jardiniere, 9½", glazed bottom, dry foot, impressed mark RANSBOTTOM 157 USA 10" ROSEVILLE, O.
Pedestal, 18", Top impressed 157/-USA. (The No. 157 design began in 1939. This glaze, 1983.) $150-175

Flower Pot, 6¾" tall x 8" across, hand painted on scalloped pot, signed Pace in front, no mark on bottom. Note inside on RRPCo (J.A. Ransbottom) card "Painted in under glaze colors by Willard Pace, ceramic artist for many years at RRPCo (approx 1950)" signed Alfred Ransbottom. $200-225

No. 01 Glaze Jardiniere, 9", with castle, ducks, tree, sailboat and house, decorated. Weak mold, green glazed bottom, Metaglow glaze. 1931. $100-125

Additional views below

Jardiniere with flower, 6" x 7", green gloss glaze, green glazed bottom, dry foot, no mark. $50-75

No. 4 Luxor Jar, 6½" x 7½", Luxor finish, plain unglazed bottom, no mark. $45-50

Dark blue Jardiniere, 6" x 7", clear glazed bottom, no mark. $75-100

No. 02 Decorated Glaze Jar with white flowers, 6½", clear glazed bottom, no mark. 1931. $100-125

Jardiniers and Pedestals

CROWN POTTERY

Floral Accessories

No. 1400/
Jardinieres

No. 1401/
Std. Jardinieres

No. 211 Florist Vases
Ideal for floral arrangements

No. 287
African Violet Jar
Glazed Jardiniere and Special Red Clay Body Growing Pot

No. 22 - E
Hanging Baskets

No. 412/
"TWEED"
Jardinieres and Pedestals

No. 412/
"TWEED"
Vases

No. 291
Stock Vases

No. 421/
Jardinieres and Pedestals

THE ROBINSON-RANSBOTTOM POTTERY CO., Main Office and Plant, Roseville, Ohio

1948 Catalog page

1960 Catalog page

1979 Catalog page

CROWN POTTERY

Patio Jars For indoor or outdoor use. Available with or without metal frames. Please see information sheet for complete range of sizes and finishes. See color page.

Illustrating No. 150
Patio Jar
with standard frame

Illustrating No. 70
Taper Pot
with standard style frame

Illustrating No. 150
Patio Jar
with "A" style frame

No. 566
Low Patio Jar
and frame

Illustrating No. 562
Oil Jar and frame

No. 160
Patio Jar and frame

THE ROBINSON-RANSBOTTOM POTTERY CO., Main Office and Plant, Roseville, Ohio

1958 Catalog page

PATIOS, TERRACE, PORCH, INTERIOR, EXTERIOR,
the ware of many uses, in a glorious array of styles and color combinations.

16 **No. 421/9** Jardiniere and Pedestal. Glazed Four Colors.

17 **No. 421/** Jardiniere. Glazed Four Colors.

18 **No. 14** Glazed Bird Bath and Pedestal. Pink, Blue, Yellow, White.

19 **No. 150** Patio Jar, Rose and Ivory Illustrated. Glazed Three Colors. Tall Style Frame Shown.

20 **No. 70** Taper Pot and Metal Frame. White Finish Illustrated.

21 **No. 150** Patio Jar with or without Black Metal Stand. Glazed Three Colors, Ivory and Green Illustrated, Low Style Frame Shown.

22 **No. 160** Patio Jar with or without Metal Stand. Glazed Three Colors. Luxor Finish Illustrated.

1958 Catalog page

Porch and Garden Ware

No. 112 Jardiniere
5", 6", and 7" diameter

No. 163 Jardiniere

No. 208 Jardiniere

Roman Jar

No. 22-E
Hanging Basket

(Before Planting)

Luxor Porch Pot and Saucer
8", 10" and 12" diameter

Garden Urn
15" diameter, 15" tall

"Jocko"
Grass growing heads complete with special seed. An amusing and attractive novelty.

THE ROBINSON-RANSBOTTOM POTTERY CO., HEAD OFFICE AND PLANT, ROSEVILLE, OHIO
AFFILIATED WITH —
THE ROBINSON CLAY PRODUCT CO., AKRON, OHIO

1947 Catalog page

1966 Catalog detail

No. 426 Shell Bowl, 10 or 12". 1966.
$30-35

Two sides of a Crock/Sand Jar, 16″ x 12″, featuring stag, fawn and forest scene, ivory glaze, no mark, flat, unglazed bottom. 1930's. $350-375 each

Crock, 15″ x 12″, Metaglo, 1931 Catalog, flat, unglazed bottom. This mold, with stag, deer and forest scene, was used for many different glaze treatments. $250-275

Sand Jar, 15½″, no insert, stag and fawn scene, marked RRPCo USA Roseville, O., unglazed bottom. Luxor. 1931-1970.
No. 64, 1979-1990. $75-85

(Known as No.1 or No. 2 Sand Jars from the 1930's to 1969. Became No. 64 in 1970.)

No. 1 Luxor Umbrella Jar, 9½″ x 22″. 1926. $325-375

Sand Jar, 14½″, turquoise, with ships, insert, no mark. 1937-1959. $100-125

CROWN POTTERY

SAND and UMBRELLA JARS . . Smartly styled and available in a wide range of pleasing colors.

No. 7 Sand Jar
(Fitted with Sand Bowl)
10″ diameter, 15″ tall

No. 1 and No. 2 Sand Jar
No. 1—12″ diameter, 15″ tall
No. 2—13″ diameter, 16″ tall

No. 169 Sand Jar
14″ diameter, 15″ tall

No. 3 Umbrella Jar
(Fitted with Sand Bowl)
9″ diameter, 18″ tall

No. 3 Sand Jar
12″ diameter, 20″ tall

No. 157 Sand Jar
12″ diameter, 15″ tall

No. 6 Sand Jar
10¾″ diameter, 14″ tall

No. 1 Umbrella Jar
9½″ diameter, 21½″ tall

● Please refer to Information Sheet for complete details ●

1941 Catalog page

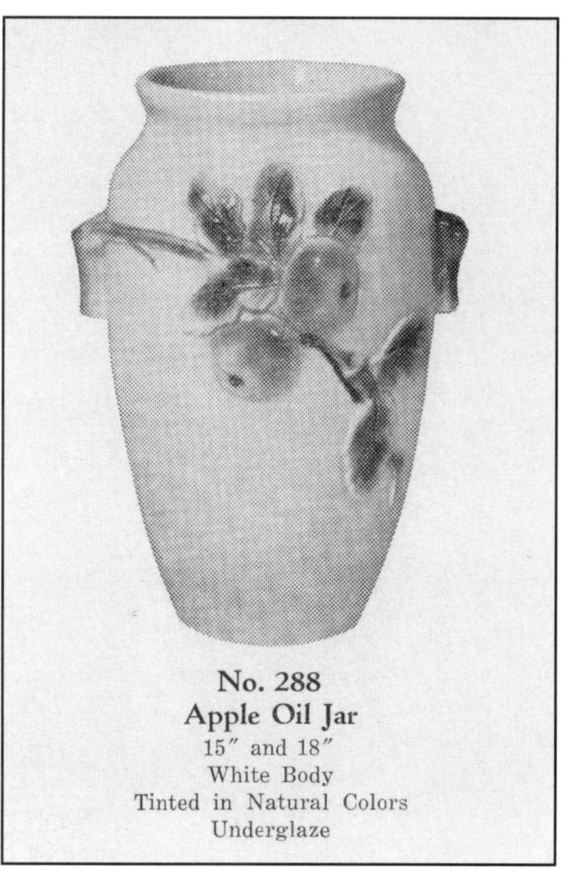

No. 288
Apple Oil Jar
15″ and 18″
White Body
Tinted in Natural Colors
Underglaze

1950 Catalog detail. No. 288 Apple Oil Jar.

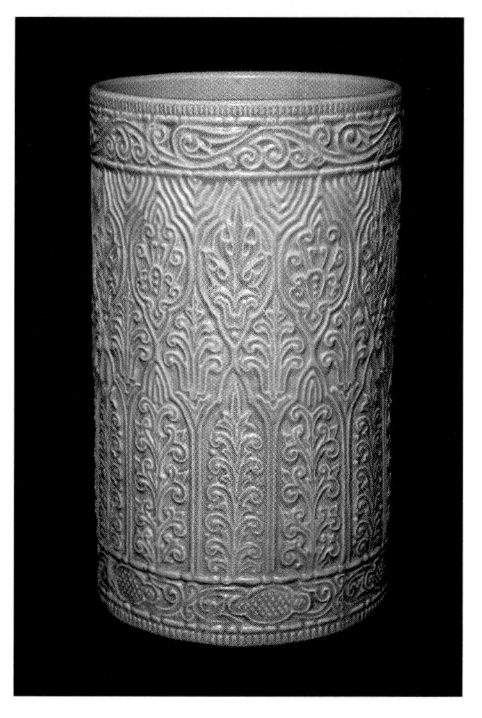

No. 67 Umbrella Stand, pink and cream, 20″, flat, unglazed bottom with IP incised. $300-350

No. 1 Decorated Luxor Umbrella Jar, 22″, plain, unglazed bottom, impressed mark: USA. 1931-1970's. $325-375

No. 67 Umbrella Stand, 20″ x 11″, rust and cream, plain, unglazed bottom. Weller mold, purchased when Weller closed. 1949-1986. $200-250

No. 3 Sand Jar, 19 3/4″ x 11 1/2″, turquoise "devil" plain, unglazed bottom, impressed USA. 1937-1948. $200-250

Green Sand Jar, 19 3/4″ x 11 1/2″, no mark. 1937-1948. Also came in ivory glaze. $200-250

No. 3 Decorated Umbrella Jar, 18″. 1940's. $325-375

1937 Catalog detail

Top: Hanging Strawberry Pot, $5^{1/2}$", glazed bottom, no mark. $65-75
Bottom: Flower Pot, 5", flat, unglazed bottom. $50-60
Strawberry Pot, 8", no saucer, glazed bottom, dry foot. $75-100
Strawberry Pot, 9", with saucer, plain bottom. $100-125
Strawberry Pot, 12", with saucer, plain bottom. $175-200
All with green glaze over orchid glaze.

CROWN POTTERY

Sand and Umbrella Jars . . Smartly styled and available in a wide range of pleasing colors.

No. 7 Sand Jar
(Fitted with Sand Bowl)
10" diameter, 15" tall

No. 67 Sand Jar
11" diameter, 19¾" tall

No. 3 Umbrella Jar
(Fitted with Sand Bowl)
9" diameter, 18" tall

No. 1 Sand Jar
12" diameter, 15" tall

No. 1 Umbrella Jar
9½" diameter, 21½" tall

THE ROBINSON-RANSBOTTOM POTTERY CO., MAIN OFFICE AND PLANT, ROSEVILLE, OHIO
AFFILIATED WITH
THE ROBINSON CLAY PRODUCT CO., AKRON, OHIO

1949 Catalog page

CROWN POTTERY

Sand and Umbrella Jars . . Smartly styled and available in a wide range of pleasing colors.

No. 7 Sand Jar
(Fitted with Sand Bowl)
10" diameter, 15" tall

No. 67 Sand Jar
11" diameter, 19¾" tall

No. 3 Umbrella Jar
(Fitted with Sand Bowl)
9" diameter, 18" tall

No. 1 Sand Jar
12" diameter, 15" tall

No. 68
Sand Jar
11½" diam., 14½" tall

No. 1 Umbrella Jar
9½" diameter, 21½" tall

THE ROBINSON-RANSBOTTOM POTTERY CO., MAIN OFFICE AND PLANT, ROSEVILLE, OHIO
AFFILIATED WITH
THE ROBINSON CLAY PRODUCT CO., AKRON, OHIO

R-100

1950 Catalog page

Jars for Umbrellas, Sand & Strawberries

Maize Ivy Jar, 5 1/2", flat, unglazed bottom, no mark. Came in 6", 8" and 10" sizes and 3 colors, Astroglow, Green with over-drip and Maize. 1960's. $20-25

Ivy Jar, 7 3/4", hole to punch out. 1939. $35-40
Hanging Ivy Jar, 4 1/2", green glazed bottom, hole to punch out on bottom. 1931. $25-30

Strawberry Jar, 11 1/2", green glaze over orchid glaze, glazed bottom, dry foot, no mark. 1930's. $150-175

Umbrella Stand, 19 1/2", flat unglazed bottom with heavy drips ground off. Late 1920's early 1930's. Jardiniere and Pedestal in background to show size. $700-900

The Strawberry Jars were made by taking a regular vase, cutting slits and pulling out the openings.

No. 2 decorated Luxor Umbrella Jar, 21 1/2", darker green inside. 1931. $150-200

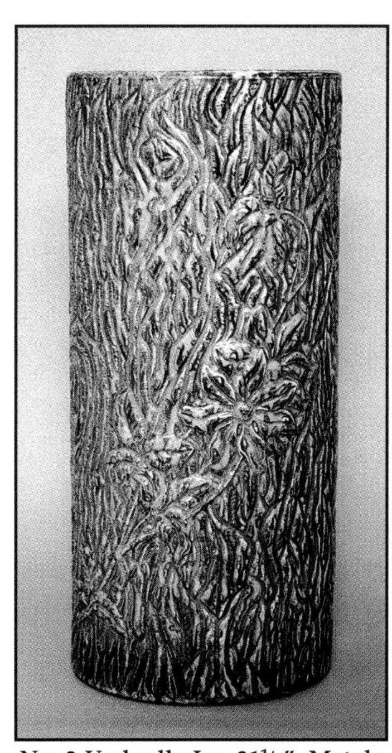

No. 2 Umbrella Jar, 21 1/2", Metglo glaze, no mark, flat, unglazed bottom. 1931. $300-350

White Aladdin's Lamp Sand Jar, 17 3/4", no mark, plain, unglazed bottom. 1955-1969. $100-125

Hanging Basket Strawberry Pot, 4" x 5 3/4", brown with white drip, RRPCo Roseville, O. USA impressed. 1970's. $20-25

Top Row: 1954-1965.
Black and yellow bands, 5", RRPCo USA Roseville O. 1953. $8-12
Cream and brown, 8", oval ink stamp. 1984. $10-12
Brown Shoulder Bowl, 4½", RRPCo Roseville, Ohio NO 391. $25-35.
Middle Row: Green, 7½", unglazed bottom, ink stamp, hand decorated at Alpine Pottery. 1988-1991. $10 15
Green, 6", unglazed bottom, ink stamp. 1988-1991. $8-10
Blue flowers, 9", glazed bottom, no mark. 1940's. $10-15
Bottom Row: Green, 10", Alpine stamp. 1988-1991. $15-20
Black, 12", footed planting dish, RRPCo Roseville, O USA. Stamp "Hand decorated by Alpine Pottery, Roseville Ohio." 1966. $15-20

Stamp on bottom

Bowls: All marked RRPCo (6", 7", 8", 9"), Roseville, Ohio, USA.
Top Row: Blue sponge, 7" $6-7
Wheat, 6" 1990-2000. $5-6
Bottom Row: Green sponge, 8" $8-9
Blue bands, 9" (also comes in 10") Williamsburg. 1970's-1990's. $11-12

Shoulder Bowls: 14" and three 12":
Top Row: Wheat. $30-35
Green sponge. $25-28
Bottom Row: blue sponge and blue stripe, R Ransbottom Roseville, Ohio, USA, 305-12". $25-30
305-14" stripe. New. $30-35

Below: Several views of the scenes and finishes available for this bowl.

No. 3 Metglo Bowl, 5½" x 2½", clear glazed bottom. 1931. $40-50

No. 3 Luxor Bulb Bowl, 2½" x 5½", dry foot, glazed bottom, no mark. $25-35

Low Bowl, 2¾" x 6", Luxor, plain stoneware bottom, unmarked, green glaze inside. 1931. $25-35

Confetti Bowl, 7¾" x 3½", blue and pink spatter, impressed crown mark. 1981. $6-8

Luxor No. 1 Bulb Bowls, 5½" x 2½", no mark: 6½" x 2½", no mark, "Daffodil". 1931. $20-25 each

No. 3 Bulb Bowl, 6½" x 2¾", green inside, green and cream outside, trees and castles. 1931. $20-25

Metglo Bulb Bowl, 7" x 3¼", dark green, with trees and castles, plain bottom, unmarkd. 1931. $50-60

Airbrushed Bowl with Flowers, 6" x 2½", glazed bottom, dry foot, USA, 163/-. 1939-1952. $10-12

Kitchen Ware Bowls

Top Row: This is the 150th Roseville Anniversary Cereal bowl dated 1840-1990, 5", RRPCo Roseville, Ohio (inset stamp). $12-18
Pie Plate, 9", blue, 186/-USA. 1941. $15-20
Spatter Bowl, 5 1/2", pink and green, glazed bottom, dry foot, no mark. $5-8
Bottom Row: Cream with blue bands, 5", oval ink stamp. $5-8
Blue Sponge Bowl, 5 1/2", clear glazed bottom, dry foot, no mark. $5-8
Brown Sponge Bowl, 5 1/2", clear glazed bottom, dry foot, no mark. $5-8

No. 720 blue sponge bowl, marked 15" bowl, R Ransbottom, Roseville, OH USA. 1980's-1990's. $40-50

Covered Bowl with Fruit Lid, 5", RRPCo Roseville Ohio, No 326-6. Bowl was produced 1949-1951. The cover was made and decorated by Pace for Mrs. Alfred Ransbottom. $175-225

The Ransbottom Pottery Story

"In 1803, Ohio became the 17th state, the first to be carved from the huge Northwest Territory. Then the massive migration to this fertile land began.
From Massachusetts came the Wickham family; from Virginia the Ransbottom family. Mr. Ransbottom was a gentleman of the old school, a fancier of fine horses. Settling in Delaware county, he became a potter and a broker. The Ransbottom pottery-making tradition had begun.
The Wickham covered wagon contained, among the family's prized possessions, thirteen (a baker's dozen) milk crocks, all but one of which have disappeared. The sole remaining crock is owned by fourth generation descendant Alfred Ransbottom, of Roseville. There crocks had been custom-made in New England during the 1700's."

Deep Bowl, 11 1/2" x 4 1/2", painted by Pace. 1948. $75-100

Alfred Ransbottom's Old brown ware bowl, 4 1/2" x 10 1/2", rings.

Brown with white drip Casserole, no lid, 3 1/4" x 6", marked RRPC Roseville, O. U.S.A. 1960's. $15-20

Left: Metglo Bowl, 4", RRPCo. $25-35

Blue mixing bowl, icicle, 10 1/4" x 5 1/4", glazed bottom, no mark. 1916-1918. $65-75
Orchid mixing bowl, 9 1/4" x 5", glazed bottom, no mark. 1928-1929. $65-75

Pair of 8" Marble Ware mixing bowls. 1972. Shown on page 51 on catalog page. $25-35 each

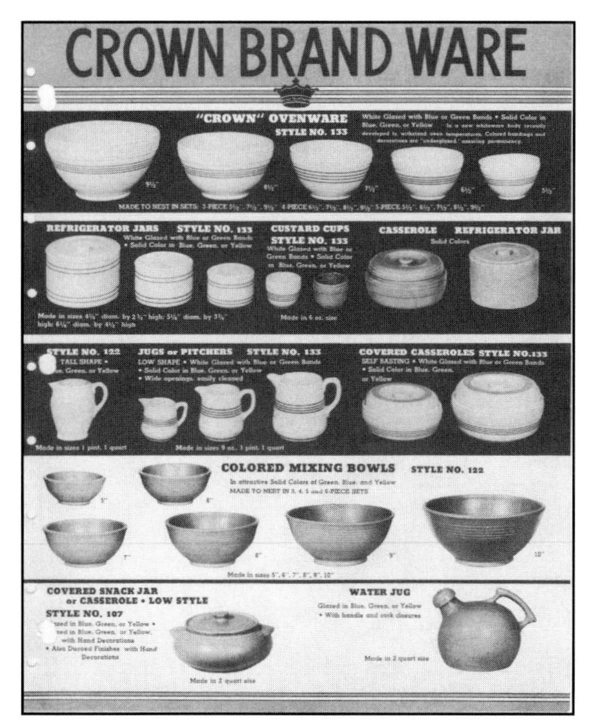

1937 Catalog page

1947 Catalog page

1955 Catalog detail

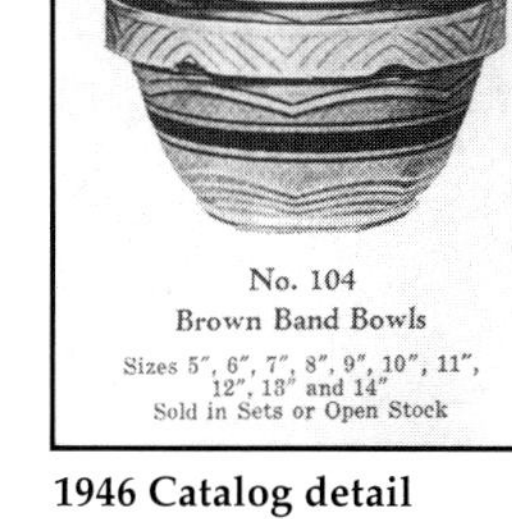

1946 Catalog detail

Bowls: Top Row: Brown, 7", RRPCo Roseville Ohio. 1950. $15-18
Orchid, 6", glazed all over. 1930's. $40-50
Cream with 6 blue and white bands, 6", RRPCo Roseville Ohio. $20-25
Middle Row: Blue Shoulder Bowl, 10", USA, glazed all over, not RRP $50-60
Green Shoulder Bowl, 9", 103/-USA. 1939. $35-45
Bottom Row: Cream with blue and red bands, 12", RRPCo Roseville OH USA. $30-35
Cream with blue bands, 12", ink stamp Robinson Ransbottom, Roseville, Ohio USA, No 303 SH Mixing Bowl, 12"/5qt. $25-30

Bowls. Top Row: Girl with Watering Can, 8", 166-8" USA impressed, also USA ink stamp. 1941-1948, 1964 and mid 70's. $20-25
Girl with Watering Can, 6", RRPCo Roseville Ohio, USA. 1941-1948, 1964. $15-20
Hobnail Set, all with impressed crown: 5½", orange, 207; 7½", green; 7½", brown, 207 8"; 8½" yellow, 207 9"; 9½" aqua, 207 10". 1941-1943. $75-85 set
Bottom Row: No. 120 Bowl Set, red and blue bands, all marked RRPCo Roseville, Oh.: 5", No 326-5; 6" No 326-6; 7" No 326-7; 8" No 326-8; 9" No 326-9. 1949-1951. $60-70 set
Yellow and Green Spatter Set, with scallops, all marked RRPCo Roseville, Ohio: 5", 370/5"; 6", 370/6"; 7", 370/7"; 8", 370/8"; 9", 370/9". 1954-1957. $50-60 set
Light Blue No. 206 Plaid (made in five sizes, this is the largest one) with impressed crown. 1941-1946. $15-18

Kitchen Ware Bowls

Three Piece Mixing Bowl Set: 10"/3qt; 8"/2qt; 6"/1qt. Didn't make many, also in dark green, ink stamped Robinson Ransbottom, Roseville, Ohio U.S.A. 1980's or 1990. $15-20, $10-15, $8-10.

Milk Pans: Top Row: White, 8", USA. 1914-1968; Brown, 8", USA-both are icicle design. $45-50 each
Bowl, 8 1/2", points on shoulder, cream and blue, glazed bottom, no mark. $60-70
Woven blue, 6", crown impressed. $40-50
Bottom Row: Mottled Blue and Red, 10", no mark. 1931. $80-90
Green with crown, 8", 8 under glaze. 1930's. $35-40
Cream banded with white and red, 5 1/2", RRPCo Roseville O No 391. 1954-1965. $20-25

Top Row:
Bowl, 6 1/2", glazed bottom, dry foot. $45-50
Bowl, 6 1/2". $60-70
Butter Crock with Lid, 3 3/4", flat unglazed bottom. $150-175

Bottom Row:
Bowl, 8 1/2". $70-80
Bowl, 10 1/2". $90-100
All DeDonatis decorated, but jiggered or molds. All late 1920's.

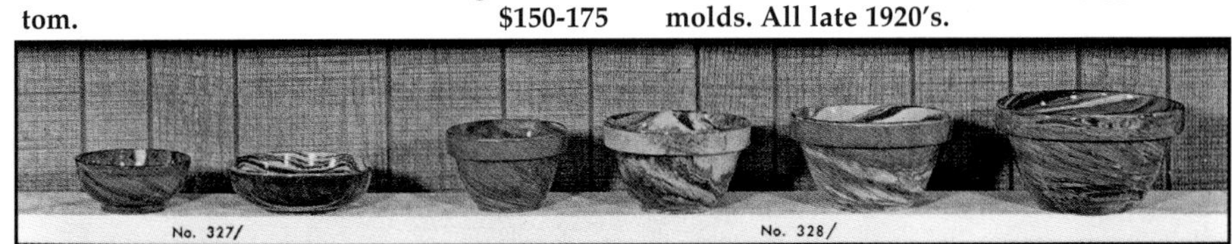

1972 Catalog detail

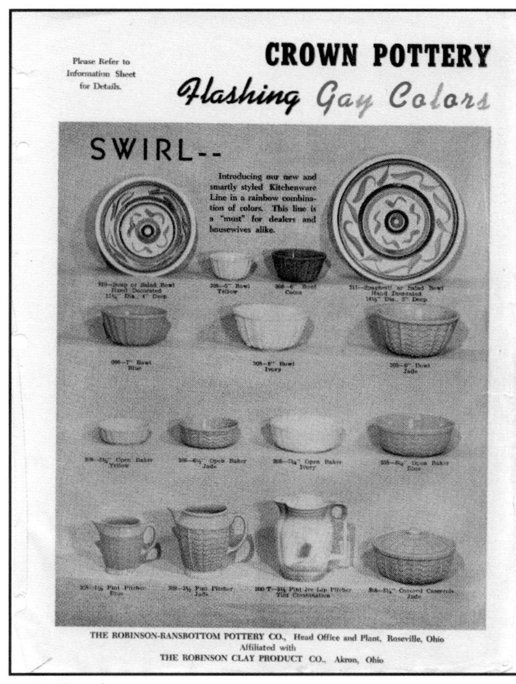

1950 Catalog page

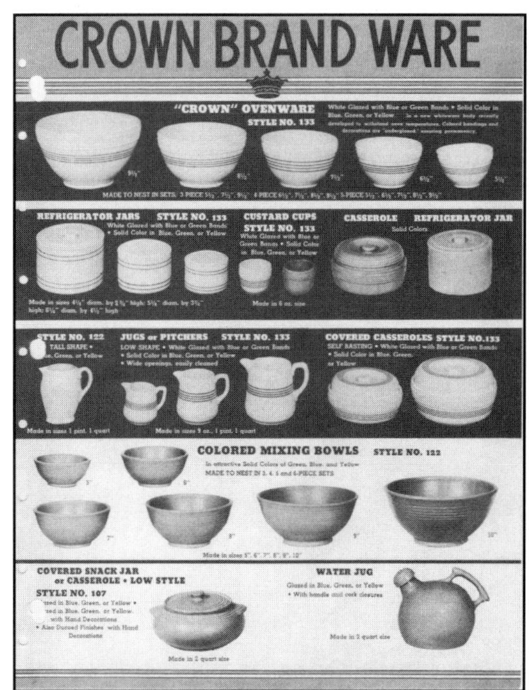

1937 Catalog page

1972 Catalog page

Kitchen Ware
Bowls and Confetti

1981 Catalog page

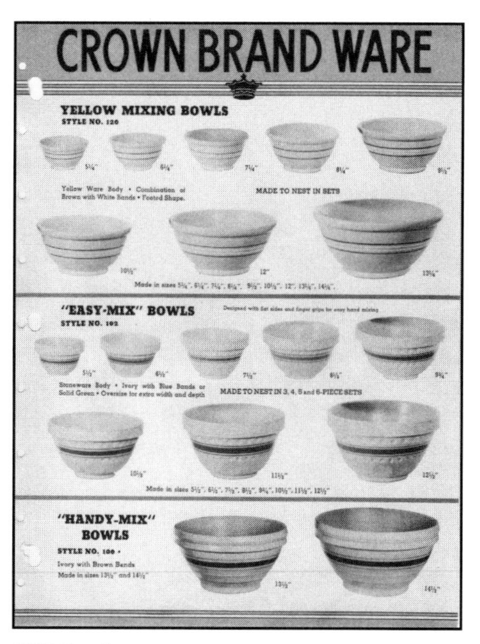

1937 Catalog page

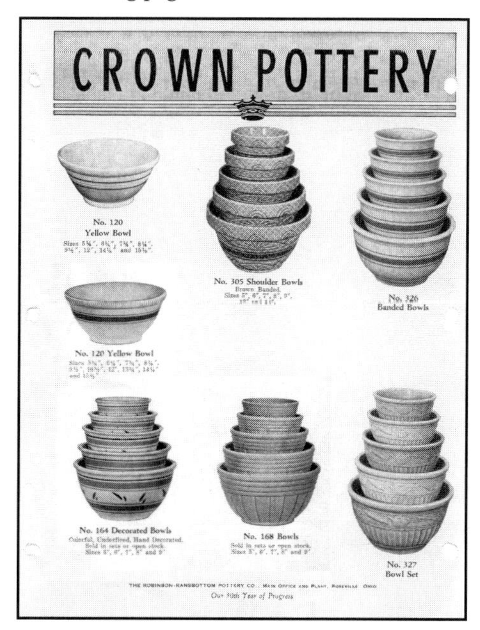

1951 Catalog page

1954 Catalog detail

1954 Paper Sticker

1945 Catalog page

NEW 6 pieces of Gala Line, 1999.

Top Row:	
Baker.	$5-6
Mug.	$8-10
No. 46450 Ice-lip Pitcher.	$23-25
No. 46130 2qt Kitchen Crock.	$12-14

Bottom Row:	
No. 46440 Platter.	$22-25
No. 46012 Bowl.	$25-28

Catalog notes: "Morning Blue, Golden Harvest, Sunset Russet" 1999

1999 Catalog page

Catalog Notes: "The Gala Collection: Natural White, Midnight Blue." 1999

NEW 6 pieces of Gala Line, 1999.

Top Row:	
No. 46008 Bowl.	$8-9
Souffle Dish.	$16-18
No. 46010 Bowl.	$17-19

Bottom Row:	
Oval Baker.	$20-22
Pie Plate.	$14-16
Covered Casserole.	$20-22

Kitchen Ware
Hot Caramel

1983 Catalog page

Hot Caramel Custard Cup. 1983. $

A selection of the New Line 1000, 1983 Fall Season Kitchen Accessories.

Kitchen Ware in production.

KITCHEN WARE
KITCHENETTE

NO. 165 NAPPIES
4 Pc. set in Rainbow Combination - 5" Blue 6" Pink 7" Turquoise 8" yellow (Solid colored sets may be had on special order with the exception of pink) Sold in sets or open doz. lots.

NO. 165 MUSTARD JAR & COVER
Capacity...5 Ozs.
Turquoise, Blue & Brown

NO. 165 CUSTARD CUPS
5 Oz. Capacity
Turquoise, Blue & Brown

NO. 165 REFRIGERATOR JAR AND COVER
Made in Sizes 5½" and 6½"
Turquoise, Blue & Brown

NO. 165 CASSEROLES
7½" & 8½" Sizes
Turquoise, Blue & Brown

NO. 165 SUGAR COVERED
Turquoise, Blue & Brown

NO. 165 PIE PLATES
9½" Diameter
Turquoise, Blue & Brown

NO. 165 PITCHERS..(Plain)
Capacity..½, 1, 2, 3, 4, Pint Sizes

NO. 165 PITCHERS..(Covered)
Capacity 2 & 3 Pint sizes

NO. 165 PITCHERS..(Ice Lip)
Capacity 3 Pint & 4 Pint Sizes

Turquoise Blue & Brown

Turquoise Blue & Brown

NO. 165 BOWLS
5 Pc. set in Rainbow Combination of 5" Brown, 6" Blue, 7" Pink, 8" Turquoise, 9" yellow (Solid colored sets may be had on Special order with the exception of Pink) Sold in sets or open dozen lots

1938 Catalog page

No. 168 Covered Casseroles, $4^{1/2}$" x 8". Author believes these to be newer, (1950's) since they do not have a stoneware body and they are lighter weight. Both with very faint impressed 168 RRPOCo. 1938. Left, $20-25, right $30-35

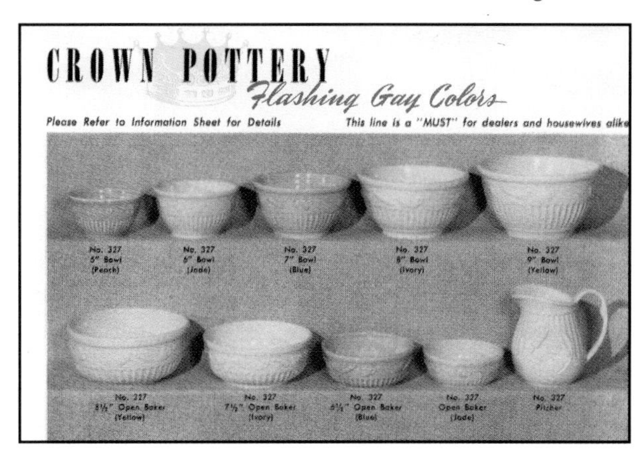

CROWN POTTERY
Flashing Gay Colors
Please Refer to Information Sheet for Details
This line is a "MUST" for dealers and housewives alike

No. 327 5" Bowl (Peach)
No. 327 6" Bowl (Jade)
No. 327 7" Bowl (Blue)
No. 327 8" Bowl (Ivory)
No. 327 9" Bowl (Yellow)
No. 327 8½" Open Baker (Yellow)
No. 327 7½" Open Baker (Ivory)
No. 327 6½" Open Baker (Blue)
No. 327 Open Baker (Jade)
No. 327 Pitcher

1949 Catalog page

Kitchenette Pantry Ware Line:
Top Row: Aqua Bowl, 7", 165/- USA $20-25
Aqua Pitcher, 8", 165/8 USA $45-50
Peach Bowl, 7", 165/7 inside $25-30
Aqua Bowl, 8" $30-35

Bottom Row: Blue Covered Casserole, $6^{1/2}$", 165/- USA. $30-35
Green Sugar Bowl, $3^{1/2}$", 165 USA. Cream Pitcher, 4", 165/ USA., 1938-1940, 1951. $25-30 each

Kitchen Ware
Modern Apple

Apple Coffee Pot, 12″, no marks, flat unglazed bottom. 1978. $50-60

All Apple Pattern: 1978
Top: Coffee Mug, 3 1/2″, ink stamp RRPCo Roseville, O, USA (in an oval), flat unglazed bottom. $10-12
Mug, 5 1/2″, no mark, flat unglazed bottom. $12-15
Covered Sugar Bowl, 5″, ink stamp, flat, unglazed bottom. $15-18
Pitcher, 8″, clear glazed bottom, dry foot, RRPCo Roseville, O, USA impressed. $35-40
Bottom: Canister, 10″, flat unglazed bottom. $30-35
Canister, 9″, flat unglazed bottom. $25-30
Canister, 6 1/2″, flat unglazed bottom. $20-25

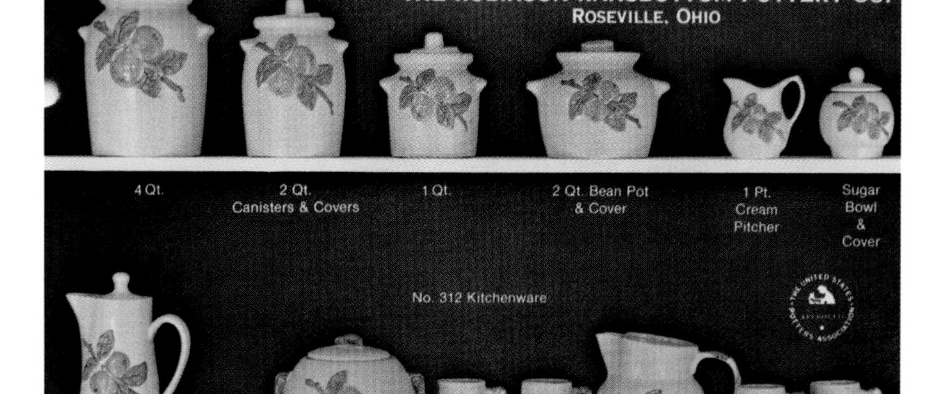

1978 Catalog pages

Apple Bean Pot, 6 1/2″, flat bottom, no mark, 1978. $25-30

Modern Serving Pieces and Accessories.
Modern as Tomorrow.
All hand decorated.
Blends well with any decor.

Modern Apple Ware pieces were first shown in 1949. The line continued through 1979-80.

Deluxe Beverage Set, 11″ Pitcher, 6 pt., 5½″ mugs, 16 oz., glazed bottom with dry foot, no marks. 1931. Mottled glaze. (Also came in solid brown glaze with white inside.) $600-700 set

Pitcher Vase with handle and batter pitcher spout, 11″, hand turned, blue stained bottom. 1920's. $200-225

Grecian Beverage Set, Grey-blue 10″ Pitcher, 4¾″ mugs, glazed bottom with dry foot, no marks. $600-700 set

Brown Sponge Pitcher, 9″, Bowl, 11″, square ink stamp: No. 700K. Bowl also has RRPCo Roseville, Ohio. 1979 $35-40

Top Row: White, glazed bottoms, no marks. 1949.
Aqua flowers, 6″. $25-30
Pink flowers, 6″. $25-30
Aqua flowers, 6½″. $30-35
Center Row: White with pink flowers, 4″ glazed bottom, no mark. 1950's. $20-25
Pink with blue, white and red flowers, 4″ glazed bottom, no mark. 1950's. $20-25
Blue Vase, 3½″, 133/-. $15-20
Red clay with hand painted flowers, 4½″ 1977. $15-20
Bottom Row: No. 46440 Platter. $22-25
No. 46012 Bowl. $25-28
Bottom Row: Green Pitcher, 7″, glazed bottom, no mark. 1950. $25-30
Hobnail Pitcher, 7″, crown impressed mark under glaze. 1941-1943. $35-40
Barrel Pitcher, 7″, pewter glaze, RRPCo Roseville, O USA. $20-25

Rose on Trellis Pitchers: <u>Top Row:</u> Pitchers, 9″, 8″ and 7″, plain clear glazed bottoms, no mark. 1931. 9″, $200-225. 8″, $175-200, 7″ $150-175
<u>BottomRow:</u> Pitchers, 7″, 9″ and 8″ green glazed bottoms, dry foot, no mark. 1938. 9″, $200-225. 8″, $175-200, 7″ $150-175

No. 300—1½ Pint Pitcher Yellow Illustrated
No. 300—2½ Pint Pitcher Ivory Illustrated
No. 300—3½ Pint Ice Lip Pitcher Robin Egg Blue Illustrated

1947 Zephyrus Catalog page

<u>TopRow:</u> Mug, 4½″, glazed bottom, dry foot, no mark. $30-40
Pitcher, 9″, glazed bottom, dry foot, no mark. $90-110
Mug, 4¾″, glazed bottom, dry foot, no mark. $50-60
Pitcher, 8¼″, blue glazed bottom, dry foot, no mark. $150-200
<u>Bottom Row:</u> Batter Pitcher, 10″, glazed bottom, dry foot, no mark. $200-250
Pitcher, 8¼″, glazed bottom, dry foot, no mark. $100-125
Pitcher, 8¼″, RRPCo Roseville, O. (Pitcher with woman and lyre is similar to Red Wing, but woman is turned in opposite direction.) 1931. (Green re-issued 1950) $90-100

Rose Trellis Pitcher, 8½″, Bowl, 12″, glazed bottom, dry foot. 1931-1932. $250-300 set

Zephyrus Ship Pitchers, color glazed bottoms, dry feet, no marks. 1947.
<u>Top Row:</u> Pink Pitcher, 7½″; Cream Pitcher, 7½″ $45-50 each
<u>Bottom Row:</u> Cream Pitcher 6″ $25-35
Aqua Pitcher 7½″ $35-45
Aqua Pitcher 6″ $25-35

Zephyrus: Introducing our new and smartly styled Kitchenware Line in a rainbow combination of colors. This line is a must for dealers and housewives alike.″ *1947 catalog.*

<u>Top Row:</u> Brown Pitcher, 4½″, RRPCo Roseville, O. 1960′s. $10-12
Brown Drip Pitcher, 4½″, RRPCo Roseville, O. 1960′s. $10-12
<u>Bottom Row:</u> Blue Sponge Wall Pocket Pitcher, 6½″ R. Ransbottom, USA. $30-35
Green Pitcher, R-RPCo, Roseville, O No 237/2-. 1960′s. $12-15
Brown Sponge Wall Pocket, 4½″, R. Ransbottom USA. 1980. $25-30

Pitcher, 9″, with green drip glaze over olive green, grey glazed bottom, grey base. 1920's. $200-350

Yellow Pitcher, 7″, yellow glazed bottom, dry foot, RRPCo Roseville, Ohio No 327-3. Late 1940's. $35-40

Pitcher with green stripes, $3^{1}/_{2}$″, cream glazed bottom, dry foot, 133/-. 1937. $40-50

Brown and White. 1960-1970's:

<u>Top:</u>
Pitcher "Jimmie Balthis, Brownsville, Ohio, USA" glazed bottom, dry foot. $35-40

<u>Bottom:</u>
Pitcher, 11″, RRPCo Roseville, O $25-30
Pitcher 10″, no mark. $20-25

Five Banded Thistle Refrigerator Pitchers (1931) and one Stag and Deer Pitcher (1916).

<u>Top Row:</u>
Green glazed bottoms, dry foot, no mark. $4^{1}/_{2}$″, $75-85 8″, $250-300 $5^{1}/_{2}$″, $90-110

<u>Bottom Row:</u>
Blue glazed bottoms, dry foot, no mark. $4^{1}/_{2}$″, $100-125 $5^{1}/_{2}$″, $125-150 7″, $150-175

$35-40

$25-30

Banded Refrigerator Pitchers with Thistle decoration, glazed bottom, dry foot. 1931.
4″ (2 pt.), $75-85 6″ (3 pt.), $125-150 5″ (6 pt.), $90-110

Mahogany glaze Pitcher, 8 1/2", plain unglazed bottom, Indian peace sign. 1914. $100-125

White Grecian Pitcher, 8 1/4", marked RRPCo Roseville, Ohio 321, probably made in 1950's if marked on bottom, white glazed bottom with dry foot. $75-85

White Pitcher with sailing ships, 8 1/4", Zephyrus line, glazed bottom, dry foot, no mark. 1947-1948. $50-60

Stoneware Pitcher, 6 1/2", made from Bosh Farm clay, flat, unglazed bottom. 1910. Not confirmed to be Ransbottom.

Blue-tint deer and fawn Pitcher, 8 1/2". 1916. $175-225

Blue-tint Indian peace sign Pitcher, 8 1/2". 1914. $225-250

White Ewer, 12", came with basin, in 1914 catalog, glazed bottom, dry foot, no mark. 1916-1918. $125-150

Green Stoneware Pitcher, 5", green glazed bottom, dry foot, no mark. Rosella, 1931. $50-75

Ship Ice-Lip Pitcher, 6 3/4", white glazed bottom, dry foot. $60-70
Also made in 5 1/4" size, Zephyrus Line. 1950. $40-50

CROWN POTTERY

Meal Makers . . . An attractive array of items for gifts or personal use. Designed for catering to the needs of "THE INNER MAN"

No. 391 Shoulder Bowls (Sets or Open Stock.)

Illustrating a combination of No. 1504/IL Pitcher and No. 1504/M Mugs

No. 1503 5-9" Bowl Set Rainbow Combination

No. 370 Covered Casserole

No. 1504/ Pitchers (4 Sizes)

No. 1506/ Juice Jugs (2 sizes)

Steam Table Jars Solid White Glaze.

Boston Bean Pot Brown and White Glaze.

No. 120 Yellow Bowl Sizes 5½", 6¼", 7¼", 8¼", 9½", 12" and 14¼".

THE ROBINSON-RANSBOTTOM POTTERY CO., Main Office and Plant, Roseville, Ohio

1958 Catalog page

Stained Glass Look, all marked RRPCo Roseville, O. USA.

Top Row: Yellow Mug, 4"	$10-15	Bottom Row: Pitcher, 6".	$20-25
Peach Mug, 4"	$10-15	Icelip Pitcher, 8¾", 1504/6.	$35-40
Pitcher, 4½", 1504.	$15-20	Pitcher, 7½", F/1504.	$25-30
Juice Jug, 6"	$25-35	1958-1959 all.	

Brown Drip Pitchers
All marked RRPCo Roseville, O USA.
Top Row: 6", $15-18 each; 7½", $20-25
4½", $12-15 each
Bottom Row: 10" $25-30; 10½", $30-35

No. 207 Icelip Peach Hobnail Pitcher, 8½", crown mark impressed in bottom. 1943. $40-50
Right: Bottom of Hobnail Pitcher, showing impressed mark.

Green or white and green pitcher.
Catalog detail.

CROWN POTTERY

No. 170-B Ball Jug (Victoria Finish Illustrated) Ice Lip 4-pint capacity	Ice Water Jug 4-pint capacity	No. 170 Ball Jug Ice Lip 4-pint capacity
No. 186 Cookie Jar	No. 186 Ball Jug Sizes 3 and 5 pint have ice lip, 1½ pint size has plain lip	No. 172-C Ball Cookie Jar (Victoria Finish Illustrated) Capacity 5 and 8 pints

1939 Catalog page

Cream with Brown Drip Pitcher, 4¼", cream glazed bottom, dry foot, RRPCo USA impressed, large capital G with R inset carved into clay. Sample glaze 1960's. $10-15

Molding ware

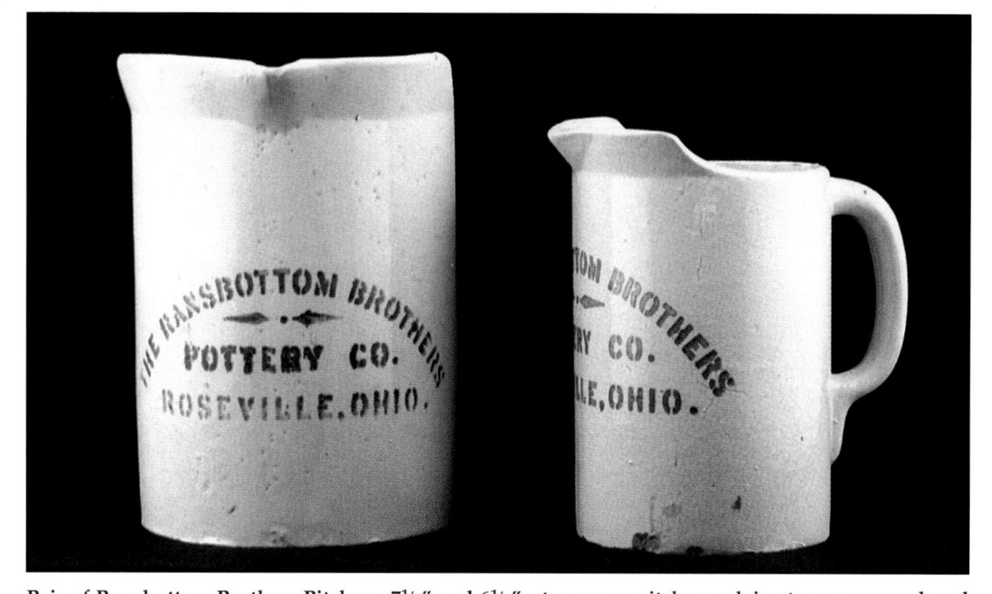

Pair of Ransbottom Brothers Pitchers, 7½" and 6½", stoneware pitchers, plain stoneware unglazed bottom, marked The Ransbottom Brothers Pottery Co. Roseville, Ohio 1908-1916.

7½" $200-250 6½" $175-200

Red Clay Pitcher, 6¾", marked outside J. Walter Ransbottom, marked Ransbottom, 1930 with a crown, and Roseville. One-of-a-kind.

Kitchen Ware Pitchers

Hand Decorated pieces, all marked RRPCo Roseville, O USA. 1974-1977.

Top Row:		Bottom Row:	
Mugs, 5¼"	$15-20	Pitcher, 8"	$75-100
Pitcher, 6"	$35-45	Mug, 5¼"	$15-20
Pitcher, 4¼"	$25-35	Pitcher, 7¼"	$60-70

Top Row:
Vase, 8", USA 139/. $60-80
Vase, 6", RRPCo Roseville, Ohio No. 357/2. $25-30
Bottom Row:
Pitcher, 8", no mark. $50-60
Vase with handles, 8", 235/. Later lines, probably Pace, but not Old Colony. $75-95

Pitchers, 8", White, RRPCo Roseville, O USA. $75-100
Light green, 243/. 1941-1949. $50-60

Yellow Pitcher, 6", yellow glazed bottom, dry foot, impressed, RRPCo Roseville, O No. 11/-. 1970's. $30-35

Pitcher, 8" dry bottom. $150-175
Pitcher, 10½", glaze footed. $200-250
Both DeDonatis decorated, molded shapes. 1928-1929

ASTROGLO

In February of 1962, Lt. Col. John Glenn became America's first astronaut, heralding our entry into mysterious, limitless outer space. In New Concord, Ohio, across the hill from Roseville, friends in Col. Glenn's home town followed his free flight in space with burning intensity and, when his successful landing was announced, their cheering was America's symbol of elation and pride. Our space exploration, during the ten months that followed, was fantastically successful,climaxedby Mariner's reaching, orbiting and sending back information from Venus, a planet 33,000,000 miles from Earth. But the romance of Col. Glenn's venture remains, due in part to his wonderful sense of humor and his wholesome, adventuresome spirit.

One of the mysteries he encountered in the dark void of his flight was the appearance of a myriad of tiny flecks or pin-points of light, which stretched into needle length as he sped through them.

Our progress from the oldest science, ceramics, to the newest, astronautics, has brought us a long, long way. But pottery still endures to remind us of our ties to the earth. As a salute to Col. Glenn and his observing the needles of light, Robinson-Ransbottom has developed a new and unusual glaze finish which we have named Astroglo. Astroglo is a blending of white glaze with a facile brown-green dark glaze, the blending resulting in flecks or intermingling needles of light.

The above information came from the inside sheet of the 1963 catalog

Top Row: Spatter Pitcher, 6", in pink and green, oval RRPCo Roseville, O, USA. 1981. $15-18
Cream and brown Pitcher, 6 1/4", square ink stamp No. 121-J. 1960's. $15-18
Green Pitcher, 6 1/4" RRPCo, Roseville, O USA. 1986. $15-18
Bottom Row: Red Pitcher, 8 1/4" rough bisque with hand painted flowers, no mark. $25-30
Black Pitcher, 11" with white drip, Astroglo (see information at left), RRPCo Roseville, O USA. 1960's. $25-30
Green Spattered Pitcher, 8 1/4", ink stamp. 1990's. $20-25

Top Row: Green Gloss Pitcher, 5 1/4" RRPCo Roseville, O USA. $15-18
Green Sponge, 4 1/2", ink stamp Robinson Ransbottom. $10-12
Pitcher, 1pt. USA, Roseville, Ohio. 1990's. $15-18
Red Sponge, 6 1/4", square ink stamp, #700-R. Late 1970's. $15-18
Center Row: Pink Hobnail, 5" crown under glaze. 1941-1943, $25-30
White, 5 1/2", RRPCo, Roseville, O impressed. 1949. $20-25
Gold and green drip, 4 3/4". RRPCo USA1960's. $10-12
Cream and blue stripe, 4 3/4", square ink stamp, #303-G. 1960's. $10-12
Bottom Row: Rust and yellow, with stripes, 7", R-RPCo Roseville, O No 357/3. 1960's. $20-25
Cream with blue and red band, ink stamp with No. 550 pitcher 1 qt. 1990's. $15-18
Orange, 6 1/2", USA 195/- impressed on dry bottom. $15-18
Green, 6 1/2", RRPCo Roseville O USA impressed under glaze. $20-25

Plymouth Colony Early American Stoneware, 1970.
Produced for only one year.
Salt and Pepper, 4 1/2", no mark, glazed bottom. $12-15 pair
Cream Pitcher, 4 1/2", 3/4 pt., no mark, glazed bottom. $12-15
Sugar, 4 1/2", RRPCo. Roseville, Ohio. $12-15
Mug. $10-12

Plymouth Colony Early American Stoneware, 1970. All but Tumbler and Ewer marked: RRPCo Roseville, Ohio USA.

<u>Top Row:</u> Ale Mug, 5 1/2"	$10-12	<u>Bottom Row:</u> Pitcher 8", 5 pt.	$25-30
Tumbler, 5 1/2", 1 pt., no mark.	$10-12	Ewer and Basin, 9" Ewer plain bottom.	$40-50
Pillar Vase, 9"	$18-20	Milk Pitcher, 7", 3pt.	$20-25
Wine Jug Vase, 8 3/4"	$15-18		
Spirits Jug, 8", 1 qt.	$18-20		

"Seventy years bring a lot of changes. Poultry fountains would be out of place on today's big poultry farms, and electric blankets replaced stoneware foot warmers long ago. Among other products we used to make, no longer in demand, are preserve jars and chamber pots.

However, not all of our early products are obsolete, but are still made to fill a genuine need. Our stoneware jars (crocks) are used in every section of the U.S. and Canada. The No. 38 Luxor porch pots and saucers have been popular for more than forty years. Water (iced tea) kegs, bean pots, and stone pitchers have been, of necessity, part of our annual production for fifty years or more. And we have made jardinieres ever since our opening day.

In this modern world, the past still holds its charm. We have tried to capture some of it in our new Plymouth Colony ware. The various pieces are not necessarily authentic, in shape or in appearance, to the pottery ware made in the 17th century. Rather, they suggest what may have occupied a captain' s table, or a settler's cupboard." *1970 catalog*

1970 Catalog page

Pasta Bowl, 15 1/2", ruffled style, signed PACE under flower and PACE backwards in the mold. $75-85

Pasta Bowl, 14 1/4", signed Pace, Young, 1953 in brown glaze, ink stamp: Rustic Ware, hand dec., RRPCo Roseville, O. $75-85

Pasta Bowl, 14 1/2", not signed, ink stamp, Rustic Ware, Hand dec. RRPCo Roseville, O. $40-45

Pasta Bowl, 14 1/2", green with brown bands, braided applied handles, RRPCo Roseville, Ohio (impressed). $50-60

Pasta Bowl, 14 1/4", RRPCo Roseville, Ohio 311-. $45-50

Pasta Bowl, 14 3/4", blue flowers and band, turquoise blue outside RRPCo Roseville, Ohio (impressed). $60-70

Pasta Bowl, 14 1/2", with stylized tulips, RRPCo Roseville, Ohio (impressed). $40-45

Pasta Bowl, 14 1/2", rose and turquoise, RRPCo Roseville, Ohio (impressed). $45-50

Pasta Bowl, 14 1/2", Tweed-type design, no mark. $40-45

Pasta Bowl, 14 1/2", with 2 circles and rose flares, RRPCo Roseville, Ohio. $40-45

Pasta Bowl, 14 3/4", green and pink stripes and brown band, RRPCo Roseville, Ohio. $40-45

Pasta Bowl, 14 1/2", turquoise and brown bands, ink stamp "Rustic Ware" Hand dec. by RRPCo Roseville, Ohio. $40-45

All of the bowls on this page were made in the 1940's-1950's and decorated mostly by Willard Pace.

Pasta Bowl, 10 1/2", turquoise and brown stripes, RRPCo Roseville, Ohio 311-. $40-45

Pasta Bowl, 10 1/2", turquoise flowers, RRPCo Roseville, Ohio. $45-55

Pasta Bowl, 10 1/2", rose and burgandy bands, RRPCo Roseville, Ohio 311-. $35-40

Pasta Bowl, 10 1/2", yellow inside with apples and brown bands, signed Pace in a brown glaze. $35-40

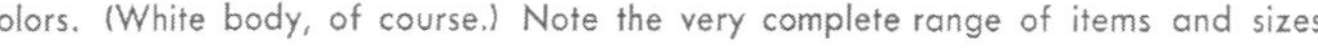

"RUSTIC WARE", with the gaiety and charm of the Old World. Freehand decoration under the glaze in flashing colors. (White body, of course.) Note the very complete range of items and sizes.

No. 311/ Bowls
5", 7", 10", 12" and 14"

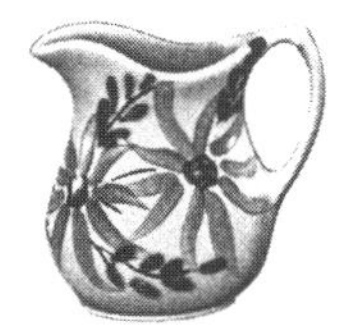

No. 311/ Pitchers
12, 32, and 48 ounces.

No. 311/1
Condiment Jar and Cover

No. deep Bowl

No. 311/15
Cookie Jar

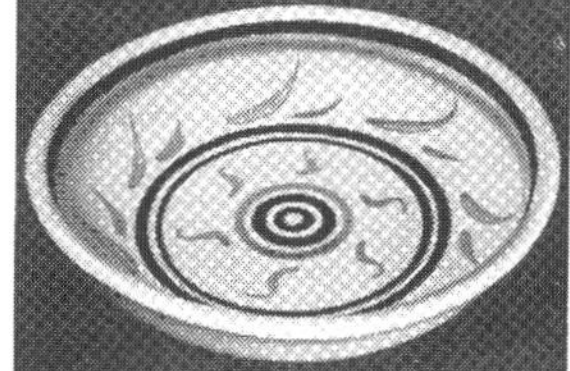

No. 311/14"
Shallow Bowl

1953 Catalog page

Bowl, $10^{1/2}$", marked: RRPCo Roseville, O 311- Rev. Holtzhauser Christmas 1951. $125-150
Covered Bowl, $2^{1/2}$" tall, 30-5, hand decorated by RRPCo Roseville, O. $45-50

Plate, 8", Pace signed plate, clear glazed back with dry foot, no mark. $40-50

Plate, $10^{1/2}$", Pace signed, RRPCo Roseville, Ohio, 311-$10^{1/2}$. 1953. $125-175

Rustic Crock, $5^{13/4}$" x $9^{1/4}$", flat, plain unglazed bottom. $15-20

Kitchen Ware
Rustic

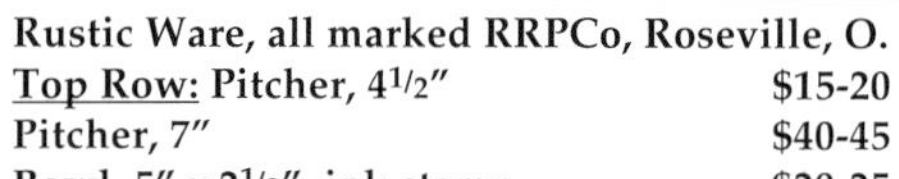

Rustic Ware, all marked RRPCo, Roseville, O.
Top Row: Pitcher, $4\frac{1}{2}$" $15-20
Pitcher, 7" $40-45
Bowl, 5" x $2\frac{1}{2}$", ink stamp. $20-25

Bottom Row: Three pitchers, 6", No. 357/2 $30-35 each

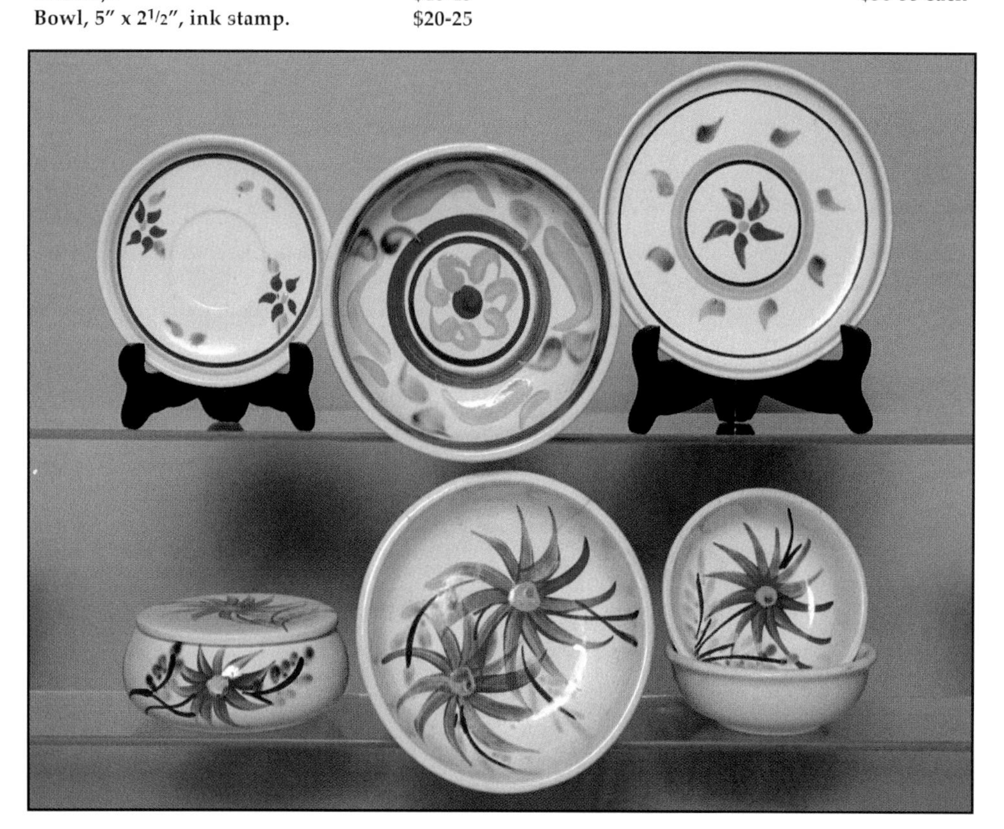

Rustic Bowls and Plate:
Top Row: All marked RRPCo Roseville, Ohio.
Saucer, 6", 311-. $15-20
Bowl, $7\frac{1}{4}$", rose and turquoise, 311-7" and ink stamp. $45-50
Salad Plate, $7\frac{1}{2}$", 311-$7\frac{1}{2}$" $20-25

Bottom Row: Covered Bowl, marked RRPCo Roseville, Ohio and ink stamp. $45-50
Bowl with rose flowers, $7\frac{1}{4}$", marked RRPCo Roseville Ohio and ink stamp, 311-7" $60-65
Two cereal bowls, $5\frac{1}{2}$", both with ink stamp, one with impressed 311. $25-30

Two deep bowls, $11\frac{1}{2}$" x $4\frac{1}{4}$", one ink stamped. $55-60 each

Rustic Salt and Pepper set, 3", no mark. $10-15

Yellow square Pace plate, $7\frac{1}{4}$", glazed bottom, mark illegible. $30-35

New Rustic Items
"Rustic Ware, with the gaiety and charm of the Old World. Freehand decoration under the glaze in flashing colors. (White body, of course.)"
1954 catalog *1954-1960*

Kitchen Ware
Suburban (aka) Spongeware

High Jar, 1 qt.; High Jar 2 qt.; High Jar, 4 qt. $7-8, $10-12, $12-15

No. 700 Water Keg, 14" Blue Spongeware, square ink stamp, USA impressed, 1983. $50-70

Left: Blue Spongeware No. 125 Water Keg Set. 1990's
Set came boxed with keg, faucet and 4 mugs.
Mugs, 4", square ink stamp
Water Keg, 11", square ink stamp, flat unglazed bottom. $80-100 set

Top Row:	
Mug	$5-6
High Jar	$7-8
Salad Bowl	$6-7
Covered Bowl	$8-10
Bottom Row:	
Kitchen Crock, 1 qt.	$7-8
Ewer and Basin	$30-35 set
Cookie Jar	$25-28

"The charm and beauty of earlier years. Each piece is hand decorated in spatter which creates a one of a kind look-- no two pieces exactly alike. For the young of all ages."

In 1979, items were available in October Blue and Buckeye Brown.

Kitchen Ware

Suburban (aka) Spongeware

Some of the many steps in making this beautiful ware.

1981 Catalog page

1979 Catalog page

1979 Catalog page

Kitchen Ware
Tea Pots

Hand Painted Tea Pot, 6″, glazed bottom, dry foot, no mark. $100-125

Top Row:
Black Tea Pot, 4½″, red clay, Crown impressed mark, 1940's. $25-35
Other pots have glazed bottom, dry foot, no marks:
Green Tea Pot, 6″, 6 oz., 1931. $70-80
Mauve Tea Pot, 5½″, 30 oz., 1931. $60-70
Bottom Row:
Mottled Tea Pot, 7″, 36 oz. $100-125
Mauve Tea Pot, 7″, 42 oz., 1931. $80-100

Yellow Octagonal Tea Pot, 4½″ glazed bottom, dry foot, marked: RRPCo Roseville Ohio 306-2. 1949. $20-25

Yellow Stackable Tea Pot, 8″, each piece marked RRPCo Roseville, Ohio. $20-25
Aqua Tea Pot, 5½″, RRPCo Roseville Ohio 306-6. $20-25
Aqua Stackable Tea Pot, 8″, each piece marked RRPCo Roseville, Ohio. 1949. $20-25

Kitchen Ware
Terra

No. 850 Terra Flower Pot and Saucer.
$10-15

1984 Catalog page

Terra 1982-1989

Kitchen Ware
Wheat

1990 Catalog page

NEW. Grouping of Wheat Pattern Ware, No. 600. 1990 -1997.

Top: No. 06020 Low Jar,1 pt.	$5-6
No. 06030 Flared Crock, 1 qt.	$7-8
No. 06090 Pitcher, 2 qt.	$20-22
No. 06080 Pitcher, 1 qt.	$14-15
No. 06070 Pitcher, 1/2 pt.	$10-12
Bottom: No. 60420 Pasta Bowl 12"	$10-12
No. 60220 Pie Plate 10 3/4"	$15-20
No. 60190 Covered Casserole, 2 qt. (also came in 1 qt.)	$17-20
Plate, 6".	$7-8
Pizza Plate, 14", 1990-2000.	$12-14

NEW. Grouping of Wheat Pattern Ware, No. 600. 1990 -1997.

Bottom: Covered Canisters	$9-11, $10-12
Cup	$4-5
Bread Pan	$18-20
Baker	$24-28
Top: Custard Cup	$4-5
Bean Pot 4 qt.	$20-24
Double Boiler.	$7-8

Kitchen Ware
Williamsburg Pioneer

Williamsburg Water Keg, 14", cream with blue stripe, Crown (2). 1974. $45-55

Williamsburg. NEW, Crown, RRP6 Roseville, OH
Water Keg, 2 gal. $45-50
Water Keg, 4 gal. $65-70
Churn, 3 gal. 1974. $48-52

Williamsburg Barrel Salt and Pepper set. Blue stripes on grey. 3", no mark, red clay. 1974. $10-12 pair

Catalog Note: "RRP Williamsburg Pioneer. Serving Pieces and Accessories. Our popular #303 line adds nostalgia to any kitchen. Ovenproof. Dishwasher Safe and can be used in microwave oven. Do not place on open flame."

RRP Williamsburg Pioneer
Serving Pieces and Accessories
Our popular #303 line adds a nostalgic touch to any kitchen.
Ovenproof, Dishwasher Safe, and can be used in microwave ovens. Do not place on open flame.

1979 Catalog page

Williamsburg Blue Band Kitchen Ware. 1974.

Top:

Covered Casserole	$11-13
Covered Casserole	$15-20
Bean Pot with Cover, 1 qt.	$12-15

Bottom:

Flared Crock with ice holder	$7-8
Ice holder	$6-7
No. 303 Cookie Jar	$22-25
Cereal Bowl	$5-6
Bread and Dessert Plate	$7-8
Dinner Plate	$14-16

Crown Pottery Color Chart: 7-Tan, 8-Victoria Blue, 9-Yellow, 10-Victoria Green, 11-Victoria Rose, 12-Gloss Blend, 13-Pastel Blue, 14-Pastel Pink, 15-Pastel Brown. 1939.

Hand decorated covered utility jar with lids, plain crock bottoms, DeDonatis decorated. 1931. 7½" $125-150 9" $150-175

Top Row:
Morning Glory Steins $35-50 each
Pitcher, glazed bottom, dry foot: 5½, 5 and 4½ cup Stein $65-75

Bottom Row:
Covered Casseroles with rippled (sunburst) heat-radiating bottoms. 7½" $75-85 8½" $80-100
All DeDonatis Morning Glory. 1928-1929.

Ribbed bottom

Covered Casserole dish, 3½ x 7½", plain ribbed bottom, 1928-1930. $100-125

Hand decorated Snack Dish, 1937. $35-40

Left: Bean Pot with yellow and black sponge painting, RRPCo Roseville, O USA. 1950's. $25-35

Caramel Kitchen Crock 5¾", Oval ink stamp, RRPCo Roseville, O USA. $12-15

Pink Rosella Stein, 4½", plain pink glazed bottom, dry foot, Rosella. 1930's. $50-60

Early American Brown Bean Pot, 2 qt., ink stamp, Robinson Ransbottom, Roseville Ohio USA. $20-25

Early American
<u>Top Row:</u> Cup, 4½", glazed, USA $6-8
Pitcher, 6½", unglazed, ink stamp (square) with #121-J at bottom of stamp $15-18
Pitcher, 4½" $10-12
Jug, 7¼", #121-K. $25-30
Bank, 8½", glazed bottom, RRPCo. Roseville, O, USA $35-40
<u>Bottom Row:</u> Crock, 3¼", square ink stamp $6-8
Crock, 6", square ink stamp, no shape # $8-10
Pitcher, 8½" USA, #121-E. $20-25
Bean Pot, 6¾" ink stamp, no square, Robinson Ransbottom Roseville, Ohio, USA. $20-25
1960's-1980's.

1960 Catalog page

Kitchen Ware

Snack Sets, 8" tall, in three colors, RRPCo Roseville, Ohio, USA. 1972-1973
$25-30 each set

Blue sponged mug with blue flower, 5¹/4", no mark, glazed bottom, dry foot. Sample. $35-40 each

Covered Casserole, 3¹/2", ink stamp Americana. 1970's. $15-20
Covered Casserole, 9¹/2", cream with orangestripes, Americana ink stamp. 1970's. $25-30
Caramel Casserole 5", no mark, glazed bottom. 1980's. $20-25

Mugs, 5¹/4", especially made for The Pot Shop, 1974-1975.
Bottom showing The Pot Shop mark.
$25-30 each

Snowmen: 1999. Produced 1 year only.

Pie Plate	$25-40
Dessert Plate	$20-30
Cookie Jar	$40-50
Pitcher	$35-45

Below:
Ramekin, 2", RRPCo USA, Roseville, OH,
Pot, 3", RRPCo Roseville, Ohio, 10 oz. Kitchen crock;
Ramekin, 2", red and blue, Roseville, Ohio;
Carmel Ramekin, 2" Roseville, Ohio. All 1980's.
$5-8 each

1999 Catalog page

CROWN POTTERY

No. 120
Yellow Bowl
Sizes 5¾", 6¾", 7¾", 8¾", 9½", 12", 14¼" and 15½".

No. 305 Shoulder Bowls
Brown Banded.
Sizes 5", 6", 7", 8", 9", 12" and 14".

No. 194 Cookie Jar
Assorted Backgrounds and Decorations.
7 Pint Capacity

No. 306
Octagon Teapot
Sizes 2, 4 and 6 Cups

Boston Bean Pot
Brown and White Glaze.

No. 307 Cookie Jar
10 Pint Capacity.
Assorted Backgrounds and Decorations.

Steam Table Jars
Solid White Glaze.
Sizes 6½", 8½" and 10½"

"OSCAR"
Children Can't Resist Him
9 Pint Capacity

No. 104 Cookie Jar
Assorted Backgrounds and Decorations.
8 Pint Capacity

CROWN POTTERY

SO NEW - - - These attractive items were too late to be placed upon their proper pages. Smartly styled, they make ideal gifts or prizes.

No. 218/ Bowls
Sizes 5¾", 7¼", 9¼" Diameter. White glazed, hand overglaze decorations

No. 218/ Pitchers
Sizes ½, 1½, 2½, 5 Pint
White glazed, hand overglaze decorations

No. 302 Stackaway Four-Piece Tea Service
"Tea for Two"

No. 304
Jumbo Salt and Pepper
4¼" Tall

No. 303
Four-Piece Kitchen Set
Salt and Pepper 5½" Tall
Conserve Jar 4¾" Tall

No. 306
Octagon Teapot
Sizes 2, 4 and 6 Cups

No. 500
Flower Pot and Saucer
Hand Decorated

(See price sheet for complete details)

THE ROBINSON-RANSBOTTOM POTTERY CO., HEAD OFFICE AND PLANT, ROSEVILLE, OHIO
AFFILIATED WITH —
THE ROBINSON CLAY PRODUCT CO., AKRON, OHIO

1949 Catalog pages

The "Pot Shop" retail outlet store at the plant.

Personalized Stoneware Crockery Program

Item # 99902
See Price Sheet for Program Details

The 2 gallon (9" Dia. x 9" Tall, Wt. 15 lbs.) stoneware crocks are beautifully personalized and deeply etched to last for generations. They are great for indoors or outdoors, they can be used as a housemarker, a warm welcome for guests, a planter or a container. They are a unique gift for a special occasion like a housewarming, wedding, anniversary, holiday or a family heirloom. Place them wherever desired; a porch, driveway, hallway, garden or hearth. The crocks are food safe so they can also be a wonderful addition to a kitchen.

Etching can be filled with the following colors (one color per crock).

Etched Crock Program

Celebrate a grand opening, anniversary, hometown event, or promote clubs, landmarks, colleges, cities, counties or states. Whatever you choose it can be beautifully etched into a stoneware crock.

99250 - Mug
99919 - 1 Gallon
99929 - 1 Pt. Low Jar
99939 - 1 Qt. Low Jar
99949 - 2 Qt. Low Jar
99959 - 1 Qt. High Jar
99969 - 2 Qt. High Jar

See Price Sheet for Program Details

5

1999 Catalog page

Low Crock for Centennial made for employees.
$25-35

Crock production

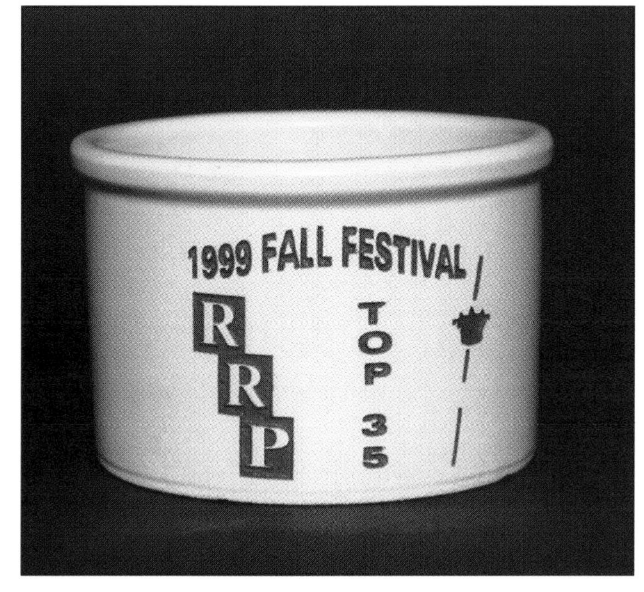

New Crock, 4" x 6", given away at 1999 Fall Festival for the top 35 cars, limited, marked: RRPCo 1 qt. low Roseville, Ohio, USA.
$35-50

Three Crocks, all new. Top: 1 gal. size. $45-50
Bottom: 2 gal size. Left, $50-60, right, $60-75

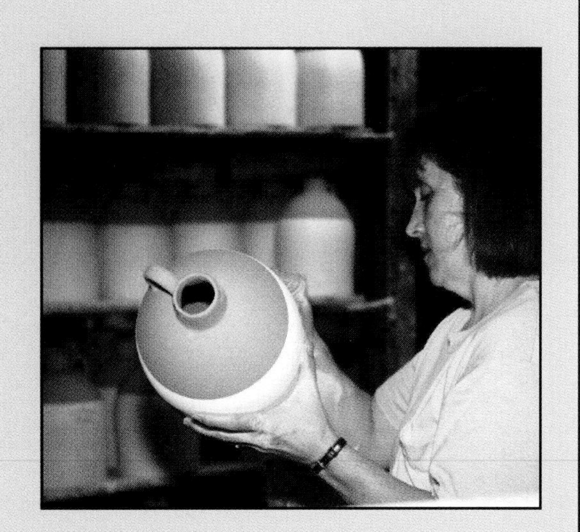

Employee inspecting ware.

Stamping crown logo on a jug.

Ware going through the automatic spray machine to apply glaze.

CROWN POTTERY

No. 186 Pie Plate
9½″ diameter

Steam Table Jars
Solid White Glaze.
Sizes 6½″, 8½″ and 10½″

No. 186 Casserole
Sizes 7½″ and 8½″

Individual Bean Pot
Handled and Covered.
8 Ounce Capacity

Ice Cube or Butter Tub
9½″ diameter, 6″ tall

Low Ice or Butter Tub
White Glazed, Blue Banded
9½″ diameter, 5¾″ tall
Capacity 1 gallon

Bean Baker
Open Top.
Solid Brown Glaze.
Sizes 8, 16 and 32 ounces

Stone Acid Pitcher
For Factory or Laboratory Use.
Sizes ½, 1, 1½ and 2 gallons

Dutch Oven
Self-Basting Casserole.
9¾″ diameter

Boston Bean Pot
Brown and White Glaze
1, 2 and 3 quart sizes have one handle;
4, 6 and 8 quart sizes have two handles.

● *Please refer to Information Sheet for complete details* ●

1941 Catalog page

Meal Makers

Designed for catering to
the needs of "THE INNER MAN"

Please refer to information
sheet for complete details

No. 1503
5-9″ Bowl Set
Rainbow Combination

No. 391 Shoulder Bowls
(Sets or Open Stock.)

No. 1504
Pitchers
(4 Sizes)

No. 370
Covered Casserole

Steam Table Jars
Solid White Glaze.
Sizes 6½″, 8½″ and 10½″

Boston Bean Pot
Brown and White Glaze.

No. 120
Yellow Bowl
Sizes 5⅓″, 6⅓″, 7⅓″, 8¼″,
9½″, 12″ and 14¼″.

THE ROBINSON-RANSBOTTOM POTTERY CO., Main Office and Plant, Roseville, Ohio

1957 Catalog page

Brown Drip. Top Row: Salt and Pepper set, 3″ $5-8 pair
Salt and Pepper set, 5″, no marks. $12-15 pair
Bottom Row: Snack plate, 12″ RRPCo USA, Roseville, O, $15-18

Brown Drip
Top Row:
Bowls, 9″ and 8″, RRPCo Roseville O USA. $16-20, $10-15
Covered Casserole with handles, 8″, RRPCo Roseville, O USA. 1960's. $20-25
Bottom Row: Bowl, 9″, RRPCo Roseville, O, USA. $15-20
Vase, 8 1/2″, plain flat bottom $20-25
Covered Casserole, 8″, flat bottom, RRPCo, Roseville, O. $20-25

Top Row: No. 1211 Rectangular Dish, 9″, RRPCo Roseville, O. USA, $20-25
Flower Dish, 12″ x 7″, RRPCo USA, Roseville, O. $20-25
Bottom Row: Oval Bowl, 8″ x 3″ $15-18
Ash Tray, 7 3/4 x 5 3/4″, RRPCo USA, Roseville, O. $15-18
Early 1960's.

Lamp Bases

1994 Catalog page

Sleeping Peon, 8" Lamp Base, plain, unglazed bottom with large hole and hole in the back for cord. 1937-1940. $100-150

Apple Lamp Base, 8½", factory made, 1950's, $35-45

Also see Old Colony lamp bases on page 121.

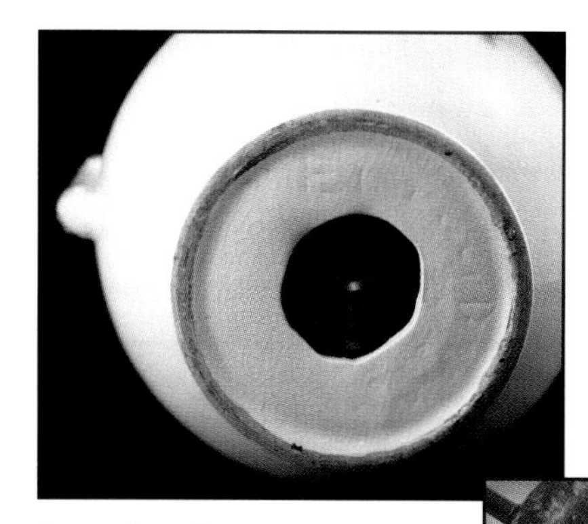

Base of Apple Lamp.

Green over Orchid glaze Drip Lamp, 9", production piece, concave, plain bottom. 1930's. $200-225

Miscellaneous
Desert Dwellers

Desert Dwellers, red clay, no marks, 1976-1977
$20-25 each

Top Row:
No. 604 Road Runner, 6",
No. 601 Owl on a Log, 8 1/2"
No. 608 Desert Fox, 4"

Bottom Row:
Road Runner on a Log, 2 pieces, 9"
Lizard on a Log, 7 1/2"
Toad and Coyote also made

Below: No. 605 Iguana, 5" $20-25

1976 Catalog page

Lead Pots were pots that Robinson Ransbottom made during the depression for a leading lead oxide manufacturer. The lead manufacturer used the pots purchased from Robinson Ransbottom in their bisque form to produce their lead. There is no example of the original bisque pot. The pots pictured below were decorated for Mort Ransbottom's 60th birthday, Nov. 25, 1938. Depicted are the clay veins, some folk art and rhymes playing off the lead pot production.

Cuspidors, 4½" x 7", blue, green and brown; no mark on blue and green, color glazed bottom, dry foot, 1930's; brown marked RRPCo Roseville Ohio, 193. 1937-1970's. First two: $35-50, last one: $15-18

Cuspidor, 4½" x 7", hand decorated, cream glazed bottom, dry foot. 1928-1930. $45-65

Several views of "Lead Pot", 9" x 8", special birthday pot for Mort Ransbottom. 1938.

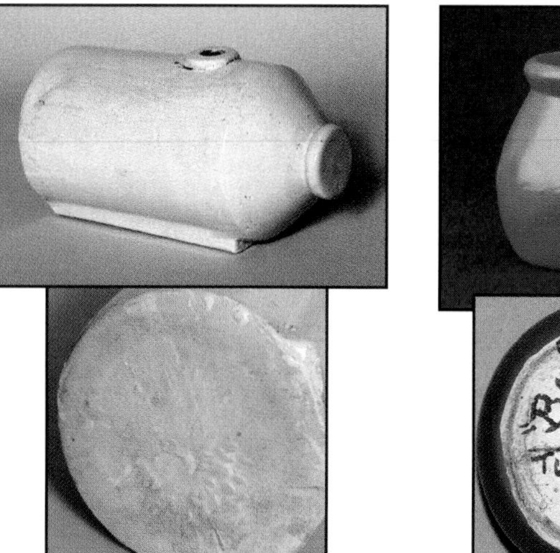

Foot Warmer, 10½". 1930's -1946. $35-45

Scarab Paper Weight, 4¼", marked on bottom in raised letters. $100-125

Golden Anniversary employee give-away, 2¼", no mark on bottom. 1951. $25-35

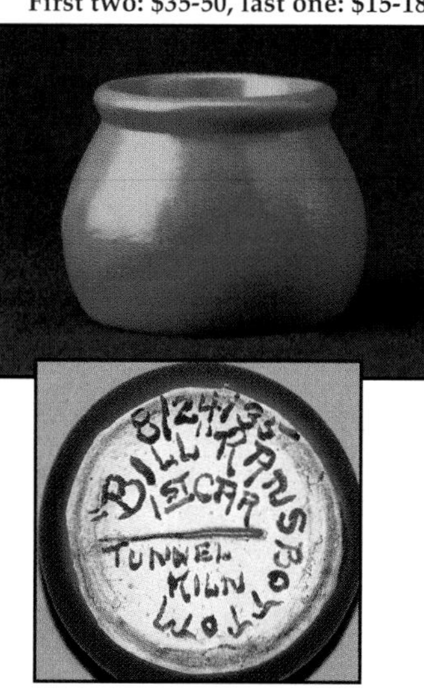

Pot, 2¾", orange. This pot was fired on the first car through the new tunnel kiln on 8-24-1935.

Match Holder, 5½", white, hand painted, crown on bottom. Early 1940's. $15-20

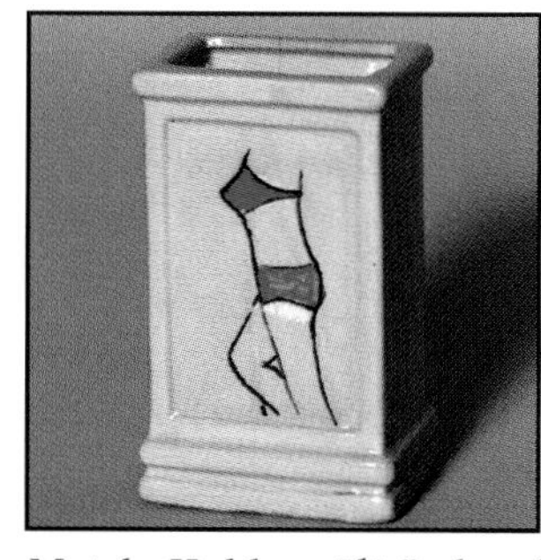

Match Holder, 5¼", hand painted girl, pink glazed bottom, impressed crown mark. $15-20

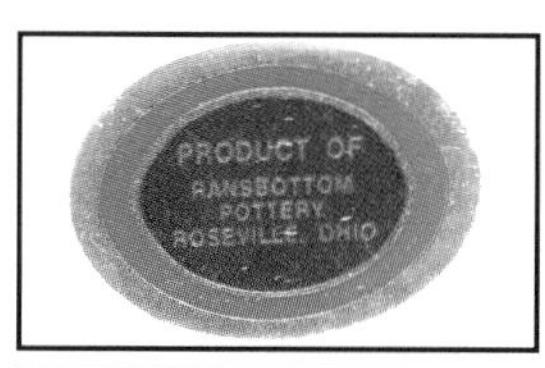

Barrel Churn, 16½", 37" overall with stand, Crown with 5, STONE BARREL CHURN, Pat. Aug. 15, 1905. $200-250

Miscellaneous Pottery

Rose on Trellis Chamber Pot with handle, 5 1/4", cream and blue, ivory glaze and blue tint. Late 1920's to early 1930's. $85-100

Bowl, 5", with bird and applied flowers inside, Robinson Clay Products Co 301 over USA. $20-25

Grass Growing Heads: Barnacle Bill (the sailor) and Elmer (the doughboy), 7", the army head, marked on back: Patent Pending. 1941-1943.
Jocko (the monkey), 5 1/2", plain unglazed (bottom also). 1948.

Bisque growing heads remained moist, so that grass seeds, planted in deep cuts, could grow.

Bill and Elmer $40-50
Jocko $30-40

Salesman Sample Vases and box, vases are 3", variety of glazes. 1970's. Rare.

Pot, 6", hand thrown with applied handles, glazed bottom with 3 stilt marks and "O' What Night 6-21-34" (in clay by hand). On the outside: F.W. Ransbottom (inscribed).

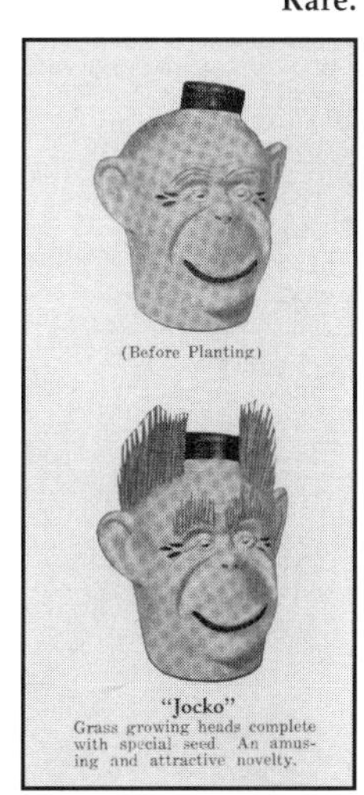

1948 Catalog detail

1974 Catalog page

Left: Pair of sinks, 28" x 25" x 16", buff clay, pink (flesh) glaze, made for Frank Ransbottom's fish camp cabin.

No. 322/6
Square Dish Garden
No. 322/8
Rect. Dish Garden
No. 325/
Casual Bowls
No. 289
4" Crocus Urn
After Planting
No. 291
Stock Vase
10", 12", 15" and 18"
No. 287
6" African Violet Jar
Glazed Jardiniere and
Special Red Clay Body
Growing Pot
THE ROBINSON-RANSBOTTOM POTTERY CO., MAIN OFFICE AND PLANT, ROSEVILLE, OHIO
AFFILIATED WITH
THE ROBINSON CLAY PRODUCT CO., AKRON, OHIO

1950 Catalog page

Planter, 4½", brown with white drip, RRPCo Roseville, O. $10-15
Planter, 3¼" x 7½", green, RRPCo 1210-75, USA. $8-10

CROWN POTTERY
Floral Accessories
GRACEFUL STYLING—Designed to give the utmost utility for beautiful floral arrangements.
No. 1286
Stork Planter
No. 1245/
Flower Bowl
No. 1244/
Oval Dish Garden
No. 1321/
Pedestal Dish Garden
No. 1242
Rectangular Dish Garden
No. 1204/
Planting Dish
No. 285 Shoe
Hand Decorated
No. 1210/
Footed Oval Dish
No. 1400/
Jardinieres
No. 1401/
Std. Jardinieres
No. 1243/
Jardiniere-Planter
No. 211/ Florist Vases
Ideal for floral arrangements
THE ROBINSON-RANSBOTTOM POTTERY CO. Main Office and Plant, Roseville, Ohio

1959 Catalog page

No. 213 Flower Box, 12" x 4". All marked with impressed crown, rust, white and green. $35-45 each
Green with white has RRPCo in crown and USA, Roseville Ohio beneath. See bottom at inset.
"Complete with 3 pots" from 1941 catalog.

No. 264/
Dish Gardens

1947 Catalog detail

Bottom right photo: Top Row:
No. 270 White Flower Pot, 4¾", RRPCO Roseville, Ohio 270, 1949-1952. $8-10
No. 205 Spattered Flower Pot, 5", RRPCO Roseville, Ohio 205, 1958-1959. $8-10
No. 266 Yellow Flower Pot, 4¾", RRPCO 266, 1947. $8-10

Center Row:
No. 263 Pink Flower Box, 3½" x 6", RRPCO 263/6 Roseville, Ohio 270. $12-15
No. 270 Yellow Flower Pot, 4", RRPCO Roseville, Ohio 270. $8-10
No. 263 Yellow Flower Box, 3½", RRPCO 263/6 Roseville, Ohio. $12-15

Bottom Row: White Flower Box, 16" x 5¾", RRPCO 263/16" Roseville, Ohio 270. 1947-1950. $35-40

Planters & Dish Gardens

Window Box, 12″ x 4$^{1}/_{2}$″, blue, plain, unglazed bottom, no mark. 1926. $150-200

Decorated Lennox Window Box, 18″ x 6″, green and cream, no mark. 1926. $100-150

Lennox Ware is made on a Stoneware body, no glaze on the inside, matt green outside on the low parts, natural Terra Cotta finish on the high parts.

Drip Dish Gardens, marked RRPCo USA Roseville, O. 1960's.

Top Row: No. 311 Oval Bowl, 8″ x 3″	$15-20
No. 311 Round Bowl, 10″ x 3″, 311-10″	$15-20
Bottom Row: Flower Pot, 4$^{1}/_{4}$″	$15-20
Footed Bowl, 3$^{1}/_{2}$″ x 5″, USA.	$15-20
No. 1217 Bowl, 3$^{1}/_{2}$″ x 8″. Late 1960's.	$15-20

Green Footed Planter, 7$^{1}/_{2}$″, RRPCo Roseville, O USA. 1960's. $15-20

No. 119 Light Green Planter, 6$^{1}/_{4}$″, green glazed bottom, dry foot, 119/ - impressed. Late 30's. $15-20

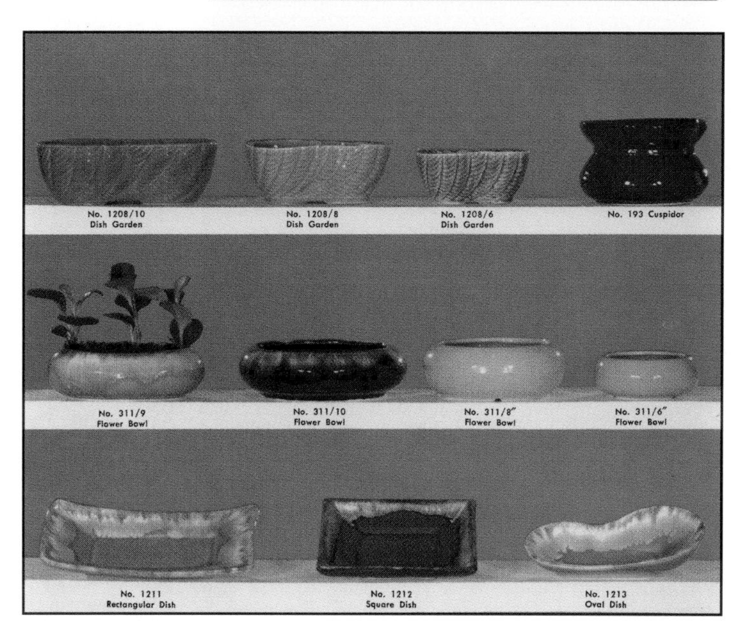

1961 Catalog page

1960 Catalog page

No. 213 Flower Box
12″ long
Complete with three pots

1941 Catalog detail

Yellow Ribbed Planter, 9" x 11", glazed bottom, dry foot, USA. 1960's. $15-20

1969 Catalog detail

No. 850 Terra Flower Pot and Saucer. $10-15

R. E. Pots & Saucers
Hanging Baskets
Standard
Azalea
Bulb Pan
R.E.
No. 22E
No. 200
No. 100
Bisque
No. 553
No. 592

1969 Catalog detail

CROWN POTTERY

FLOWER POTS . . . A most complete line of Flower Pots,—glazed colors, hand lacquer decorated and plain red in a variety of shapes and sizes.

Standard Shape

Lois Shape

Azalea Pot

Fern or Bulb Pot

No. 600 Lois Shape
Lacquered Shoulders
Natural Light Buff Body

U and T Hand Decorated Flower Pots and Saucers
Assorted Decorations on Green (T) or Red (U) Background

Swing Pot
Hand Decorated
(Indentation in bottom, can punch for drainage)

Swing Pot
Solid Lacquer Colors or Natural Stoneware Buff
(Indentation in bottom, can punch for drainage)

Sprayed Pot and Saucer
Solid Colors: Red, Green and Blue.
3¼" to 12¼" diameters inclusive

No. 121 Jardiniere

No. 214 Flower Pot
(Saucer Attached)

No. 121 Flower Pot
(Saucer Attached)
5¾", 6¾", 7¾" and 8¾" diameters

Cemetery Vase
5" and 6" diameter

1941 Catalog page

1972 Catalog detail

Planters
Flower Pots

Flower Pots and Saucers, 7", RRPCo USA Roseville, Ohio, in white and blue. New. $10-12 each

Left: 1990 TANTONE Catalog page

Planter, 10", in green with spatter glaze, glazed bottom, dry foot, no mark. $15-20

White Footed Planter, 5½", RRPCoRoseville. $10-15

No. 548 "Flame" flared bowl, planter. 1979. $15-20

1971 Catalog detail.

Flower pots: $10-12, $8-10, $5-6

Outer Space Planters, 1955. No. 415-420. Six in the series.
$65-75 each

Top Row: Caterpillar, 3½", 418
Beetles, 6", 420, in yellow and aqua

Middle Row: Caterpillar, 3½", 418
Bees, 3½", 417, aqua and yellow
Butterfly, 4½", aqua, 419

Bottom Row: Snails, 4½", green and cream, 415
Grasshopper, 5" rust, 416
Butterfly, 4½", yellow, 419
All marked RRPCo Roseville, Ohio.
Not shown in catalog, but listed on price sheets.

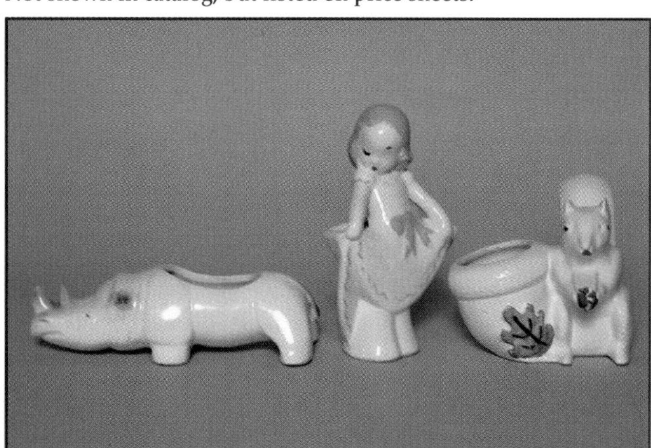

Rhino Planter, 10" x 3", flat feet, unglazed, no mark. $15-20
Shy Anne Planter, 8½", crown impressed mark. $15-20
Squirrel and Acorn Planter, 6½", x 5½", flat, unglazed bottom, $15-20
Early 1940's.
Rhino, color under glaze; girl and squirrel, cold painted.

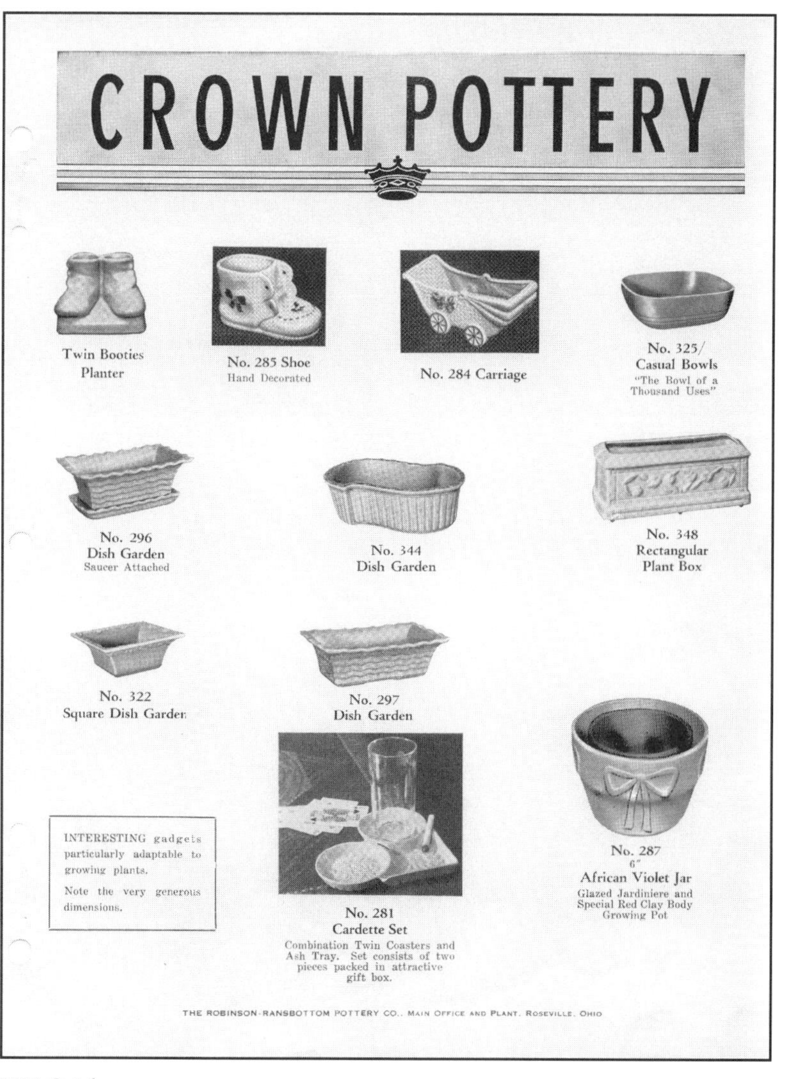

CROWN POTTERY

Twin Booties Planter

No. 285 Shoe
Hand Decorated

No. 284 Carriage

No. 325/ Casual Bowls
"The Bowl of a Thousand Uses"

No. 296
Dish Garden
Saucer Attached

No. 344
Dish Garden

No. 348
Rectangular Plant Box

No. 322
Square Dish Garden

No. 297
Dish Garden

INTERESTING gadgets particularly adaptable to growing plants.

Note the very generous dimensions.

No. 281
Cardette Set
Combination Twin Coasters and Ash Tray. Set consists of two pieces packed in attractive gift box.

No. 287
6"
African Violet Jar
Glazed Jardiniere and Special Red Clay Body Growing Pot

THE ROBINSON-RANSBOTTOM POTTERY CO., MAIN OFFICE AND PLANT, ROSEVILLE, OHIO

1952 Catalog page

Novelty Planters

Top Row: Parakeet Planter, 5″
Wren Planter, 5″, with hole in back for wall pocket
Wren Planter, 5″
All marked RRPCo Roseville, Ohio, USA (raised).
Bottom Row: Parakeet Planter, 7″, 1957.
Wren Planters, 7″ $35-40 each
All marked RRPCo Roseville, Ohio, USA impressed. 1957.

Planter of "Cow Jumped Over the Moon", 3½″, no mark. $30-35

No. 6 Rabbit Planter, 7″, flat, unglazed bottom with unpunched drain hole. 1931. $75-100

Pelican Planters, 5″ and 8″, glazed bottoms, dry foot, no mark. 1941.
5″ $25-30
8″ $35-40

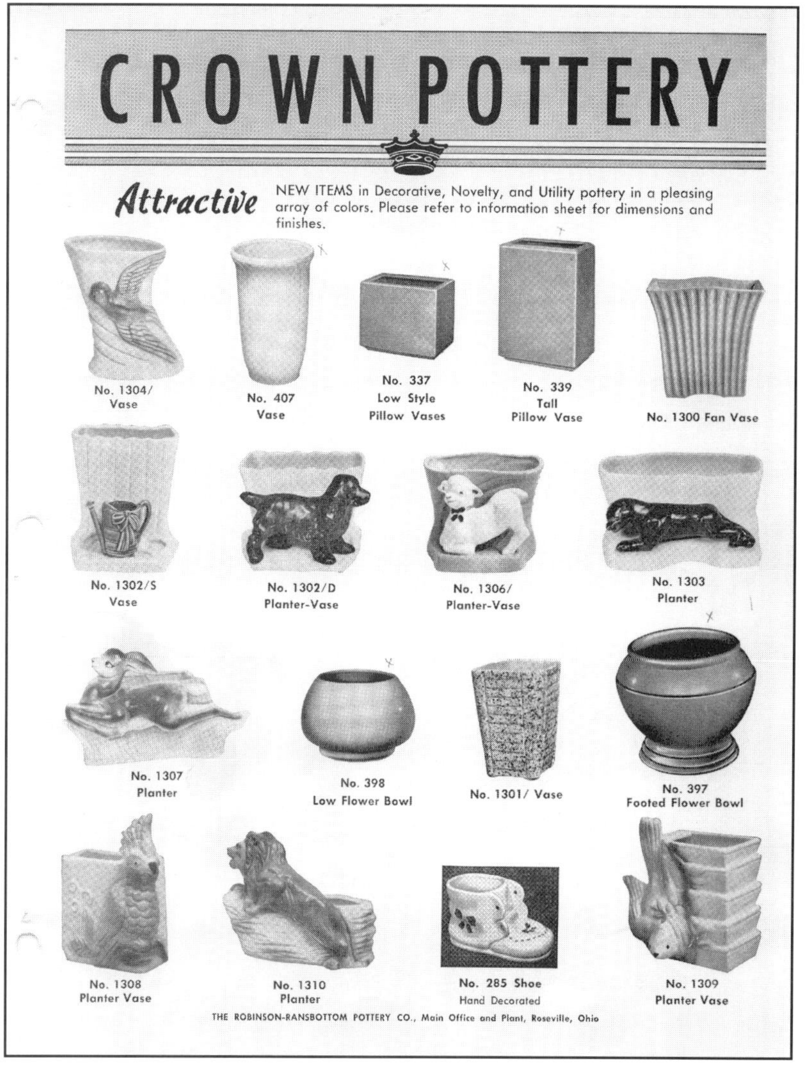

CROWN POTTERY

Attractive NEW ITEMS in Decorative, Novelty, and Utility pottery in a pleasing array of colors. Please refer to information sheet for dimensions and finishes.

No. 1304/ Vase
No. 407 Vase
No. 337 Low Style Pillow Vases
No. 339 Tall Pillow Vase
No. 1300 Fan Vase
No. 1302/S Vase
No. 1302/D Planter-Vase
No. 1306/ Planter-Vase
No. 1303 Planter
No. 1307 Planter
No. 398 Low Flower Bowl
No. 1301/ Vase
No. 397 Footed Flower Bowl
No. 1308 Planter Vase
No. 1310 Planter
No. 285 Shoe Hand Decorated
No. 1309 Planter Vase

THE ROBINSON-RANSBOTTOM POTTERY CO., Main Office and Plant, Roseville, Ohio

1957 Catalog page

Novelty Planters. 1957.
Dog Planter, 4 1/2", RRPCo Roseville, Ohio, 1302-4", USA (raised). $35-45
Lion Planter, 7" RRPCo Roseville, Ohio. $75-85
Watering Can Planter, 6 1/2", RRPCo Roseville, Ohio, No. 1302/6", US (raised). $40-50

No. 285 Baby Shoe Planters. 1949-1950's.
Baby Shoes, 3 1/2", hand painted, flat bottoms, unglazed.
$8-10 each

Novelty Planters
Top Row:
Open Baby Buggy Planter, 3" x 7", no mark. 1950-1956. $10-15
Stork and Buggy Planter, 7", RRPCo Roseville, Ohio, USA. 1950. $15-20
Blue Twin Booties Planter, 2 3/4", glazed bottom, dry foot, No mark. $8-10 each
Pink Twin Booties Planter, 2 3/4", glazed bottom, dry foot, RRPCo Roseville, Ohio, 1941-1947 and 1952-1953. $8-10 each
Bottom Row: Stork and Buggy Planters, all marked RRPCo Roseville, Ohio, USA. 1959. $15-20 each

No. 340 Madonna Planters, 6 1/2":
Plain, 1952-1955. $20-25
Gold trim, 1952-1953. $35-40
No. 298 Fan Vase. Early 1950's. $10-15
All marked RRPCo Roseville, Ohio.

Novelty Planters

Novelty Planters. 1957.
<u>Top Row:</u>
Deer, 4″, glazed bottom, USA. $35-45
Rust Watering Can, 4″, RRPCo Roseville, Ohio, USA (raised), 0-1302-4″ $25-35
Black Watering Can, 4″, RRPCo Roseville, Ohio, USA (raised) 0-1302-4″ $25-35
<u>Bottom Row:</u>
Pink Lamb, 4″, RRPCo Roseville, Ohio, , 0-1306-4″ $35-45
Green Planter, 3 1/2″, with 8″ rust panther, RRPCo Roseville, Ohio, 1303-8, USA (raised). $40-50
Cream Planter, 3 1/2″, with 8″ black panther, RRPCo Roseville, Ohio, 1303-8″, USA (raised). $40-50

Novelty Planters. 1957.
<u>Top Row:</u> $40-50 each
Dog, 6 1/2″, plain bottom;
Aqua Lamb, 6 1/2″, RRPCo Roseville, Ohio.
Pink Lamb, 6 1/2″, RRPCo Roseville, Ohio. No. 1306-6″. USA (raised).
<u>Bottom Row:</u> Dog, 4″, RRPCo Rose-ville, Ohio, No. 1302-4″. $35-45
Gazelle, 4 3/4″, RRPCo 1307 Roseville, Ohio, USA (raised). $40-50
Gazelle, 4 3/4″, USA (raised). $60-70

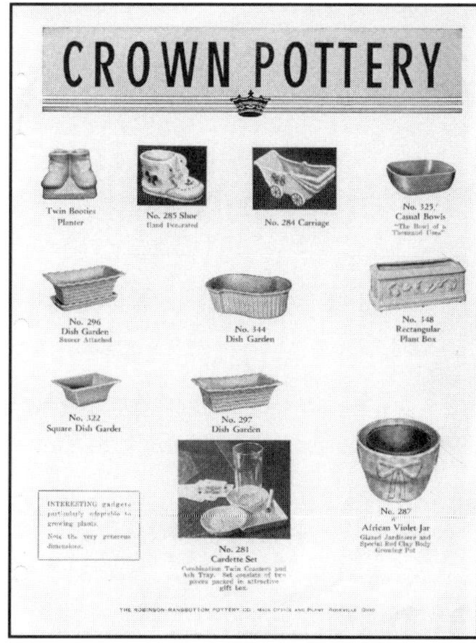

CROWN POTTERY

Twin Booties Planter

No. 285 Shoe
Hand Decorated

No. 284 Carriage

No. 325
Casual Bowls
"The Bowl of a Thousand Uses"

No. 296
Dish Garden
Saucer Attached

No. 344
Dish Garden

No. 348
Rectangular
Plant Box

No. 322
Square Dish Garden

No. 297
Dish Garden

INTERESTING gadgets particularly adaptable to growing plants.
Note the very generous dimensions.

No. 281
Cardette Set
Combination Twin Coasters and Ash Tray. Set consists of two pieces packed in attractive gift box.

No. 287
African Violet Jar
Glazed Jardiniere and Special Red Clay Body Growing Pot

THE ROBINSON-RANSBOTTOM POTTERY CO. MAIN OFFICE AND PLANT ROSEVILLE OHIO

1952 Catalog page

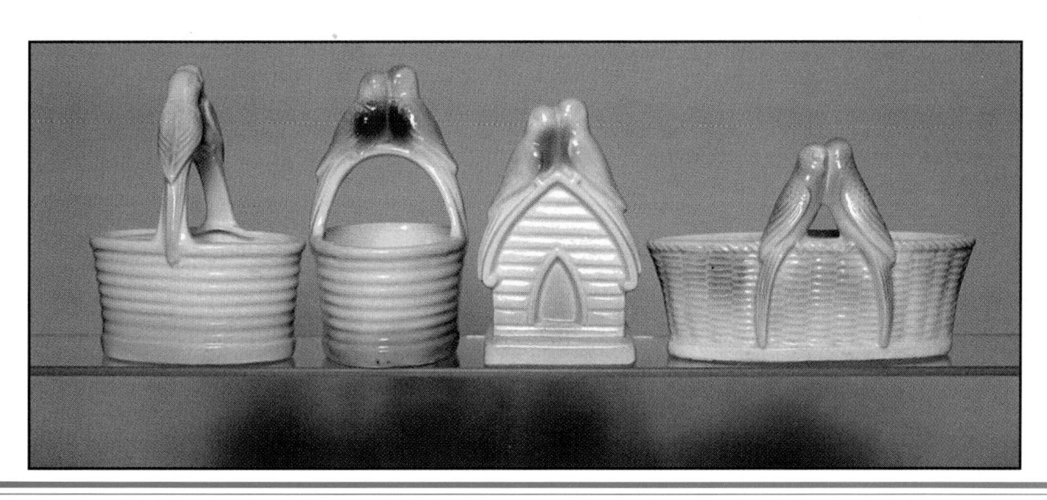

Love Bird Planters. 1949-1956.
$20-25 each
Handle Planter, 7″, RRPCo Roseville, Ohio, 254.
Handle Planter, 7″, RRPCo Roseville, Ohio, 254.
House Planter, 6 1/2″, RRPCo, 251-
Basket Planter, 5 1/2″ x 8″
USA (impressed).

Novelty Planters

Victorian Man holding a package Vase. $50-60

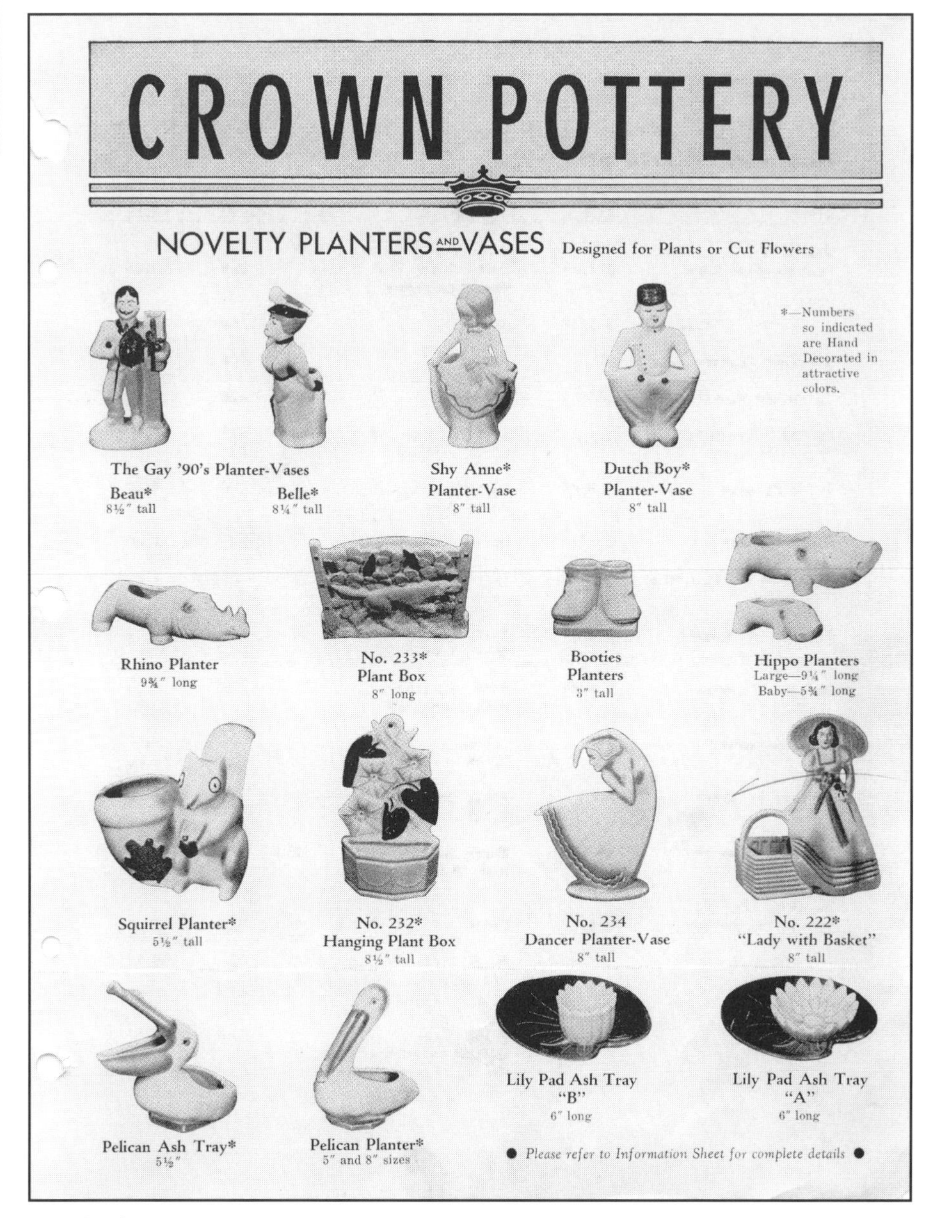

CROWN POTTERY

NOVELTY PLANTERS AND VASES

Designed for Plants or Cut Flowers

*—Numbers so indicated are Hand Decorated in attractive colors.

The Gay '90's Planter-Vases

Beau*
8½" tall

Belle*
8¼" tall

Shy Anne*
Planter-Vase
8" tall

Dutch Boy*
Planter-Vase
8" tall

Rhino Planter
9¾" long

No. 233*
Plant Box
8" long

Booties
Planters
3" tall

Hippo Planters
Large—9¼" long
Baby—5¾" long

Squirrel Planter*
5½" tall

No. 232*
Hanging Plant Box
8½" tall

No. 234
Dancer Planter-Vase
8" tall

No. 222*
"Lady with Basket"
8" tall

Pelican Ash Tray*
5½"

Pelican Planter*
5" and 8" sizes

Lily Pad Ash Tray
"B"
6" long

Lily Pad Ash Tray
"A"
6" long

● *Please refer to Information Sheet for complete details* ●

1941 Catalog page

The Gay "90's" Beau and Belle Planter Vases. $50-60 each

Victorian Man holding package (Vase), cream glazed bottom, dry foot, impressed Crown mark. 1941.

Above, Lady Planter Vase, 8½", Belle, crown mark impressed on bottom; Man Planter, 9". 1941-1950's, 1982. $50-60 each

Bottom right: Lady Planter Vase, 8½", cold painted, crown mark impressed on bottom; Man Planter, 9". 1941-1944, 1950's, 1982. $50-60 each

RIO

CROWN POTTERY

COLORFUL HAND DECORATIONS

All items decorated by hand over lacquered backgrounds in vivid and attractive colors.

No. 121-J Jardiniere
Sizes 5½", 6½", 7½" and 8½"

No. C-139 Vase
Sizes 6", 8", 10", 12", 15" and 18" tall

No. C-121-P Flower Pot
(Saucer Attached)
Sizes 5¾", 6¾", 7¾" and 8¾" diameter

Mexican Sombreo Novelty Ash Tray
5" diameter

No. 177-F Flower Bowl
5½" diameter

No. 178 Bulb Bowl
5½" diameter

No. 139-B Vase
"Sleeping Peon"
Sizes 6", 8", 10", 12", 15" and 18" tall

No. 176 Popcorn Bowl
5½" diameter

No. 177-B Hanging Basket
(With Chain)
5½" diameter

C-MPS Pot and Saucer
Hand decorated in the Mexican Motif.
Sizes: 3¼", 4¼", 5¼", 6¼", 7¼" and 8¼" diameters.

No. 175 Cactus Bowl
3½" diameter

1939 Catalog page

Rio Line and Sleeping Peon;
Vase, 8", red, USA, 139/ impressed. $50-60
Vase, 6", USA 139/. $35-45
Three hats, 4¾", no marks. $15-20 each

Inset Piece: Rio Line Pot, 5½", dark red clay with blue and white stripes and pink and blue flames. $15-20

NEW
DIFFERENT
ATTRACTIVE

"RIO"

DISTINCTIVE
HAND APPLIED
DECORATIONS

C-139
C-178
C-121-P
C-177-B
C-139
C-176
C-SOMBRERO
C-175
C-MPS
C-121-J
C-177-F

1938 Catalog page

Rio Vase, 15½", plain, unglazed bottom with small foot, 139/-USA. $75-85

Rio Vase, 12", 139/-USA. $65-75

Rio Vase, 10¼", USA 139/. $55-65

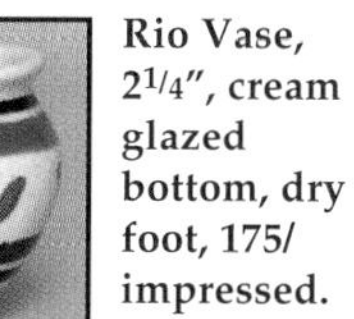

Rio Vase, 2¼", cream glazed bottom, dry foot, 175/ impressed. $12-15

RIO "Brilliant hand decorating against red or black background. Colorful and charming for interior or out-of-doors. Flower Pots, Jardinieres and Vases in a well chosen variety of sizes. Don't overlook RIO for quick sales and profits."
1938 catalog

No. 1332, 11″ Fluted Vase, 1960's-1970's. $20-25

No. 412 Tweed Vase, 10″, RRPCo Roseville, Ohio, No. 412 10. 1955-1968. $40-50

Order label Aqua Fan Vase

Top Row:
No. 124 Maroon Vase, 8″, 124/-. $20-25
No. 123 White Vase, 123/-. 1937-1938. $30-35
No. 188 Maroon Vase with Lily Pads, 8″, 188/-. $30-35
White Vase, 9¼″, flat, unglazed bottom. $30-35

Bottom Row:
No. 272 Dragon Vase, 8″, RRPCo Roseville, Ohio -272, 1949-1950. $20-25
No. 272 Dragon Vase, 6″, RRPCo Roseville, Ohio -272, 1949-1950. $20-25
Flower Vase, 7½″, RRPC RO USA oval. $20-25
Flower Vase, 5½″, RRPC Ro USA oval. 1978-1982. $20-25

Top Row: Aqua Fan Vase, 7″, sticker: Robinson Ransbottom, 1330 Royal Stem $15-20
Fan Vase, 10″, brown with white drip, RRPCo Roseville, O. $20-25
Brown Drip Fan Vase, 7″, RRPCo, Roseville, O/ USA. 1958-1968. $15-20
Bottom Row: No. 121 Yellow Vase, 7¾″, 121/-. $20-25
White Vase, 8″, crown impressed. 1941-1947. $30-35
Deer Insert Vase, 8″, green, RRPCo Roseville, Ohio, 230. 1941-1947. $20-25
Deer Insert Vase, 8″, white, 230. $20-25

Top Row: All marked RRPCo Roseville, Ohio.

No. 394 Lime Fan Vase, 6″, No-394.1954-1956.	$15-20
Green Bird Vase, $6^{1}/_{2}$″, USA (raised), No-1304-8″. 1957.	$20-25
Light green Fan Vase, 6″, No 498. 1954-1956.	$15-20

Bottom Row: Yellow Bird Vase, 8″, RRPCo, Roseville, Ohio, 1304-8″, USA. 1957. $20-25

No. 225 Blue Art Deco Fan Vase, 225/-. 1941-1946. $15-20

Green Bird Vase, 8″, RRPCo Roseville, Ohio., 1304/8″, USA. 1957. $20-25

Green Bird Vase bottom

Top Row: No. 140 Yellow Vase, 6″ 1937-38	$10-12
No. 143 Pink Vase, 5″, 143/-USA. 1937-38	$15-18
No. 143 Green on green Vase, 143/-USA. 474M (Scratched M). 1937-38	$15-18
No. 163 Cachepot, $3^{1}/_{2}$″, 163/5, USA, punch hole for drainage. 1939-52	$18-20
Bottom Row: No. 575 Green drip Vase, plain, unglazed bottom. Late 1960's.	$35-40
All the rest marked RRPCo Roseville, O USA	
No. 1332 Green Vase, $7^{1}/_{2}$″ (also came in 9″ and 11″). 1960's.	$25-30
No. 340 Brown with green drip Vase, $9^{1}/_{2}$″. 1960's.	$10-12
No. 340 Brown with white drip Vase, $7^{1}/_{2}$″. 1960's.	$10-12
No. 340 Rust with brown Vase, $7^{1}/_{2}$″. 1960's.	$10-12

Top Row:

No. 214 Aqua Console Vase, 6″, crown impressed on bottom, white glaze bottom, dry foot. 1941. $15-18

Aqua and white planter box, $3^{1}/_{2}$″ x $9^{1}/_{2}$″, crown impressed, white glaze bottom, dry foot. 1940's. $18-20

Pink Console Vase, 6″, crown impressed, pink glaze bottom, dry foot. 1940's. $15-18

Bottom Row:

No. 214 Pink Vase, 10″. 1941-1947. $25-30

No. 1332 Royal Fluted Vase, $10^{3}/_{4}$″, RRPCo Roseville, O USA. 1960's $25-30

Yellow Vase, 10″, 81/-. 1937-1938. $25-30

No. 225 Aqua Fan Vase, 7″, bottom glazed (numbers illegible), wiped foot. 1941-1946. $15-20

No. 1318 Green, two-handled Vase, $10^{1}/_{2}$″, glazed bottom, dry foot. 1960's. $30-40

Drip Vases, RRPCo, USA, Roseville, O

Top Row: Vase, 7 1/2", blue and pink. 1961.	$35-40
Vase, 7 1/2", green and brown.	$35-40
Coffee Pot, 10 1/2", green and brown.	$30-35
Bottom Row: Globe Vase, 5 1/2", green and brown.	$15-20
Vase, 5 1/2", blue and pink.	$20-25
Vase, 5 1/2", blue and pink. 1961-1970's.	$20-25

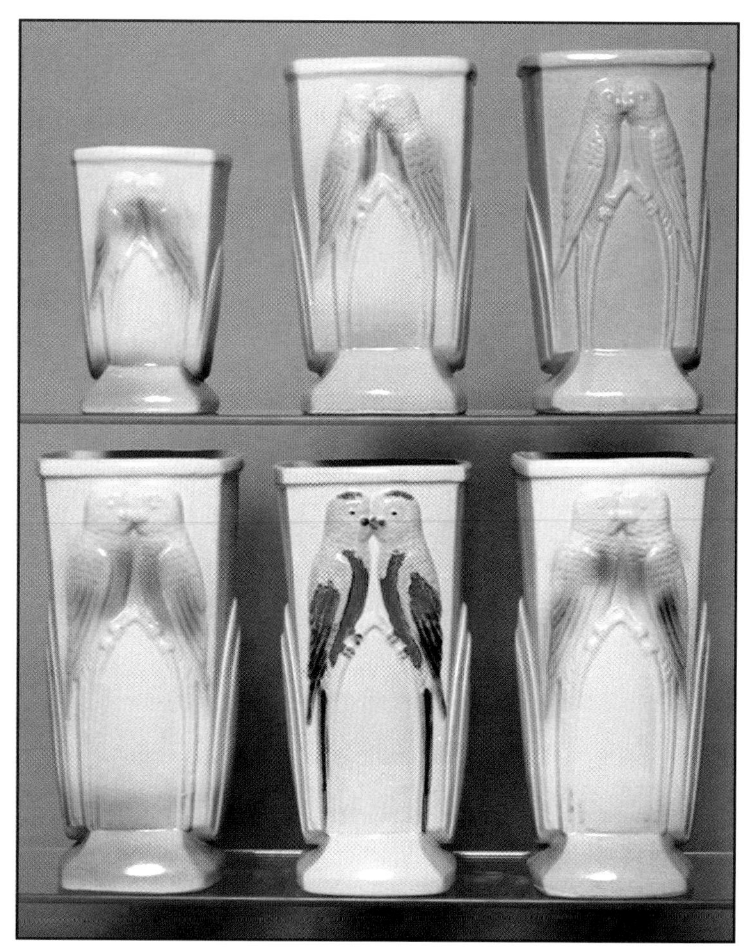

Top Row: Lovebird Vase, 6", flat, unglazed bottom.	$20-25
Lovebird Vase, 8", RRPCo Roseville, Ohio, 260/8, glazed.	$35-40
Lovebird Vase, 8", glazed bottom, unmarked.	$20-25
Bottom Row: Lovebird Vase, 10", glazed, unmarked.	$35-40
Lovebird Vase, 10", John Ransbottom, 1942 under glaze.	$35-40
Lovebird Vase, 10', glazed, unmarked. 1947-1950.	$35-40

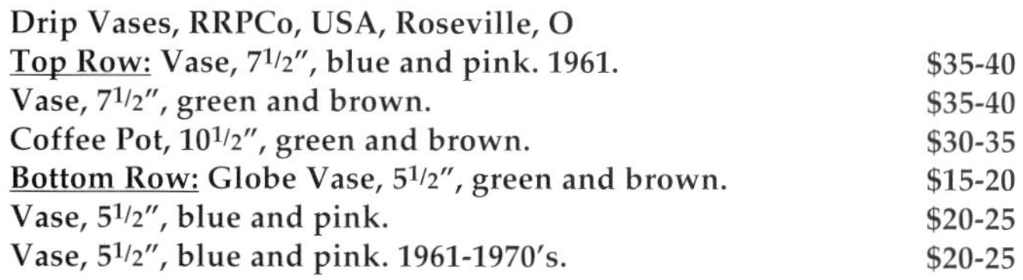

Yellow Lily Pad Vase with handles, 8", gloss glaze, yellow glazed bottom, dry foot. $30-35

Aqua Lily Pad Vase with handles, 8", flat glaze, aqua glazed bottom, dry foot, 138/- impressed, 1937-1938. $30-35

Metglo Vase, 7 1/4", glazed bottom, dry foot, no mark. 1930's.	$55-65
Metglo Vase, 11", glazed bottom, dry foot. 1930's.	$75-85
Luxor Vase, 7 1/4", unglazed bottom with small foot, no mark. 1931.	$40-50

Green Vase, 7 3/4", green glazed bottom, dry foot, 127/- USA. 1937-1938. $20-25

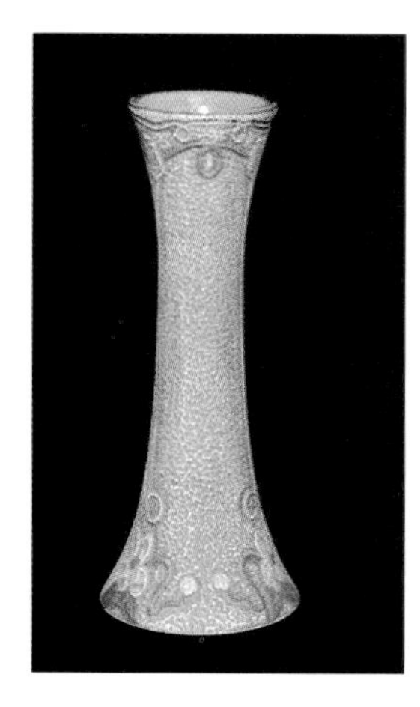

Luxor Vase, 7 1/4". 1931. $40-50

Top Row: All marked RRPCo Roseville,O USA. All 1950's, Not shown in catalogs.
White Leaf Vase, 5" $10-12
Pink with gold Vase, 5 1/2. $10-12
White Vase with Red Flowers, 5 1/4" $10-12
Pink Vase with White Flowers, 5 1/4" $10-12
Pink Leaf Vase, 5" $10-12
Center Row: Brown Vase with green drip, 5 1/4", USA. 1960's. $12-15
Green Fan Deco Vase, 6", USA, 157/- test. $20-25
Dark Blue Deco Fan Vase, 6" $20-25
Yellow Ribbed Vase, 6", RRPCo Roseville, Ohio, 273. $12-15
Bottom Row: No. 229 Light Blue Vase, 6", no mark, blue glazed bottom, dry foot. 1941-1947. $18-22
Pink Decorated Vase, 7", no mark, pink glazed bottom, dry foot.1950's. $12-15
Pink Decorated Vase with Gold Trim, 7", no mark, pink glaze bottom, dry foot. 1950's. $12-15
White Vase with Red Flowers, 5 1/4", 257-5". 1950's. $12-15
Green single-handled Vase, 8 1/2", RRPCo, USA, Roseville, O. 1960's. $12-15

Old Weller molds, white glazed bottoms, dry foot on both. 1950-1971.
Stack Vase, 16", marked RRPCo Roseville, O. 291-16 USA. $35-40
Stack Vase, 12 3/4", marked RRPCo Roseville, O. $20-25

Blue Vase, 6 3/4", blue glazed bottom, dry foot, 143/-impressed. 1937-1938. $30-35

Wide Vase, 6 1/2", cream with orange and yellow wiped glaze, glazed bottom, dry foot, marked RRPCo Roseville, OHIO, No -396 impressed. 1954. $20-25

Left: Top Row: No. 207 Hobnail Beater Jar, 5 1/2", crown mark under glazed bottom, dry foot. 1941. $25-35
Athenian Footed Urn, 7 1/2", plain, unglazebottom, no mark. 1970's. $30-35
Three-footed, two-handled Pot, 5", cream with blue bands. $10-12
Bottom Row: Black Kettle Planters, RRPCo, USA Roseville, O. 1960's-1970's.
6" $10-12 8" $12-15 10" $18-20

No. 184 Vase. 1939. $25-30

Vase, 7", white ribbed, white glazed bottom, 142/- impressed. 1938. $25-30

Turquoise Vase, 8", turquoise glazed bottom, dry foot, USA 185/ impressed. 1939. $20-25

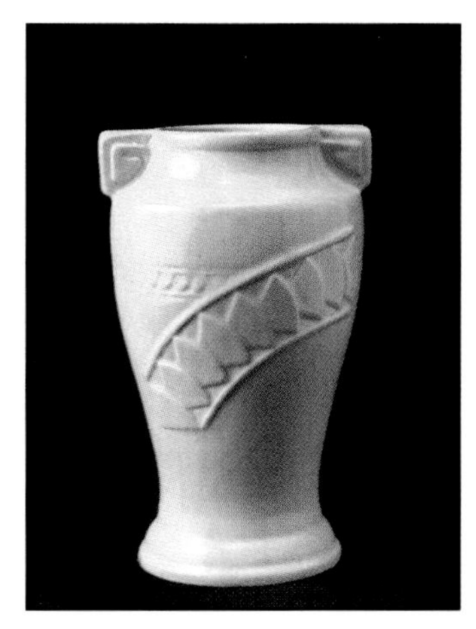

Yellow Deco Vase, 8", 185/ USA impressed in bottom. $20-25

Vase with yellow daisies, 8", 135/-. Late 1930's. $20-25

Vase, $8^{1}/_{2}$", grass green, green glazed bottom, dry foot, 136/- impressed. 1937-1938. $20-25

Top Row: Unpainted Dorothy Archer Vases, 6", green, plain unglazed; Brown and yellow, ink stamp USA oval; Brown, RRPCo USA; White, plain. $35-40 each

Bottom Row: Aladdin's Lamp Vases, 8", Aqua, 229-8; Yellow, 229-8; White, no mark; Green, no mark. 1941-1947.

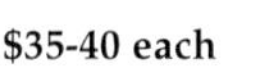

$20-25 each

Vase, 6", blue with Iris, blue glazed bottom, dry foot, 114/ impressed. Late 1930's. $20-25

Vase with Anchor, $8^{1}/_{2}$", yellow glazed bottom, dry foot, impressed mark: RRPCo Roseville, OHIO No. 403. 1950-1951. $20-25

Yellow with gold decoration, (Granville Shafer) 6", yellow glazed bottom, dry foot, impressed: RRPCo Roseville Ohio. 1949-1950. $25-30

Personalized Vase
"Titusville, Penna.
The birthplace of the oil industry.
The Famous Drake Well
August 27, 1859"
(raised lettering)

No. 215 Vase, 8″, pink glazed bottom, dry foot, crown impressed. $30-35
Green Vase, 6″, white glazed bottom, dry foot, crown impressed. 1941-1946. $20-25

Pot, 4½″, 162/4 USA $25-30
Vase, 6″, 163/6 USA. Cream with green and rose trim, glazed bottom, dry foot. $25-30

Vase, 12″, brown with cream and brown drip, unglazed bottom, impressed mark: R. Ransbottom, 12″, No. 100, Roseville, OHIO USA. Early 1980's. $20-25

Vase, 8″, pink and green, white glazed bottom, dry foot, USA 160/5, impressed. 1939-1940. $35-40

Vases with bulbous middles, 6¼″, orchid with green drip. No mark. 1930's. $150-170 each

Photo left: All 1941-1946
All have impressed crown mark.

Cream with green Planter, 4¾″, cream bottom, dry foot. $10-15
No. 214 Green Vase with handles, 10″, green glazed bottom, dry foot. $30-35
No. 215 Rose Vase, 8″, rose glazed bottom, dry foot. $20-25
Blue Planter, 3″, blue bottom, dry foot. $10-15

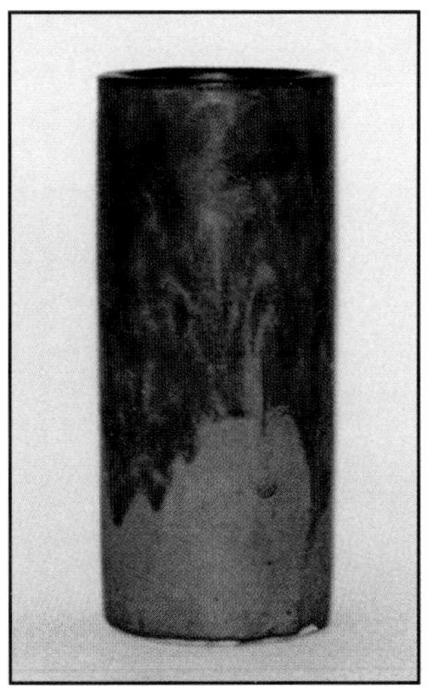

Cut Flower Jar, 12", blue glaze over orchid glaze. 1931. $200-250

Photo right:
All marked R. Ransbottom, Roseville, OH USA

Top Row:
Vase, 12", marked 12" 100, unglazed bottom. $25-30
Vase, 10", marked 10", 100. $20-25
Vase, 10", marked 10" 100. $25-30
Vase, $6^{1/2}$", marked 6" 101, glazed bottom $10-15

Bottom Row:
Jardiniere, $5^{1/2}$" x 5" marked $6^{1/2}$" 102 $15-20
Vase, 8", marked 8" 100 $15-20
Jardiniere, $7^{1/2}$" x 7" across. 1980's. $25-30

No. 571 Vase, 12", green glaze over orchid glaze. $200-250

Color Test Samples.

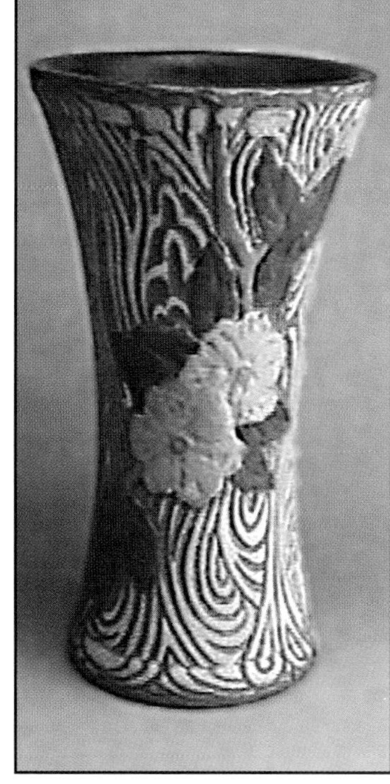

Luxor Vase, 12", green flat glazed bottom, no mark. 1926. $125-150

Luxor Wall Pocket, $9^{1/2}$", no mark $55-65
Luxor Wall Pocket, $8^{1/2}$", no mark. 1931. $25-35
Luxor Cemetary Vase, 7", no mark. 1931. $35-45
Luxor Cemetary Vase, $10^{1/2}$", no mark. 1931. $35-45

Bottoms: Vase with handles, 6"; Pitcher, 9"; Ruffled Top Vase, $9^{1/2}$".

Vase, 6", brown and green drip glaze, cream glazed bottom, dry foot, 127/- impressed. $30-40

Vase, 6", brown and green drip glazed, bottom detail.

Two-handled Vase, $9^{1}/_{2}''$, mottled drip glaze, flat, stoneware bottom, no color. 1920's. $175-200

Vase, 9″, orchid with green drip, blue stained flat bottom, no mark. 1920's. $150-170

Orchid with green drip Spill Vase, $9^{1}/_{2}''$, plain, unglazed flat bottom, no mark. 1920's. $150-175

Vase, 10″, green and blue mottled glaze, USA 157/-. 1931. $60-70

Vase, $6^{1}/_{4}''$, blue and white on maroon, unglazed bottom, no mark. $90-100

Vase, 9″, mottled blue and green on purple, unglazed bottom with finger marks. Note attached: "Hand-turned by Wm. Ransbottom (about 1927). signed Alfred Ransbottom.". $150-175

Blue Vase, 6″, flat bottom, no mark $60-70

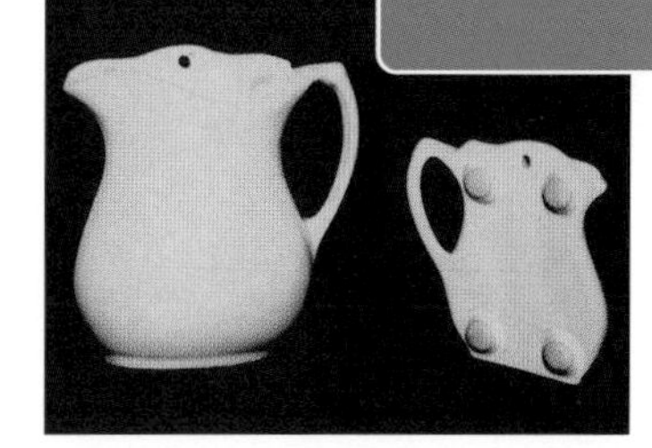

White Pitcher Wall Pockets, 7″ and 5″. R. Ransbottom, Roseville, OH, USA. $25-35

Tionesta Art Ware Sticker

Suede Vase, $12^{1}/_{2}''$. $80-100
Two-handled Suede Vase, $9^{1}/_{4}''$ $60-80
Both with red glazed bottom and hand-thrown.

Vases, 8″, flat unglazed bottoms, on the right with rope handles. $90-100 each

Tionesta Art Ware Vase. $30-35

Green drip on Green Glaze, $6^{1}/_{2}''$ no mark. $125-150

Vase, $9^{1}/_{2}''$, green glaze over orchid glaze. $150-175

Bottoms of $12^{1}/_{2}''$ Suede Vase, Ruffled Vase and Handled Vase.

Left: Ruffled-top Vase, 9″, green glaze over blue glaze, plain, unglazed flat bottom, no mark. 1920's. $150-175

Orange Flower Vase, 12 1/2", decorated by DeDonatis, twisted handles. 1928-1929. $400-450

Back side of DeDonatis Vase with curving handles, 12 1/2". 1928-1930.

Hand Painted 12" Vase. 1928-1930. $350-400

DeDonatis hand painted Vase, 12 1/2". 1928-1930. $350-400

Two DeDonatis red clay vases, 9", flat, unglazed bottoms. Late 1920's - early 1930's. $150-200 each

DeDonatis Vase, 12". Three DeDonatis Vases, 12 1/2". Cream with red and blue flowers. 1928-1929. $350-400 each

DeDonatis hand painted Vase with 2 twisted handles, 12 1/2". 1928-1930. $400-450

DeDonatis hand painted Vase with 2 twisted handles, 12 1/2". 1928-1930. $400-450

DeDonatis Vase, 9", heavily decorated. 1928-1930. $225-275

DeDonatis hand painted Vase, 12 1/2" brown sponge decoration on handles and on bottom. Late 1920's. $300-325

VASES
HAND PAINTED

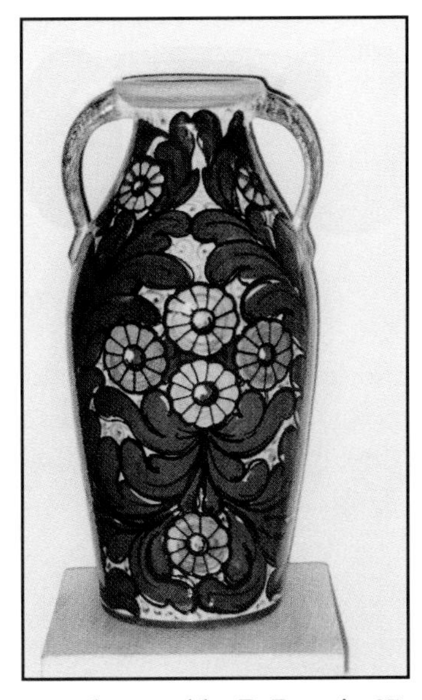

Vase decorated by DeDonatis, 27-28" tall. 1928-1930. $3,000-4,000

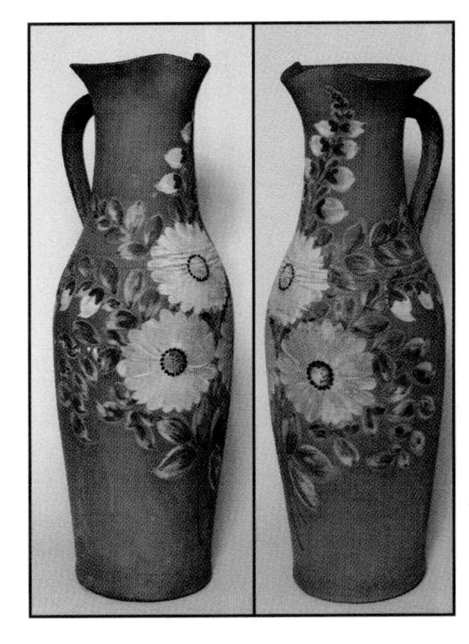

Red clay vase with one handle, 25½" unglazed, with DeDonatis flowers in blue, yellow and orange. 1929-1931. $900-1,100

DeDonatis Vase, 31", hand decorated $5,000-6,000

Red Flower Vase, 15½". 1928-1929. $800-1,000

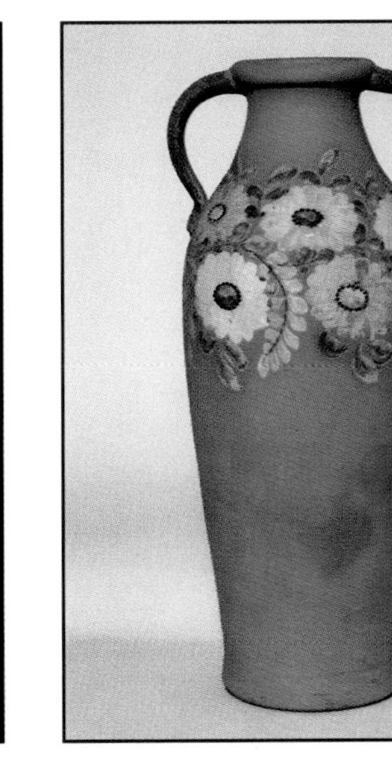

Red clay Jar, 26", two handles, hand painted by DeDonatis. 1928-1929. $900-1,100

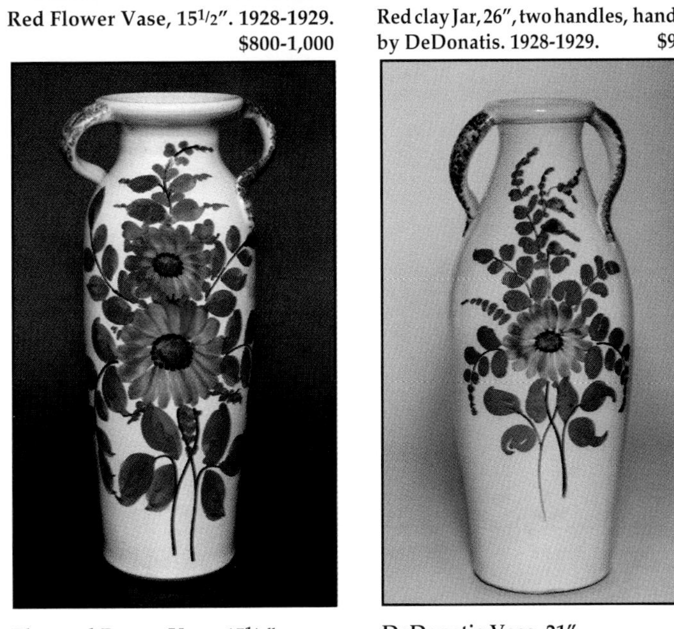

Blue and Brown Vase, 15½". 1928-1929. $800-1,000

DeDonatis Vase, 21". 1928-1930. $800-1,000

Hand decorated Vase, 26", red clay with applied handles. Similar painting on both sides. 1928-1929. $900-1,000

Two-handled hand-decorated Vase, 13", Hand turned, with flat bottom and ridges where cut off from wheel. $400-450

Vase, 9″. 1928-1929. $225-275

DeDonatis Vase with longer neck, 12 1/2″. 1928-1930. $300-325

Vase, 9″, plain bottom, no mark. 1928-1929 $225-275

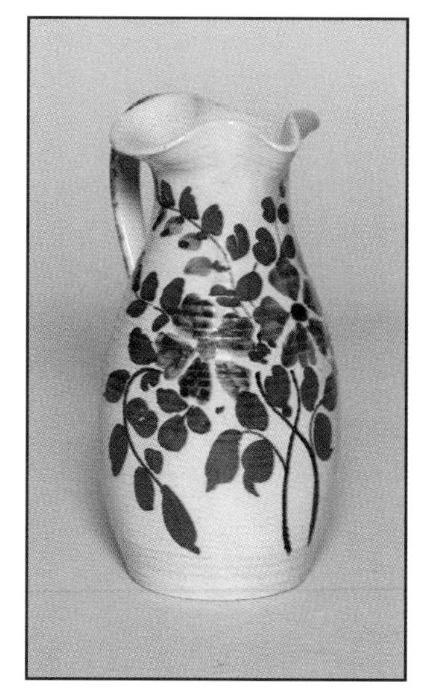

DeDonatis Pitcher with handle, 9 1/4″. 1928-1930. $300-350

DeDonatis mark inside small pot

Decorated DeDonatis Pot, 2 3/4″, signed inside. 1928-1930. $150-200

DeDonatis Vase, 21″. 1928-1930. $1,000-1,200

Hand painted vase with brown sponge on twisted handles. $1,000-1,200

Rectangular Vase, 5 1/2″, pink glazed bottom, dry foot, crown impressed mark. 1950's $15-20

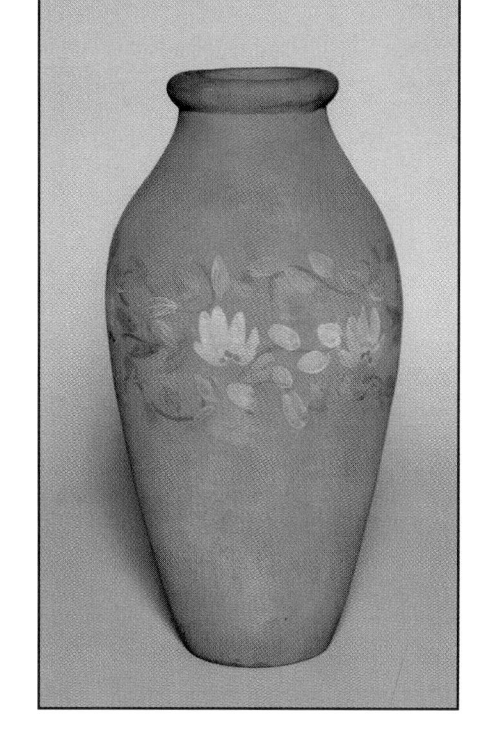

Later Period, Red Clay Vase, 20 1/2″, 1970's, RRPCo, Roseville, O, USA. $200-250

Vase, 16″. 1928-1930. $750-850

Hand-painted Vase. 1928-1930. $750-850

No. 185 Vase, 8", USA 185/ (impressed in vase), marked in front: Pace '39. Art Deco design, also done in plain colors with no painting. $175-200

No. 157 Vase, 10", USA 157 bottom mark, glazed dry foot, Probably decorated by Willard L. Pace (decorator of Old Colony). This piece was also done in plain colors. 1941. $175-200

Wall Pocket, 6½", decorated by Dorothy Archer. Not a production piece. Over-all green glazed with seven half-glazed knobs that stick out the back. R. Ransbottom Roseville, OH USA. 1970's. $125-150

Dorothy Archer Vases: 6", signed D. Archer "77"; 9" and 11", signed D.A. "77", all marked RRPCo Roseville, O in an oval ink stamp. $90-100 $100-125 $150-175

Decorated Vase, 9½", flat, unglazed bottom. $65-75

No. 139 Rio Vase, USA 139/.1937-1940. $50-60

Dorothy Archer decorated Lucia Jars:
Less than 50 5" made. Rare. 1979. Not produced and not in catalog.
12", 1977, $200-225; 10", 1978, $175-200; 8", 1977, $150-175; 6", $75-100; 5", $100-125.

No. 969-D Jar, 26", hand painted, marked: RRPCo USA Roseville, O. 1974-1979.
$350-400

No. 449-D Vase, 15 1/2", hand-painted, marked: RRPCo Roseville, O. USA. 1975.
$200-250

Vase, 26" hand decorated, no signature or mark. Late 1970's.
$300-350

No. 429-D Victorian Vase, Decorated "Mae West" Vase, 14 1/2", plain unglazed bottom, oval ink stamp: RRPCo Roseville, USA. 1977-1979.
$150-175

Oil Jar, 23", D. Archer "77", hand decorated vase, marked: 561/-USA.
$250-300

Aladdin Jar, 36", shiny glaze, hand painted, marked: 975D, signed D.A. 1978, R. Ransbottom, USA. 1977-1979. $800-1,000

Hand Painted Jar, 25 1/2", signed on bottom: DA 122 (no date), RRPCo, Roseville, O. 1974-1979.
$350-400

No. 420 "Mae West" Jar, 14 1/2", flat unglazed bottom. 1975-1976.
$100-125

Oil Jar, 22", flat unglazed bottom, impressed: 561/-USA, signed: D. Archer "77". 1976-1977.
$250-300

Mark on 26" Floor Vase.

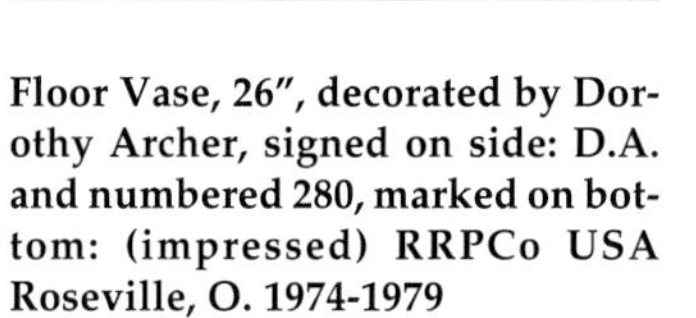

Floor Vase, 26", decorated by Dorothy Archer, signed on side: D.A. and numbered 280, marked on bottom: (impressed) RRPCo USA Roseville, O. 1974-1979
$350-400

Hand painted Dorthy Archer Jar, 31", hand painted on bottom, A. Ransbottom, 1977, Nov. 19, 1977.
One-of-a-kind

Hand painted Vase, 23", F.M. Ransbottom, 1930's. Taken from an actual photo of Frank Ransbottom and the fish he caught on the Muskingum River. "JUST ENOTHER 12 AK WALTON" written on the front.

$3,500-4,500

"Sand" glazed Vase, 36" 1970's.

$450-600

Hand painted Vase
Piece located at Zanesville Art Museum,

$3,000-3,500

Back of F.M.R. fish Jar above.

"The Pottery Maker" hand painted by DeDonatis, on red clay with handles, 24" tall.

$3,000-3,500

Back side of "The Pottery Maker".
One-of-a kind.

No. 564 Fluted Oil Jar, pink, marked: RRPCo USA Roseville, O, USA. Came in 3 sizes: 18", 20", 23", and 6 colors: white, coral, yellow, blue, apple green and pink. 1958-1959.
$150-175

Blue Vase with Snake handles, 22" plain unglazed bottom, slight foot, 283/22", RRPCo. With or without handles. 1948-1949
$175-200

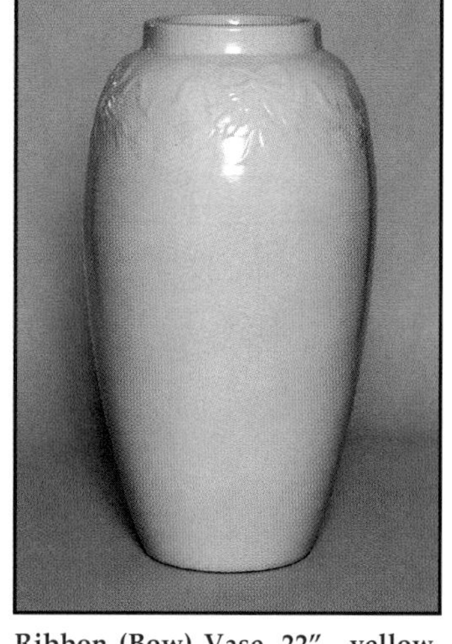

Ribbon (Bow) Vase, 22" , yellow, plain, unglazed bottom, no mark. Various colors, various years. 1941-1958 .
$150-175

Maroon with blue and white 35", 1920's-1930's.
$1,200-1,400

No. 156 Vase, 15". 1938-1940.
$75 -100

Snake-handled Jar, 18", in green, RRPCo Roseville, O 283/18. 1948-1949. $175-200

Snake-handled Jar, 14", yellow. 1948-1949. $150-175

Right: Handle Detail.

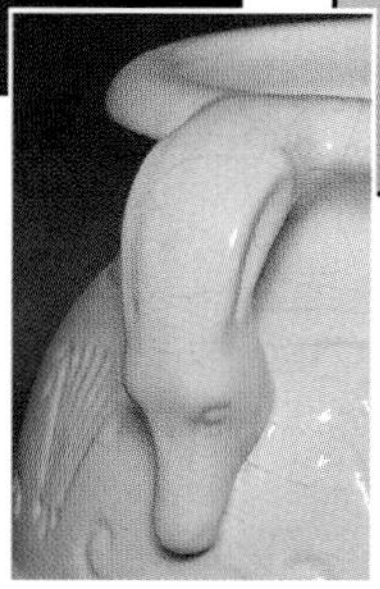

Oil Jar, 20" , persimmon, jiggered in two pieces, plain unglazed bottom, no mark. 1958-1980's, on and off.
$100-125

Curved Handled Jar, 18", plain unglazed bottom, marked: 150/-. U.S.A. 1937-1940.
$125-150

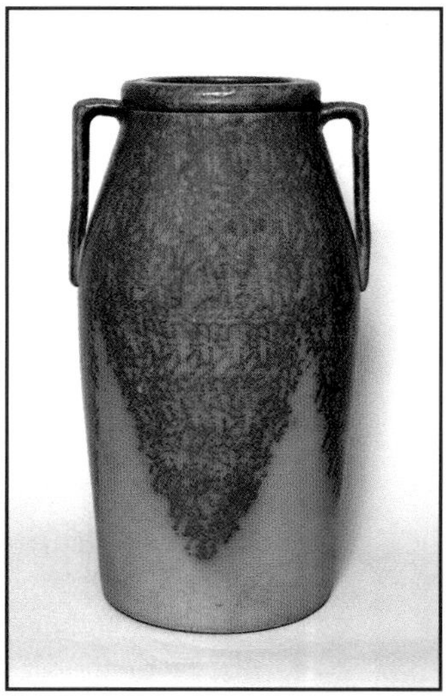

Oil Jar with handles 24", green glaze over orchid glaze, plain, crock bottom, no mark. 1930's.
$1,000-1,200

Green, two-handled floor vase, 18" 150/-USA, 1937-1943.
$125-150

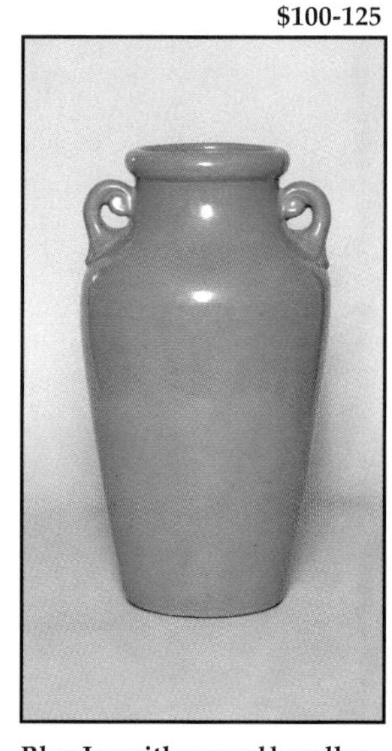

Blue Jar with curved handles, 18", plain unglazed bottom, marked: 150/-. USA. 1937-1940. $125-150

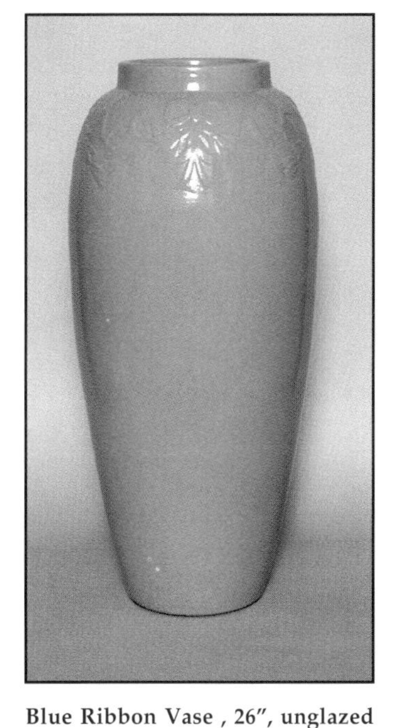

Blue Ribbon Vase , 26″, unglazed bottom, concave. 1941-1958, $175-225

No. 157 Floor Vase, 18″. Art Deco design. $100-125

1961 Catalog page

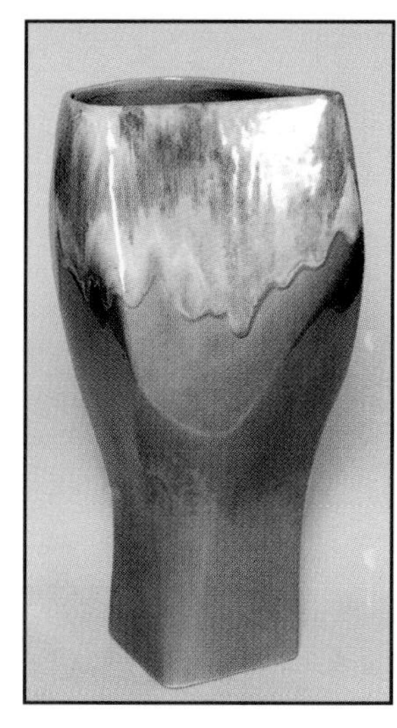

Floor Vase/Umbrella Jar 21″ green with brown drip, no mark, punch hole, sample. 1960's. $175-225

Ribbon Vase, 26″, plain unglazed bottom, no mark. 1941-1950. $175-225

No. 159 Oil Jars, 15″, maroon with twisted flower-end handles, plain unglazed bottom, RRPCo Roseville, Ohio 159/15. $75-100
Maroon with snake handles, glazed bottom with dry foot, 2383/15, USA. $150-175
Jade with twisted handle, leaf and berry design, plain, unglazed bottom, 159/-. 1938-1948. $75-100

Two-handled Vase, 14″, impressed mark: 159/ USA. $75-100

Pitcher Vase, 26″, green glaze over orchid glaze, no mark. 1930's. $1,000-1,500

Astroglo Pitcher Vase, 21″, deep brown with white drip, plain unglazed bottom, marked: RRPCo USA, ASTROGLO. 1960's. $100-125

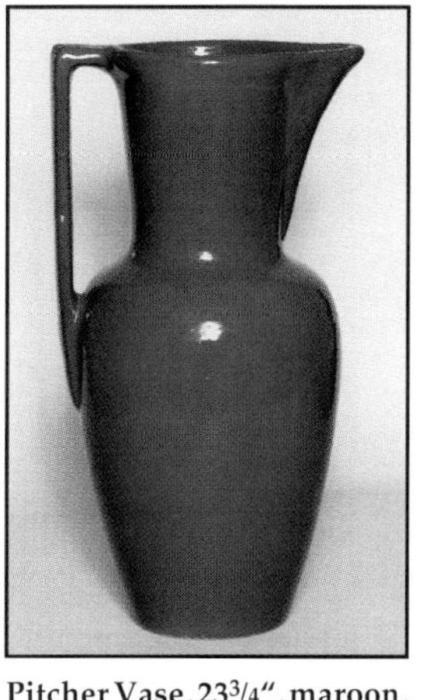

Pitcher Vase, 23¾″, maroon, plain unglazed bottom, impressed mark: RRPCo Roseville USA. $100-125

No 140 Rustic Jar, 15″, with fan decoration on bottom of piece, plain unglazed bottom with impressed marks: RRPCo Roseville, OHIO No. 140-15. 1950's, brought back in 1980's, called Embossed Urn. $50-60

Blue Vase, 15", plain unglazed bottom, impressed mark: 139/. $50-60

No. 139, Black Oil Jar, 15$^{1}/_{2}$", no mark, rare color. $75-100

No. 139 Oil Jar, 16", plain unglazed bottom, no mark. 1937-1980's. $50-60

No. 571 Nubian Jar, 15", brown with beige and green drip, RRPCo Roseville O USA. 1961-1965. $75-80

No. 167 Oil Jar, (Ribbon), 27" 1941-1958. $150-175

No. 649D Lucia Jar, 21", red clay. 1978. $125-150

Oil Jar, 22", blue with white drip, unglazed bottom, marked: 561. This glaze used 1981-1982. $225-275

Ear handled Jar, 19", marked: RRPCo Roseville, USA, No 571, Nubian Jar. 1961-1965. $90-100

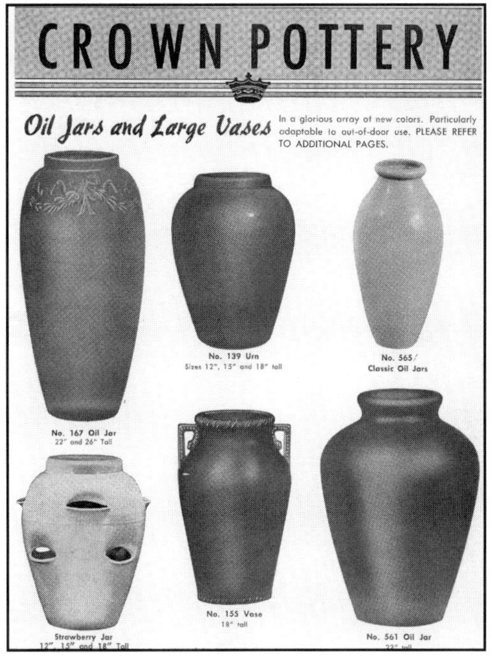

1958 Catalog page

1960 Catalog page

1963 Catalog page

VASES

Oil jar, 24″, green with white drip, marked: USA 561/-. 1967-1971 and early 1980's. $175-200

No. 139 Vase, 15¾″, brown with tan and white drip, plain unglazed bottom, no mark. $75-85

Floor Vase, 18″, blue with white drip, square handles, plain unglazed bottom, marked: USA 155 (impressed). 1930-1989's. $85-95

Floor Vase, 15¾″, 8½″ across the top, green drip, marked: RRPCo Roseville O, USA. $70-80

No. 139 Persimmon drip Oil Jar $75-85

No 139. Oil Jar, 15″, glazed bottom, dry foot, no mark. 1937-1980's. $75-85

Vase, 17½″, green with white drip, marked: RRPC, Roseville, Ohio No. 139 USA. $90-110

1962 Catalog page

1982 Catalog page

Vase, 25$^{1/2}$", with handles and rings combed in, green glaze over orchid glaze, plain unglazed bottom. 1930's.

$1,100-1,400

Two-handled Vase, 26", green glaze over orchid glaze, unglazed bottom. 1930.

$1,100-1,400

No. 571 Nubian Jar, 15$^{1/2}$", green with white and tan drip, marked: RRPCo Roseville, O USA.

$75-85

Jar, green glaze over orchid glaze, with flat, braided handles, 22", plain, unglazed bottom. 1930's.

$1,100-1,400

Jar, green glaze over blue glaze, with two heavy handles, 24", 1930's.

$1,100-1,400

Floor Vase, 22", green and copper with rope handles, plain unglazed bottom.

$1,100-1,400

Vase, 16", green glaze over orchid glaze, two-handled vase, flat, stoneware bottom, no color. 1930.

$1,000-1,400

Vase with twisted handles, 20", green glaze over orchid glaze, plain unglazed bottom. 1930.

$1,100-1,400

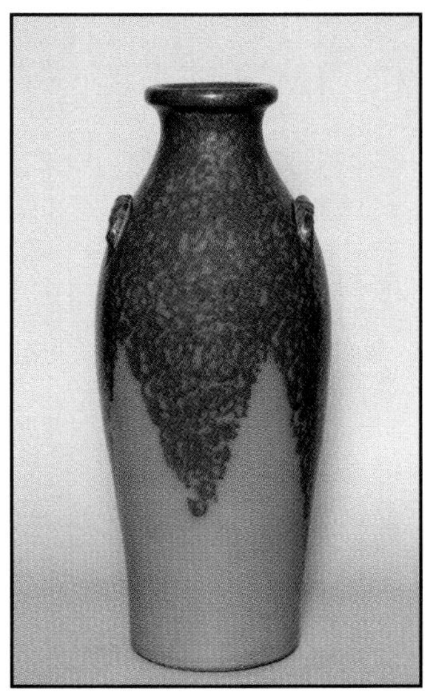

Rope-handled Jar, 22", green glaze over orchid glaze, flat unglazed bottom. 1930.

$1,100-1,400

Floor Vases

1980 Catalog page

Oil Jar, 19″, apple decorated (raised), marked: RRPCo Roseville, Ohio 257/. $125-150

Oil Jar, 15½″, apple decorated, marked: RRPCo Roseville, Ohio 288-15. 1977-1979. $90-110

Apple Vase, 15½″, tan with pink, marked: RRPCo Roseville, O 288-15. 1977-1979. $90-110

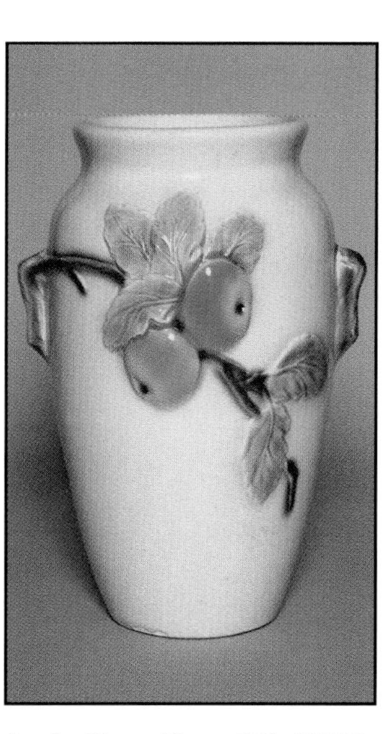

Apple Floor Vase, 18″, RRPCo Roseville, O 288-. 1950. $150-175

No. 565 Oil Jar, 26″, hand painted. $1,500-2,000

No. 162 Oil Jar with ribbons, 27″, dark blue, plain bottom, no mark. 1941-1958. $150-175

Oil Jar, 22½″, orchid with blue-green drip glaze, flat, unglazed bottom, no mark. $1,100-1,400

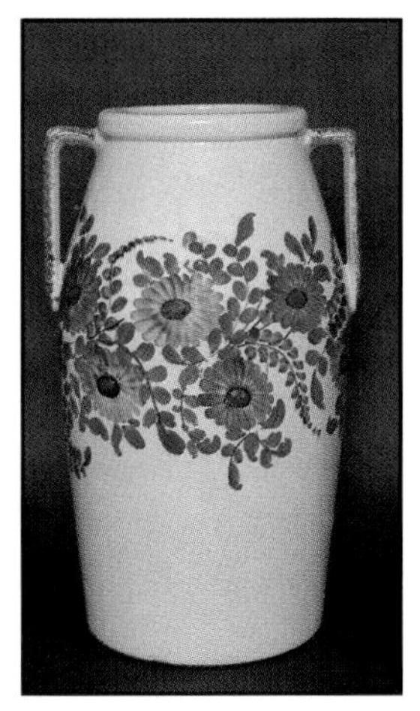

No. 545 Decorated Jar with handles, 24", DeDonatis, brown and blue flowers, 1928-1929. $1,200-1,500

Vase, 26", DeDonatis with handles, brown and gray sponge on handles. 1928-1929. $1,200-1,500

Front and Back side of 20" DeDonatis Vase, with handles, blue and brown flowers. 1928-1929. $1,000-1,200

Vase, 18", signed PACE above line in white area, marked RRPCo Roseville, Ohio No 294-13, glazed bottom, dry foot. 1951. $125-150

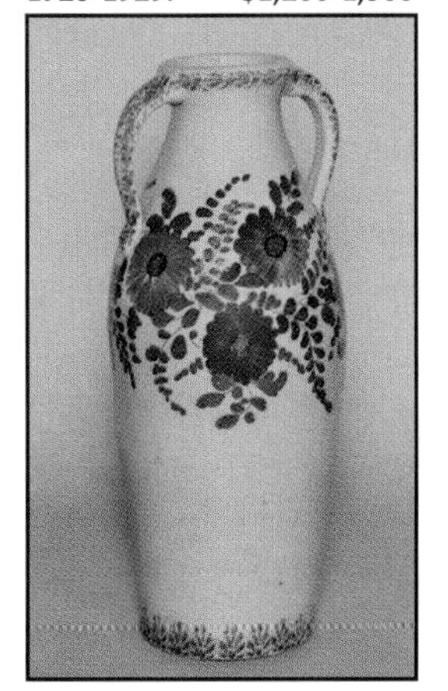

Vase, 20", 2 handles, DeDonatis, no mark. $1,000-1,200

Vase, 18½", decorated DeDonatis with handles, 1928-1930. $700-800

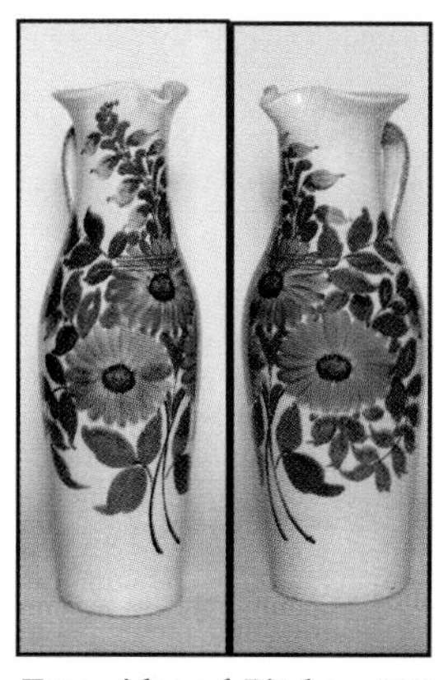

Two sides of Pitcher, 20", DeDonatis, no mark. $1,000-1,200

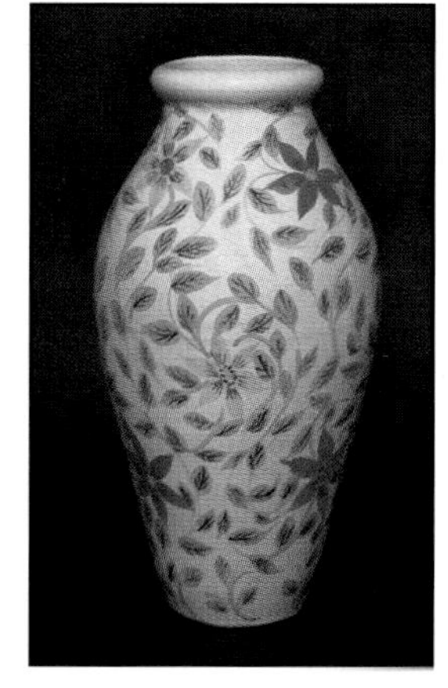

No. 969D Floor Jar, 27", Dorothy Archer hand painted. RRPCo Roseville O, D.A. under glaze, 139 in glaze at base. 1974-1979. $350-400

Hand Painted Jar, 19½", marked SG85, No 650D, Lucia Jar. 1977-1979. $500-600

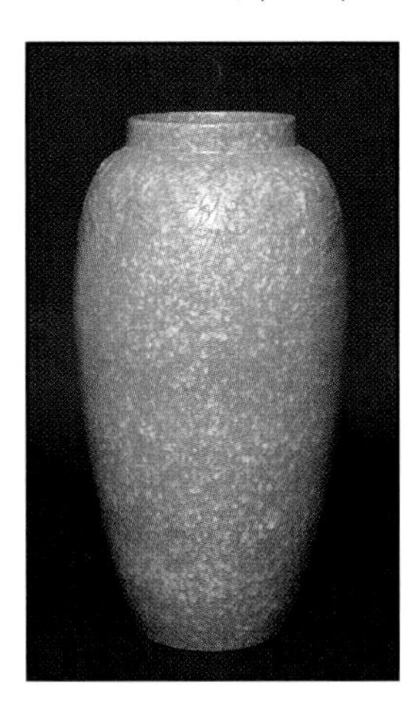

Floor Vase, 23", with ribbon decoration, plain unglazed bottom, Victoria glaze, No. 167. 1930's-1940's. $200-225

Floor Vase, 18", maroon art deco design, marked USA 157/-. 1938. $100-125

Umbrella Stand, 18", ivory brown, impressed mark, USA, hand scribed mark 157/-. 1980's. $100-125

No. 564 Fluted Oil Jar, 23" pink ribbed, plain unglazed bottom, RRPCo Roseville O, USA. $150-175

Vase, 23", red clay, hand painted, signed Don Pace, 1977, marked 561/- USA impressed. $200-250

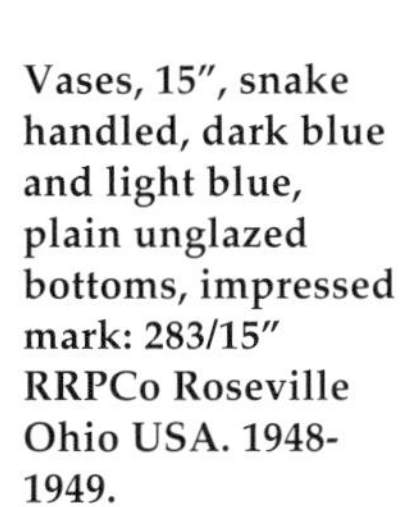

Vases, 15", snake handled, dark blue and light blue, plain unglazed bottoms, impressed mark: 283/15" RRPCo Roseville Ohio USA. 1948-1949.

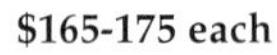

$165-175 each

No. 139 Vase, 15½", lilac, plain unglazed bottom, no mark. $75-85

Rustic Vase, 15½" marked RRPCo Roseville Ohio, No. 140-15, unglazed bottom. 1980's. $50-60

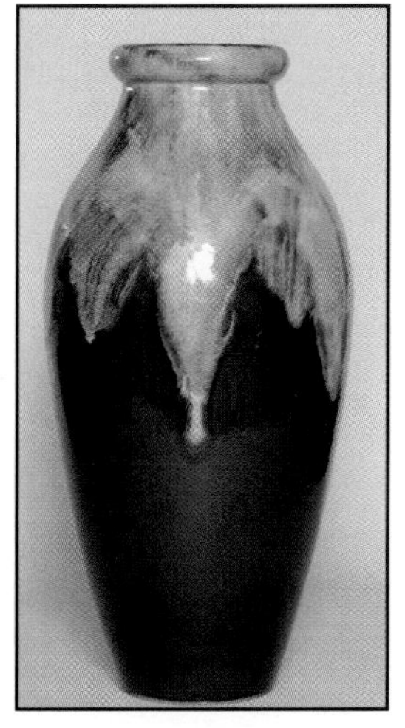

No. 565 Vase, 23", dark brown with white drip, plain unglazed bottom, impressed RRPCo Roseville, USA. 1970's-1980's. $175-200

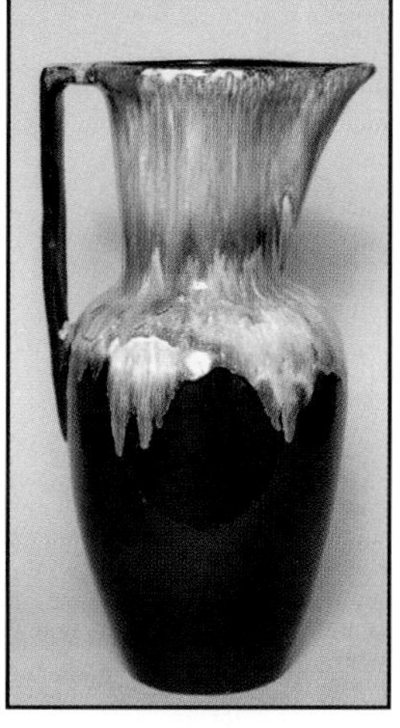

Floor Pitcher Vase, 21½", brown with tan and green drip, marked RRPCo USA Roseville O. 1961-1970, 1984. $100-125

Floor Pitcher Vase, 21½", brown Astroglow, marked RRPCo USA Roseville O. 1961-1970, 1984. $100-125

Vase, 18" blue glazed bottom, dry foot, impressed mark: 151/-. $125-150

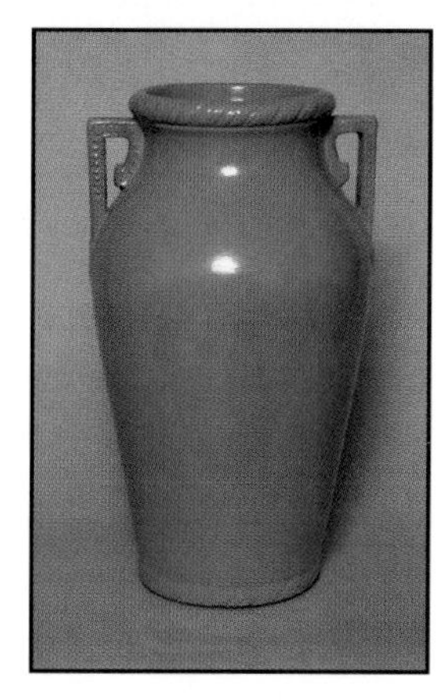

Two-handled Jar, 18", light blue, plain unglazed bottom, marked: USA 155. 1938-1980's. $80-90

No. 561 Floor Vase $175-200

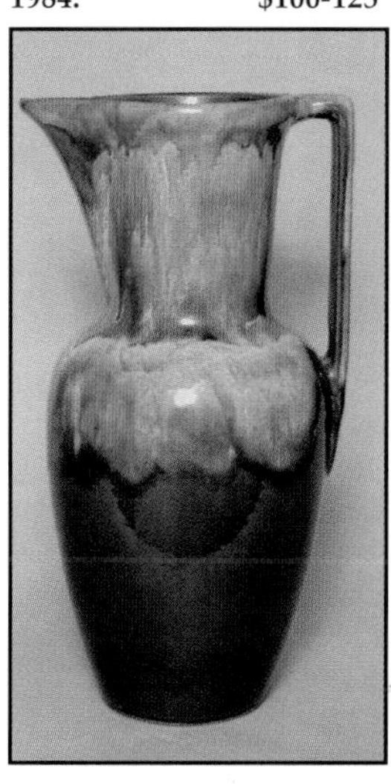

Floor Pitcher Vase, 21½", dark green drip. 1961-1970, 1984. $100-125

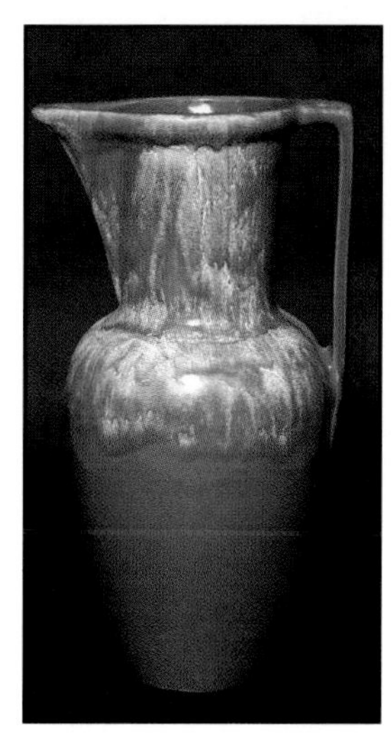

Floor Pitcher Vase, 21½", orange drip 1961-1970, 1984. $100-125

Floor Vase, 21", flat bottom, no mark, red clay. $900-1,000

Floor Vase Sample, 26", green with white drip, plain unglazed bottom, impressed marks: RRPCo Roseville, O USA. $175-200

Floor Vase, 18", brown with white drip, 2 handles, marked USA. 1938-1980's. $80-90

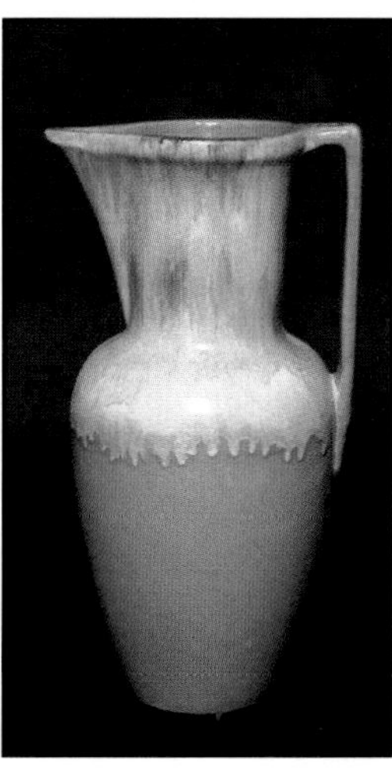

Floor Pitcher Vase, 21½", turquoise. 1961-1970, 1984. $100-125

Vase, 20", green glazed red clay, wiped on high points, signed LUCIA 1976, plain flat unglazed bottom, no mark. $150-175

Floor Vase Sample, 26", green with white drip, plain unglazed bottom, impressed marks: RRPCo Roseville, O USA. $175-200

Vase, 15", with palm decorations, brown, brown glazed bottom, dry foot, RRPCo Roseville, Ohio, No. 140-15. 1980's. $50-60

VASES

Floral Accessories

Introducing a portion of our New "TWEED" Line of Hand Decorated Ware.

No. 291 Stock Vases

No. 387 Jardinieres

No. 348 Rectangular Plant Box

No. 254 Planter Basket

No. 412/ "TWEED" Vases

No. 251 Planter - Vase

No. 352 Jardiniere and Pedestal

No. 412/ "TWEED" Jardinieres and Pedestals

No. 22 - E Hanging Baskets

No. 211 Florist Vase Ideal for floral arrangements

THE ROBINSON-RANSBOTTOM POTTERY CO., Main Office and Plant, Roseville, Ohio

1952 Catalog page

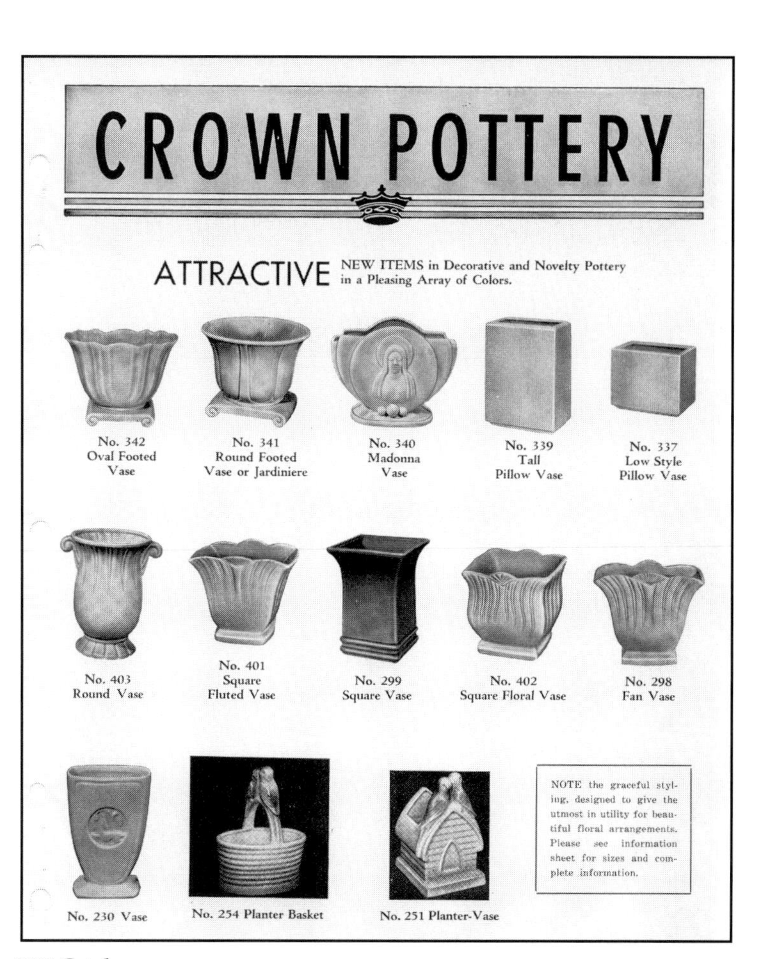

CROWN POTTERY

ATTRACTIVE NEW ITEMS in Decorative and Novelty Pottery in a Pleasing Array of Colors.

No. 342 Oval Footed Vase

No. 341 Round Footed Vase or Jardiniere

No. 340 Madonna Vase

No. 339 Tall Pillow Vase

No. 337 Low Style Pillow Vase

No. 403 Round Vase

No. 401 Square Fluted Vase

No. 299 Square Vase

No. 402 Square Floral Vase

No. 298 Fan Vase

NOTE the graceful styling, designed to give the utmost in utility for beautiful floral arrangements. Please see information sheet for sizes and complete information.

No. 230 Vase

No. 254 Planter Basket

No. 251 Planter-Vase

1955 Catalog page

CROWN POTTERY

Attractive

NEW ITEMS in Decorative, Novelty, and Utility pottery in a pleasing array of colors. Please refer to information sheet for dimensions and finishes, please see next page for additional items.

No. 407 Vase

No. 337 Low Style Pillow Vases

No. 339 Tall Pillow Vase

No. 1317 Stem Vase

No. 1320 Square Vase

No. 398 Low Flower Bowl

No. 1316 Utility Bowl

No. 1312/ Utility Vase

No. 1300 Fan Vase

No. 1504/MV. Mug Vase

No. 1301/ Vase

No. 1317 Stem Vase

No. 1311 Empire Vase

No. 1314/ Grecian Vase

No. 397 Footed Flower Bowl

THE ROBINSON-RANSBOTTOM POTTERY CO., Main Office and Plant, Roseville, Ohio

1958 Catalog page

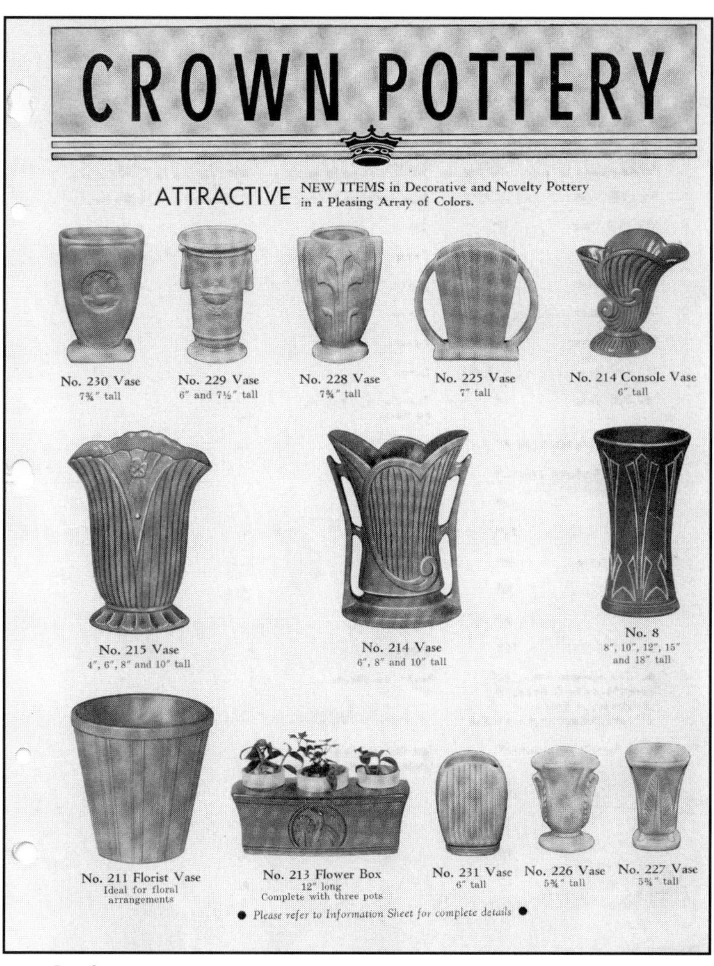

CROWN POTTERY

ATTRACTIVE NEW ITEMS in Decorative and Novelty Pottery in a Pleasing Array of Colors.

No. 230 Vase 7¾" tall

No. 229 Vase 6" and 7½" tall

No. 228 Vase 7¾" tall

No. 225 Vase 7" tall

No. 214 Console Vase 6" tall

No. 215 Vase 4", 6", 8" and 10" tall

No. 214 Vase 6", 8" and 10" tall

No. 8 8", 10", 12", 15" and 18" tall

No. 211 Florist Vase Ideal for floral arrangements

No. 213 Flower Box 12" long Complete with three pots

No. 231 Vase 6" tall

No. 226 Vase 5¾" tall

No. 227 Vase 5¾" tall

● Please refer to Information Sheet for complete details ●

1941 Catalog page

VASES

Vase, 6½", hand turned, dry foot, blue painted bottom. Sticker dated 1933. $125-150

Vase, 6½", hand turned, dry foot, blue painted bottom, $125-150

Vase, 9", green glaze over blue glaze, hand thrown, wire cut bottom, unpainted. $150-175

Vase, 12", hand thrown, twisted handles, blue bottom. $350-400

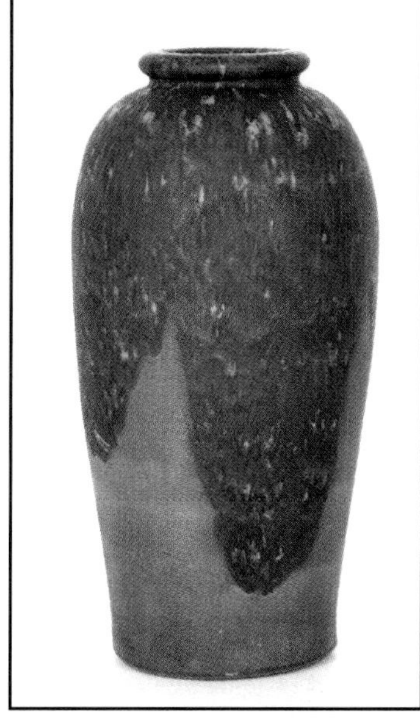

Floor Vase, 22", hand turned, flat unglazed bottom. $1,100-1,400

Vase, 8½", hand thrown, wire cut bottom, blue paint on bottom, $150-175

Floor Vase, 25½", green glaze over blue glaze, hand turned, flat unglazed bottom. 1930's, $1,100-1,400

Floor Vase, 26", jiggered, hand painted, signed D.A., numbered #290. $350-400

Floor Vase, 22", flat unglazed bottom. 1930's. $1,100-1,400

No. 294 Floor Vase, 30". 1950-1957. $150-200

No. 241 Old Colony 6" Vases:
Top Row: Marked 241; No mark.
Bottom Row: "Old Colony" Hand decorated RRPCo Roseville, Ohio. All marked 241 from 1941. $50-75 each

> Old Colony
> "Hand decorated underglaze. Each piece carries its own individual decoration and color combination. New and unique."
> *1941 catalog*

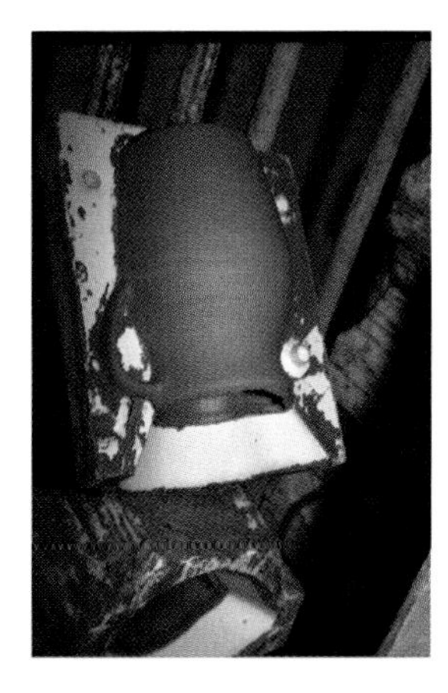

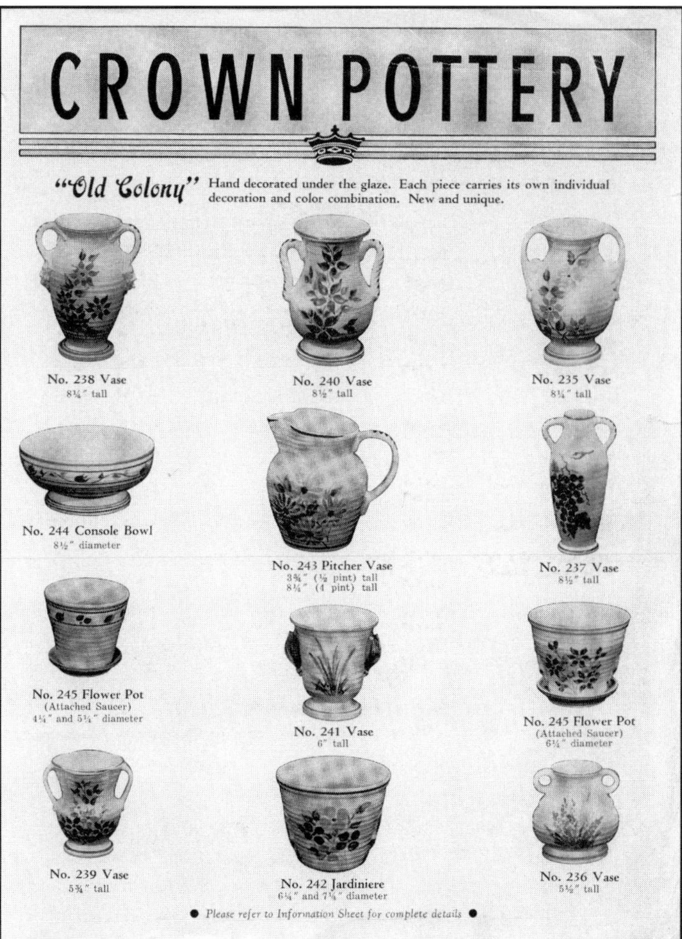

CROWN POTTERY

"Old Colony" Hand decorated under the glaze. Each piece carries its own individual decoration and color combination. New and unique.

No. 238 Vase
8¼" tall

No. 240 Vase
8½" tall

No. 235 Vase
8¼" tall

No. 244 Console Bowl
8½" diameter

No. 243 Pitcher Vase
3¾" (½ pint) tall
8¼" (4 pint) tall

No. 237 Vase
8½" tall

No. 245 Flower Pot
(Attached Saucer)
4¼" and 5¼" diameter

No. 241 Vase
6" tall

No. 245 Flower Pot
(Attached Saucer)
6¼" diameter

No. 239 Vase
5¾" tall

No. 242 Jardiniere
6¼" and 7¼" diameter

No. 236 Vase
5½" tall

● *Please refer to Information Sheet for complete details* ●

1941 Catalog page

Top Row:
Vase, 5½", 239 in mold. $50-60
Console Bowl, 8½" x 4", 244 in mold. $75-90
Jardiniere, 6¼" x 4" in mold, with circular indentation in bottom for flower pot punch out. $60-75
Bottom Row: No. 236 Vases, 5½", center one with Old Colony mark. $50-60 each
All top row items and center bottom mark "Old Colony" Hand decorated, RRPCo Roseville, Ohio. 1941

Pottery in production

Vases
Old Colony

Old Colony. No. 237 Vase with twisted handles, 8 1/2", full mark. $75-85
No. 245 Flower pot, 6 1/4" x 5 3/4" tall, full mark but no / after 245, rare. $60-75
No. 237 Vase, 8 1/2", full mark. 1941. $75-85

Top Row: $75-95 each
No. 240 Vase with braid pattern handle, 8 1/2";
No. 235 Vase, 8 1/4", handle has inside decoration.

BottomRow: $80-100 each
No. 238 Vase with gargoyle handles, 8 1/2".
All vases have "Old Colony" mark. 1941.

No. 242 Old Colony Jardiniere, 6" ribbed, white glazed bottom, dry foot, 242/- impressed, ink stamp "Old Colony" hand decorated, Roseville, O. 1941. $60-75

No. 240 Lamp Base, 8 1/2", "Old Colony" marked on bottom under glaze, hand written: W.L.Pace, Xmas '42, 235 impressed under glaze. 1941. $125-150

No. 243 Pitcher Vases, 1941, full marks:
3 3/4" (1/2 pint) $60-75
8 1/4" (4 pints) $90-110
8 1/4" (4 pints) $90-110
3 3/4" (1/2 pint) $60-75

Tionesta Art Ware

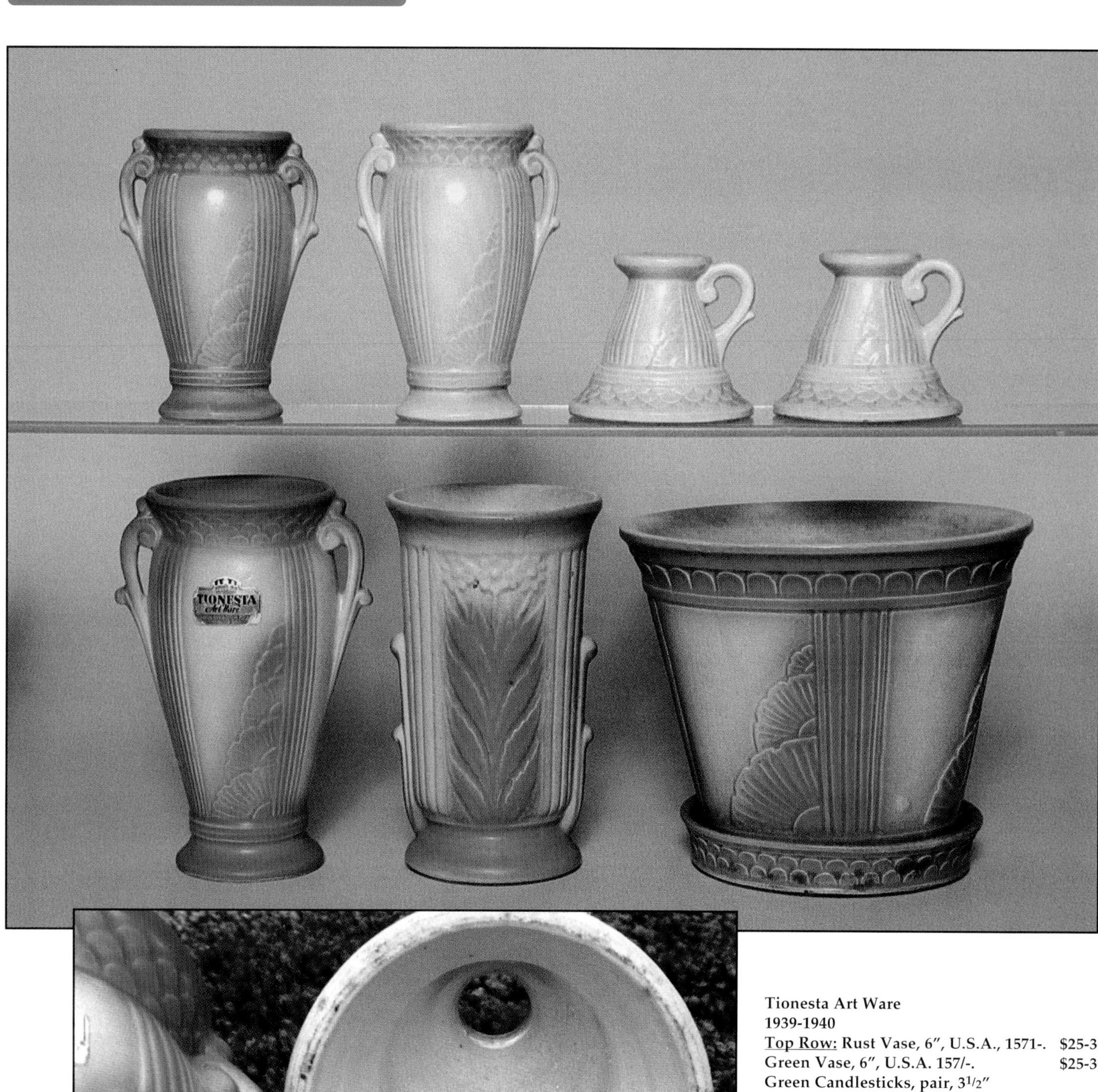

Tionesta Art Ware
1939-1940

Top Row: Rust Vase, 6", U.S.A., 1571-.	$25-30
Green Vase, 6", U.S.A. 157/-.	$25-30
Green Candlesticks, pair, 3½" open bottom, no mark, paper sticker in one. (See photo inset at left.)	$25-30 each
Bottom Row: Vase, 8" with paper label, 157/- U.S.A.	$40-50
Vase, 8", 160/5 U.S.A.	$40-50
Flowerpot, 7½", with saucer, 115/.	$35-40

Vases Victoria

CROWN POTTERY

VASES . . . Victoria Finish or Solid Color Glazes

No. 184
6" and 8" tall

No. 190
8" tall

No. 187
8" tall

No. 181
6", 8" and 10" tall

Ivy Jar
8" tall

No. 123
6", 8" and 10" tall

No. 127
6", 8" and 10" tall

No. 185
8" tall

No. 189
10" tall

No. 8
8", 10", 12", 15" and 18" tall

Cemetery Vase
5" and 6" diameter

No. 157
6", 8", 10", 12", 15", 18" and 20" tall

1939 Catalog page

Victoria glaze, 2-handled Vase, 14", glazed bottom, impressed mark, USA 159/-. 1939-1940. $100-125

Victoria Glaze Vases, 1938-1940

Top Row:		Bottom Row:	
Green, 6", USA 123/-.	$25-30	Blue, 8$^{1/4}$", USA 187/-.	$35-45
Blue, 8", USA 190/-.	$30-35	Blue, 8$^{1/4}$", USA123/-.	$45-55
Blue, 8$^{1/4}$", USA 185/.	$35-40	Blue, 10" USA 123/-.	$65-75
Red, 8$^{1/4}$", USA 187/.	$35-40	Red, 10" USA 123/-.	$65-75

Victoria Glaze Vases:

Top Row:		Bottom Row:	
Green, 6", USA 181/-	$35-45	Blue, 10$^{1/4}$", USA 127/-.	$55-65
Red, 8", USA 181/-.	$55-65	Red, 10" 181/-.	$65-75
Blue, 6", USA 127/-.	$30-35	Blue Oil Jar, 10$^{1/4}$", USA 130/.	$60-70
Red, 7$^{1/2}$", USA 127/-.	$50-55		

Victoria Glaze, 1938-1939

Top Row: Pitchers		Bottom Row: Draped Vases:	
Red, no mark.	$40-50	Green, 6", 184/- USA.	$35-40
Blue, USA 170/-.	$40-50	Blue, 8", 184/ USA.	$40-50
Green, USA 170/-.	$40-50	Red, 10" 189/USA.	$50-55

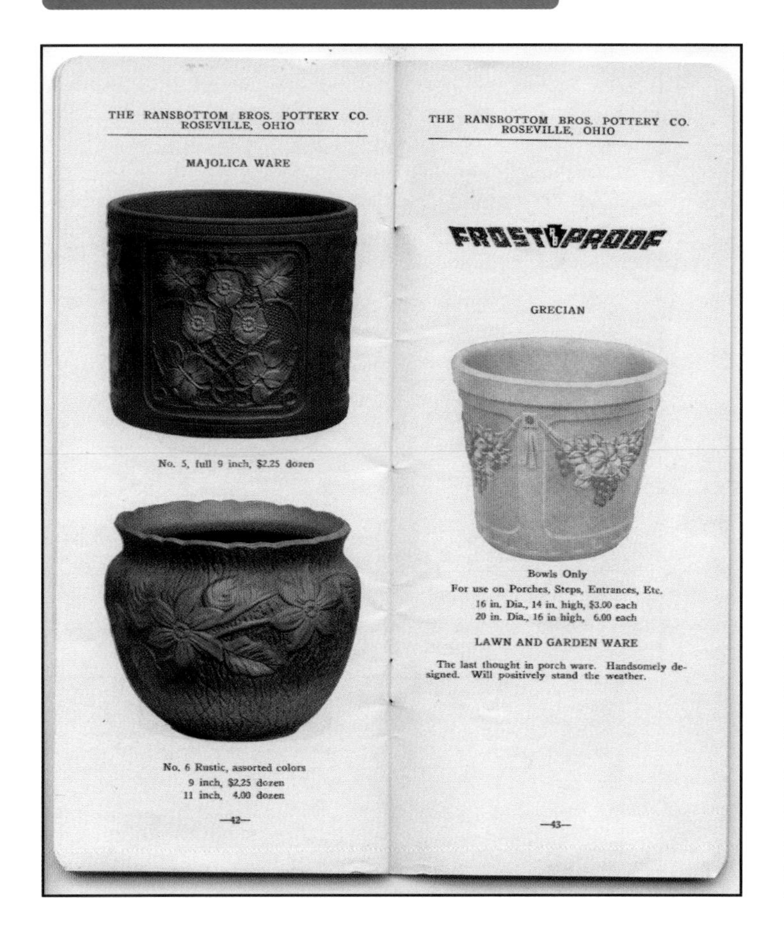
THE RANSBOTTOM BROS. POTTERY CO.
ROSEVILLE, OHIO

MAJOLICA WARE

No. 5, full 9 inch, $2.25 dozen

No. 6 Rustic, assorted colors
9 inch, $2.25 dozen
11 inch, 4.00 dozen

—42—

THE RANSBOTTOM BROS. POTTERY CO.
ROSEVILLE, OHIO

FROST PROOF

GRECIAN

Bowls Only
For use on Porches, Steps, Entrances, Etc.
16 in. Dia., 14 in. high, $3.00 each
20 in. Dia., 16 in high, 6.00 each

LAWN AND GARDEN WARE

The last thought in porch ware. Handsomely designed. Will positively stand the weather.

—43—

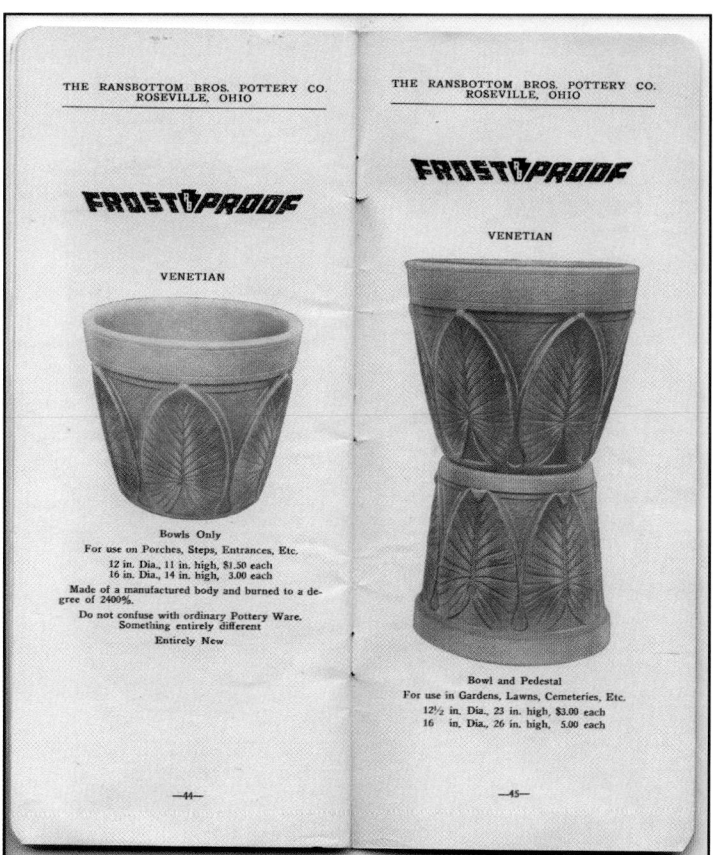
THE RANSBOTTOM BROS. POTTERY CO.
ROSEVILLE, OHIO

FROST PROOF

VENETIAN

Bowls Only
For use on Porches, Steps, Entrances, Etc.
12 in. Dia., 11 in. high, $1.50 each
16 in. Dia., 14 in. high, 3.00 each

Made of a manufactured body and burned to a degree of 2400%.

Do not confuse with ordinary Pottery Ware.
Something entirely different

Entirely New

—44—

THE RANSBOTTOM BROS. POTTERY CO.
ROSEVILLE, OHIO

FROST PROOF

VENETIAN

Bowl and Pedestal
For use in Gardens, Lawns, Cemeteries, Etc.
12½ in. Dia., 23 in. high, $3.00 each
16 in. Dia., 26 in. high, 5.00 each

—45—

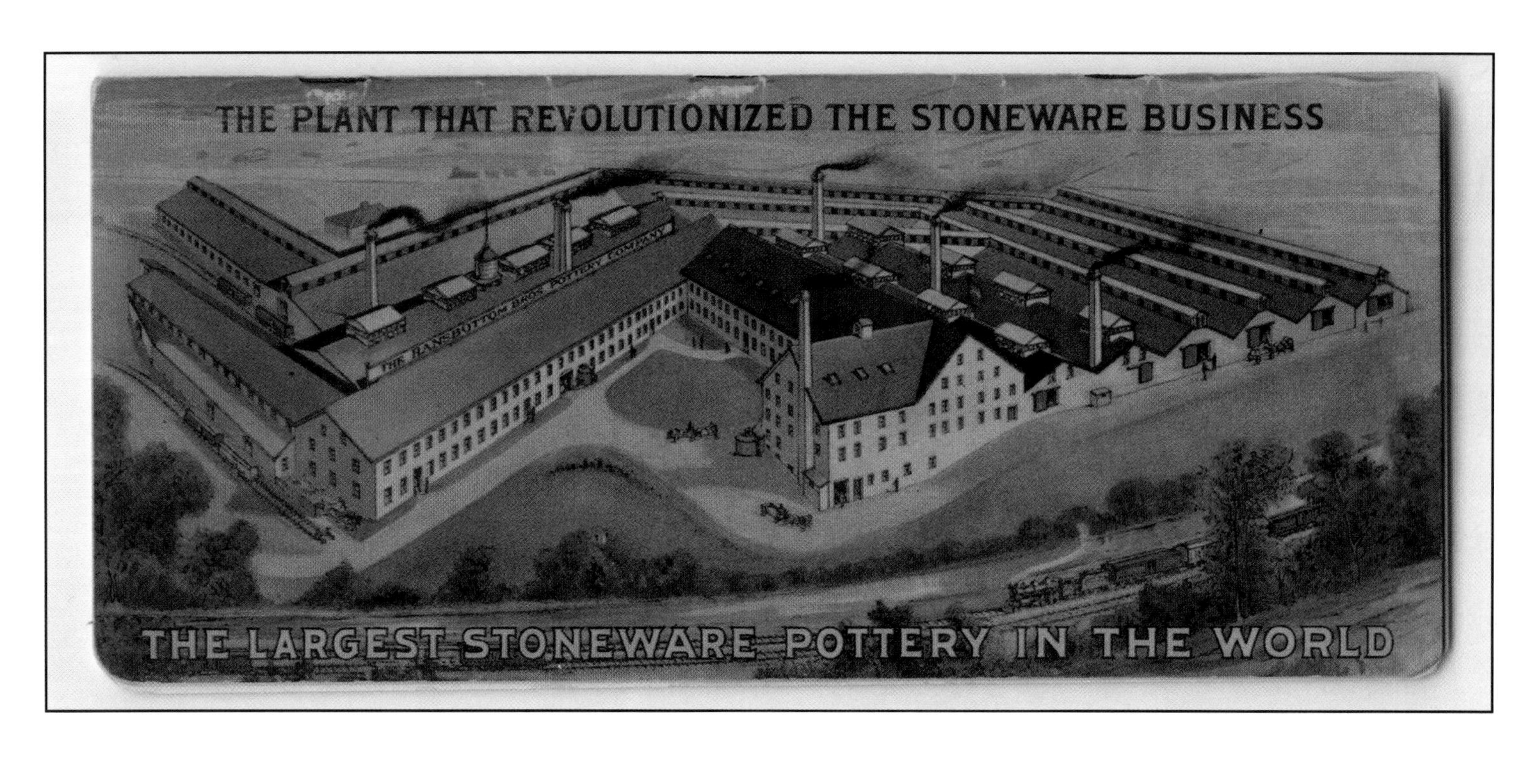

THE RANSBOTTOM BROS. POTTERY CO.
ROSEVILLE, OHIO

SHOULDER JUGS

¼, ½, 1, 2, 3, 4 and 5 Gal.
White glazed body with black tops
¼ gal., 45c per doz.
½ gal., 60c per doz.
All other sizes, 7½c per gal.

DRUGGIST JUGS

½, 1 and 2 Gal.
½ gal., 70c per doz.
1 and 2 gals., 8½c per gal.
All our jugs uniform corkage
Guaranteed no leakers or seepers

—12—

THE RANSBOTTOM BROS. POTTERY CO.
ROSEVILLE, OHIO

SYRUP JUGS

½, 1 and 2 gal. sizes
½ gal., 65c per doz.
1 and 2 gal., 7½c per gal.

½ and 1 gal. sizes
½ gal. 70c per doz.
1 gal., $1.00 per doz.

—13—

THE RANSBOTTOM BROS. POTTERY CO.
ROSEVILLE, OHIO

STANDARD JARS

10

8, 10 and 12 Gal.

STANDARD JARS OR MEAT TUBS

15

15 and 20 Gal.
For Jar Covers see Page 2

THE RANSBOTTOM BROS. POTTERY CO.
ROSEVILLE, OHIO

MEAT TUBS

25

25 and 30 gal.
35 and 40 gal.

MEAT TUBS

50

50 gal.

ROUND BOTTOM MILK PANS

⅛, ¼, ½, ¾, 1, 1½ and 2 Gal. Sizes
We make the above in Black, White and Blue Glaze

FLAT BOTTOM MILK PANS

1 Gal. Sizes Only
We make the above in Black and White Glaze

FRENCH POTS OR DEEP MILK PANS

½, 1, 1½ and 2 Gal. Sizes
We make the above in Black and White Glaze

LOW BUTTERS

⅛, ¼, ½, 1, 1½ and 2 Gals.

STANDARD JARS

¼, ½, 1, 2 and 3 Gals.

STANDARD JARS

4, 5 and 6 Gals.
For Jar Covers see Page 2

Catalog 1915

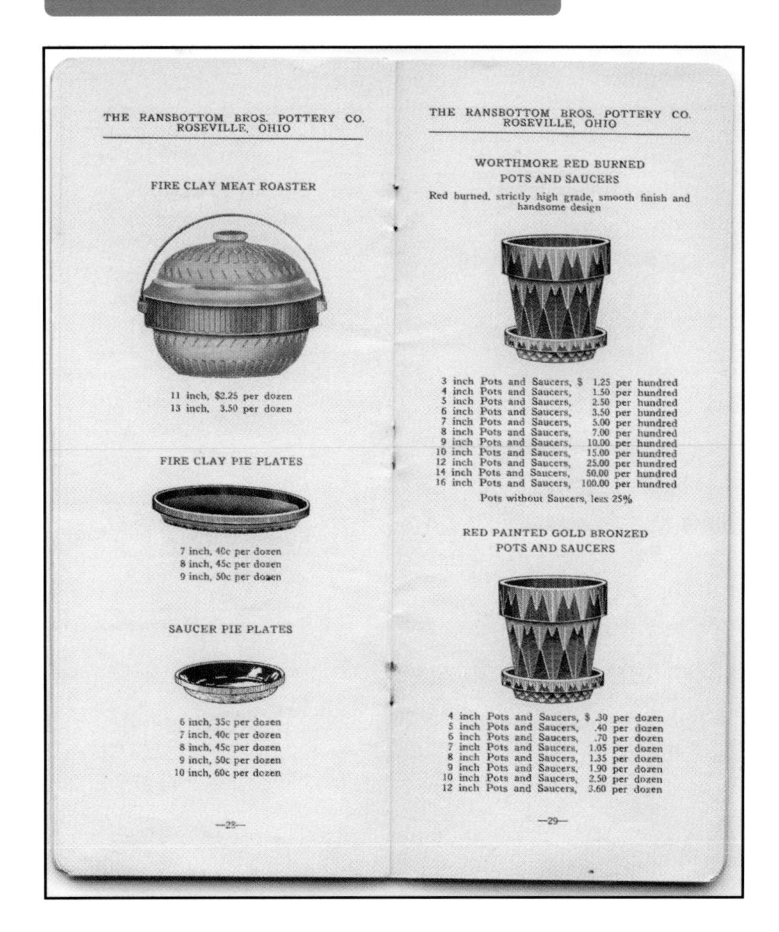

THE RANSBOTTOM BROS. POTTERY CO.
ROSEVILLE, OHIO

FIRE CLAY MEAT ROASTER

11 inch, $2.25 per dozen
13 inch, 3.50 per dozen

FIRE CLAY PIE PLATES

7 inch, 40c per dozen
8 inch, 45c per dozen
9 inch, 50c per dozen

SAUCER PIE PLATES

6 inch, 35c per dozen
7 inch, 40c per dozen
8 inch, 45c per dozen
9 inch, 50c per dozen
10 inch, 60c per dozen

—28—

THE RANSBOTTOM BROS. POTTERY CO.
ROSEVILLE, OHIO

WORTHMORE RED BURNED
POTS AND SAUCERS

Red burned, strictly high grade, smooth finish and handsome design

3 inch Pots and Saucers,	$ 1.25	per hundred
4 inch Pots and Saucers,	1.50	per hundred
5 inch Pots and Saucers,	2.50	per hundred
6 inch Pots and Saucers,	3.50	per hundred
7 inch Pots and Saucers,	5.00	per hundred
8 inch Pots and Saucers,	7.00	per hundred
9 inch Pots and Saucers,	10.00	per hundred
10 inch Pots and Saucers,	15.00	per hundred
12 inch Pots and Saucers,	25.00	per hundred
14 inch Pots and Saucers,	50.00	per hundred
16 inch Pots and Saucers,	100.00	per hundred

Pots without Saucers, less 25%

RED PAINTED GOLD BRONZED
POTS AND SAUCERS

4 inch Pots and Saucers,	$ .30	per dozen
5 inch Pots and Saucers,	.40	per dozen
6 inch Pots and Saucers,	.70	per dozen
7 inch Pots and Saucers,	1.05	per dozen
8 inch Pots and Saucers,	1.35	per dozen
9 inch Pots and Saucers,	1.90	per dozen
10 inch Pots and Saucers,	2.50	per dozen
12 inch Pots and Saucers,	3.60	per dozen

—29—

THE RANSBOTTOM BROS. POTTERY CO.
ROSEVILLE, OHIO

PLAIN RED BURNED
POTS AND SAUCERS

3 inch,	$ 1.25	per hundred
4 inch,	1.50	per hundred
5 inch,	2.50	per hundred
6 inch,	3.50	per hundred
7 inch,	5.00	per hundred
8 inch,	7.00	per hundred
9 inch,	10.00	per hundred
10 inch,	15.00	per hundred
12 inch,	25.00	per hundred
14 inch,	50.00	per hundred
16 inch,	100.00	per hundred

Pots without Saucers, less 25%

AZALEA OR LOW POTS AND SAUCERS

6 inch,	$ 3.50	per hundred
7 inch,	5.00	per hundred
8 inch,	7.00	per hundred
9 inch,	10.00	per hundred
10 inch,	15.00	per hundred
12 inch,	25.00	per hundred

Pots without Saucers, less 25%

—30—

THE RANSBOTTOM BROS. POTTERY CO.
ROSEVILLE, OHIO

GLAZED CUSPIDORS

No. 1
7½ inch Blue and White Tint, nicely Embossed
$9.60 per gross

No. 2
7½ inch Blue and White Mottled Effect
$9.60 per gross

—31—

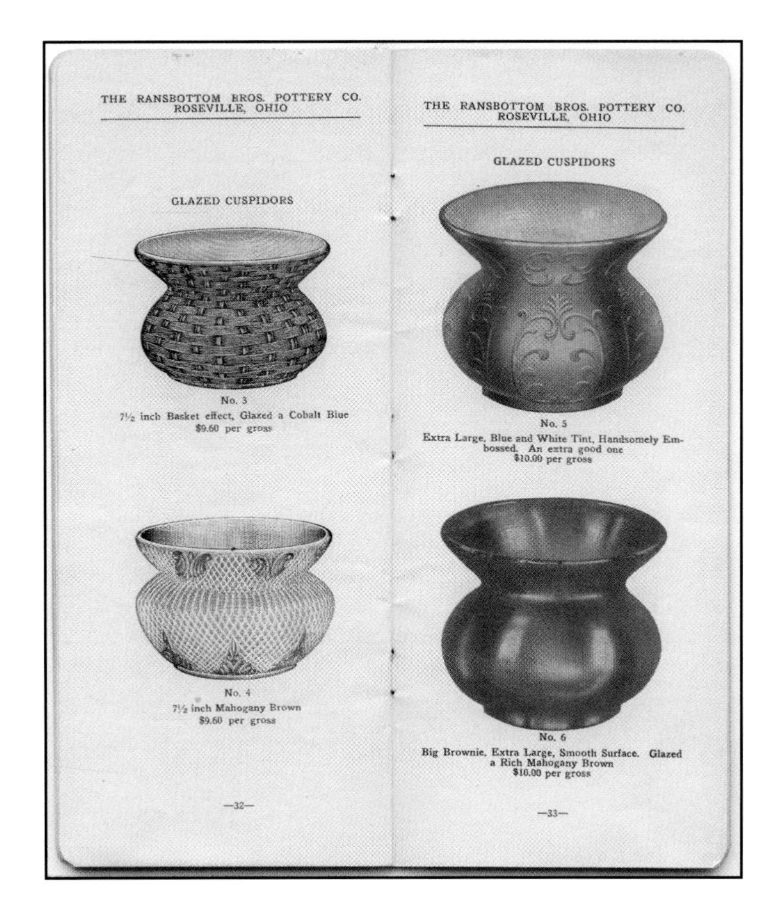

THE RANSBOTTOM BROS. POTTERY CO.
ROSEVILLE, OHIO

GLAZED CUSPIDORS

No. 3
7½ inch Basket effect, Glazed a Cobalt Blue
$9.60 per gross

No. 4
7½ inch Mahogany Brown
$9.60 per gross

—32—

THE RANSBOTTOM BROS. POTTERY CO.
ROSEVILLE, OHIO

GLAZED CUSPIDORS

No. 5
Extra Large, Blue and White Tint, Handsomely Embossed. An extra good one
$10.00 per gross

No. 6
Big Brownie, Extra Large, Smooth Surface. Glazed a Rich Mahogany Brown
$10.00 per gross

—33—

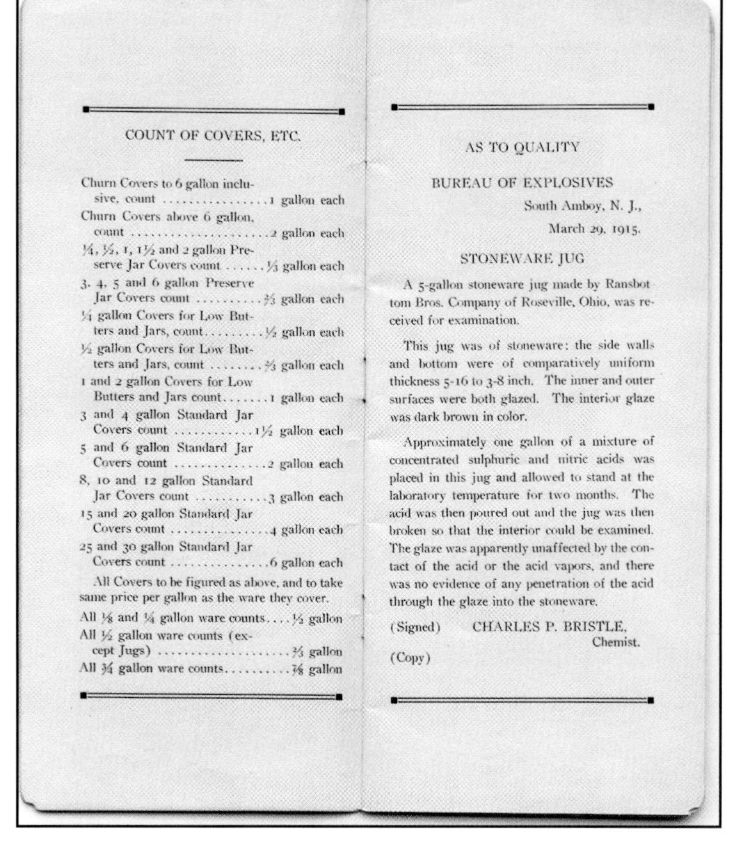

COUNT OF COVERS, ETC.

Churn Covers to 6 gallon inclusive, count ....1 gallon each
Churn Covers above 6 gallon, count ....2 gallon each
¼, ½, 1, 1½ and 2 gallon Preserve Jar Covers count ......⅓ gallon each
3, 4, 5 and 6 gallon Preserve Jar Covers count ....⅔ gallon each
¼ gallon Covers for Low Butters and Jars, count.........½ gallon each
½ gallon Covers for Low Butters and Jars, count ....⅔ gallon each
1 and 2 gallon Covers for Low Butters and Jars count.......1 gallon each
3 and 4 gallon Standard Jar Covers count ....1½ gallon each
5 and 6 gallon Standard Jar Covers count ....2 gallon each
8, 10 and 12 gallon Standard Jar Covers count ....3 gallon each
15 and 20 gallon Standard Jar Covers count ....4 gallon each
25 and 30 gallon Standard Jar Covers count ....6 gallon each

All Covers to be figured as above, and to take same price per gallon as the ware they cover.

All ⅛ and ¼ gallon ware counts....½ gallon
All ½ gallon ware counts (except Jugs) ....⅔ gallon
All ¾ gallon ware counts..........⅞ gallon

AS TO QUALITY

BUREAU OF EXPLOSIVES

South Amboy, N. J.,
March 29, 1915.

STONEWARE JUG

A 5-gallon stoneware jug made by Ransbottom Bros. Company of Roseville, Ohio, was received for examination.

This jug was of stoneware: the side walls and bottom were of comparatively uniform thickness 5-16 to 3-8 inch. The inner and outer surfaces were both glazed. The interior glaze was dark brown in color.

Approximately one gallon of a mixture of concentrated sulphuric and nitric acids was placed in this jug and allowed to stand at the laboratory temperature for two months. The acid was then poured out and the jug was then broken so that the interior could be examined. The glaze was apparently unaffected by the contact of the acid or the acid vapors, and there was no evidence of any penetration of the acid through the glaze into the stoneware.

(Signed) CHARLES P. BRISTLE,
Chemist.

(Copy)

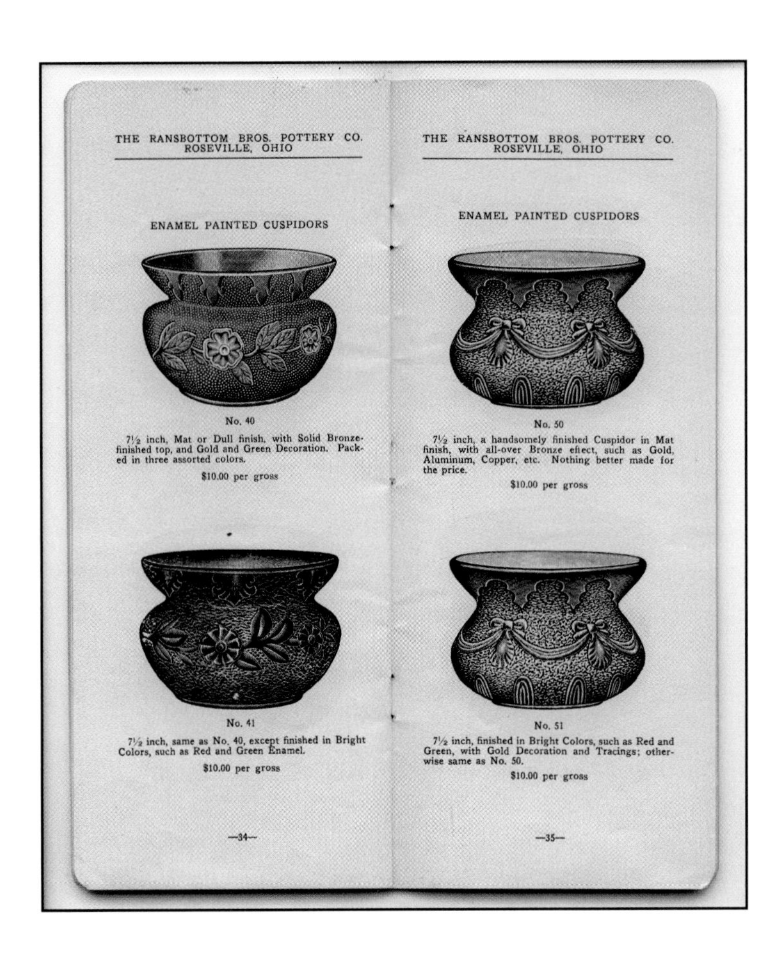

THE RANSBOTTOM BROS. POTTERY CO.
ROSEVILLE, OHIO

ENAMEL PAINTED CUSPIDORS

No. 40

7½ inch, Mat or Dull finish, with Solid Bronze-finished top, and Gold and Green Decoration. Packed in three assorted colors.

$10.00 per gross

No. 41

7½ inch, same as No. 40, except finished in Bright Colors, such as Red and Green Enamel.

$10.00 per gross

—34—

THE RANSBOTTOM BROS. POTTERY CO.
ROSEVILLE, OHIO

ENAMEL PAINTED CUSPIDORS

No. 50

7½ inch, a handsomely finished Cuspidor in Mat finish, with all-over Bronze effect, such as Gold, Aluminum, Copper, etc. Nothing better made for the price.

$10.00 per gross

No. 51

7½ inch, finished in Bright Colors, such as Red and Green, with Gold Decoration and Tracings; otherwise same as No. 50.

$10.00 per gross

—35—

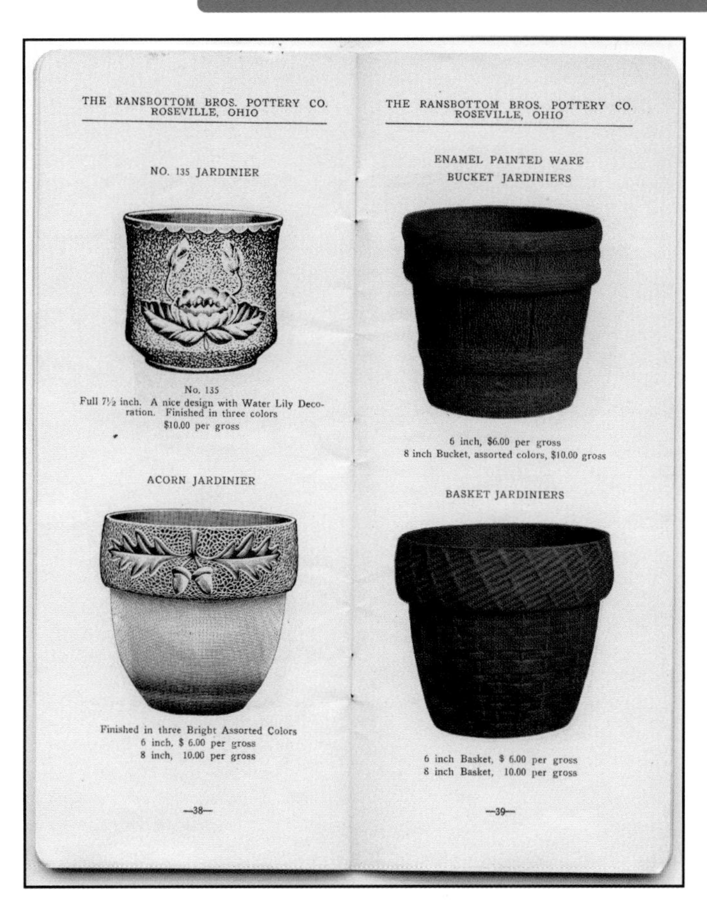

THE RANSBOTTOM BROS. POTTERY CO.
ROSEVILLE, OHIO

NO. 135 JARDINIER

No. 135

Full 7½ inch. A nice design with Water Lily Decoration. Finished in three colors

$10.00 per gross

ACORN JARDINIER

Finished in three Bright Assorted Colors
6 inch, $ 6.00 per gross
8 inch, 10.00 per gross

—38—

THE RANSBOTTOM BROS. POTTERY CO.
ROSEVILLE, OHIO

ENAMEL PAINTED WARE
BUCKET JARDINIERS

6 inch, $6.00 per gross
8 inch Bucket, assorted colors, $10.00 gross

BASKET JARDINIERS

6 inch Basket, $ 6.00 per gross
8 inch Basket, 10.00 per gross

—39—

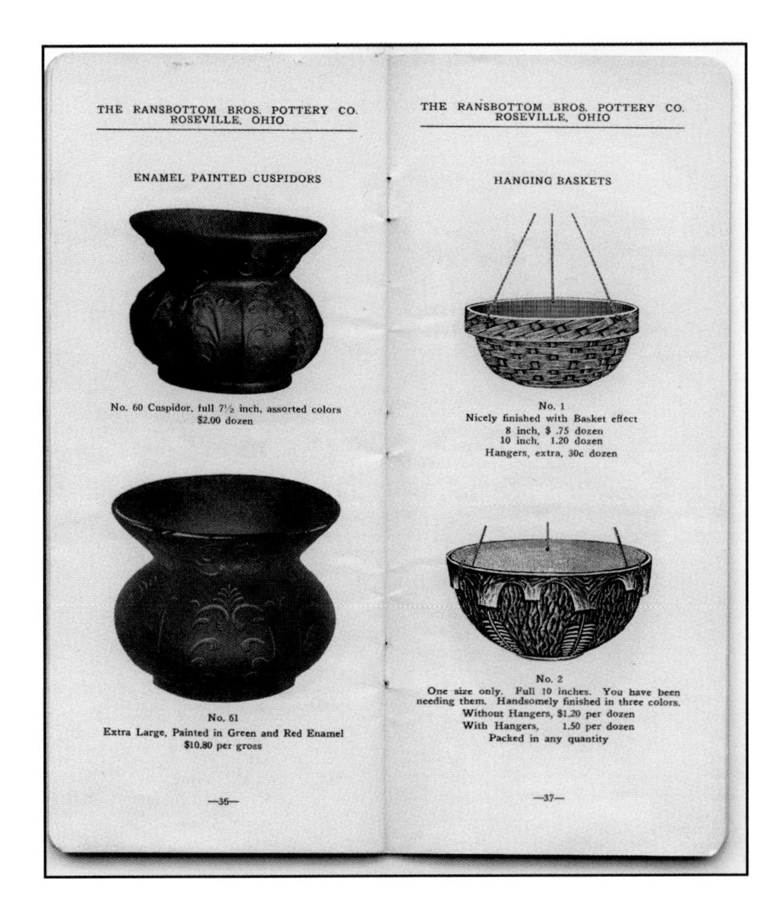

THE RANSBOTTOM BROS. POTTERY CO.
ROSEVILLE, OHIO

ENAMEL PAINTED CUSPIDORS

No. 60 Cuspidor, full 7½ inch, assorted colors
$2.00 dozen

No. 61
Extra Large, Painted in Green and Red Enamel
$10.80 per gross

—36—

THE RANSBOTTOM BROS. POTTERY CO.
ROSEVILLE, OHIO

HANGING BASKETS

No. 1
Nicely finished with Basket effect
8 inch, $ .75 dozen
10 inch, 1.20 dozen
Hangers, extra, 30c dozen

No. 2
One size only. Full 10 inches. You have been needing them. Handsomely finished in three colors.
Without Hangers, $1.20 per dozen
With Hangers, 1.50 per dozen
Packed in any quantity

—37—

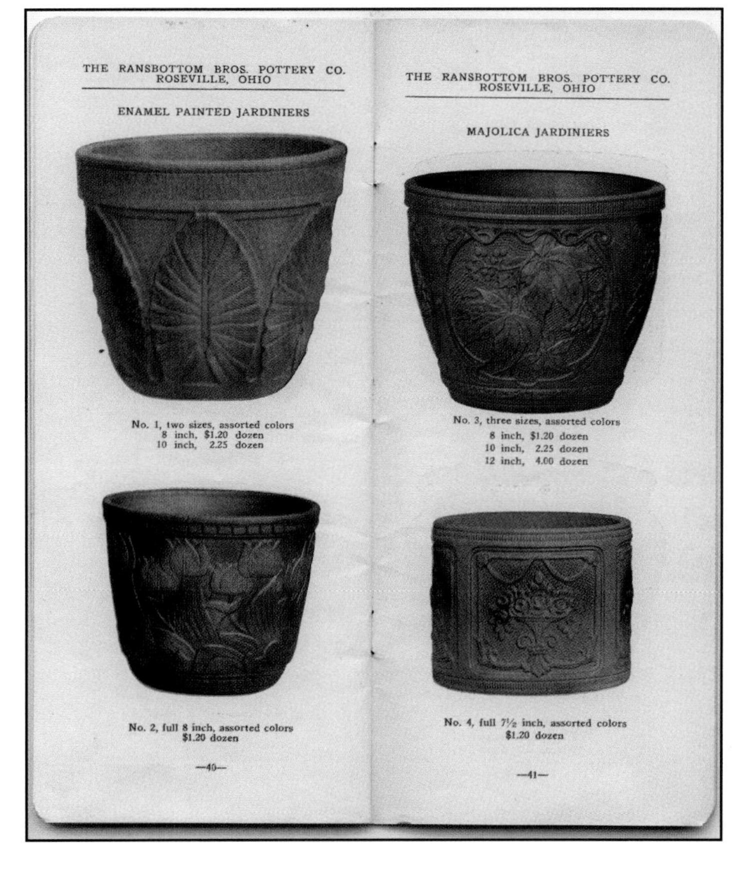

THE RANSBOTTOM BROS. POTTERY CO.
ROSEVILLE, OHIO

ENAMEL PAINTED JARDINIERS

No. 1, two sizes, assorted colors
8 inch, $1.20 dozen
10 inch, 2.25 dozen

No. 2, full 8 inch, assorted colors
$1.20 dozen

—40—

THE RANSBOTTOM BROS. POTTERY CO.
ROSEVILLE, OHIO

MAJOLICA JARDINIERS

No. 3, three sizes, assorted colors
8 inch, $1.20 dozen
10 inch, 2.25 dozen
12 inch, 4.00 dozen

No. 4, full 7½ inch, assorted colors
$1.20 dozen

—41—

Catalog 1915

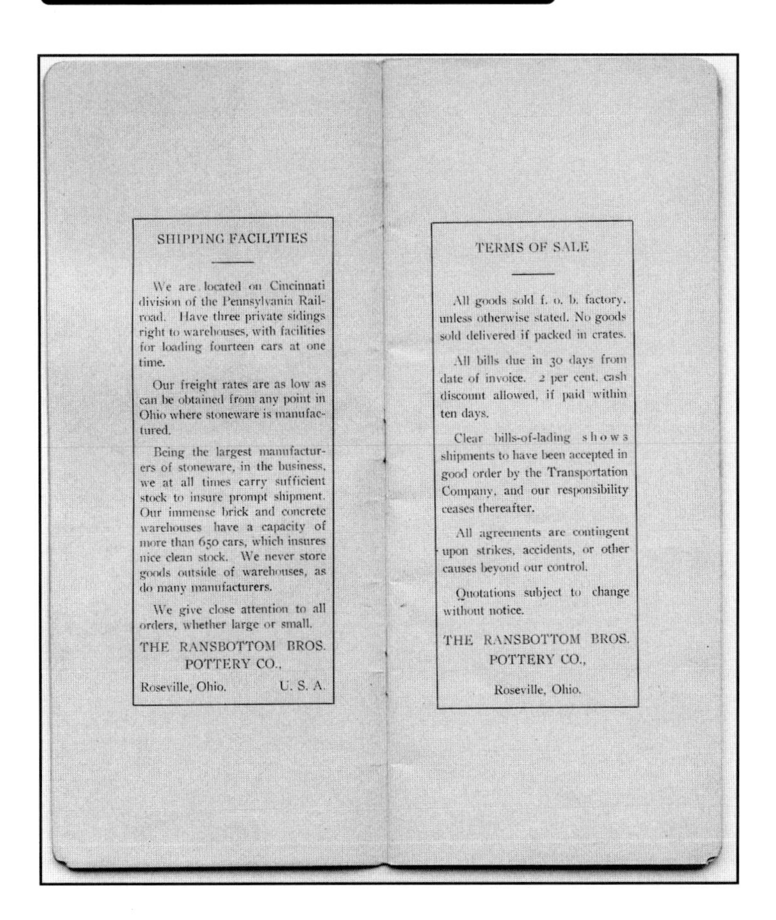

SHIPPING FACILITIES

We are located on Cincinnati division of the Pennsylvania Railroad. Have three private sidings right to warehouses, with facilities for loading fourteen cars at one time.

Our freight rates are as low as can be obtained from any point in Ohio where stoneware is manufactured.

Being the largest manufacturers of stoneware, in the business, we at all times carry sufficient stock to insure prompt shipment. Our immense brick and concrete warehouses have a capacity of more than 650 cars, which insures nice clean stock. We never store goods outside of warehouses, as do many manufacturers.

We give close attention to all orders, whether large or small.

THE RANSBOTTOM BROS. POTTERY CO.,

Roseville, Ohio. U. S. A.

TERMS OF SALE

All goods sold f. o. b. factory, unless otherwise stated. No goods sold delivered if packed in crates.

All bills due in 30 days from date of invoice. 2 per cent. cash discount allowed, if paid within ten days.

Clear bills-of-lading shows shipments to have been accepted in good order by the Transportation Company, and our responsibility ceases thereafter.

All agreements are contingent upon strikes, accidents, or other causes beyond our control.

Quotations subject to change without notice.

THE RANSBOTTOM BROS. POTTERY CO.,

Roseville, Ohio.

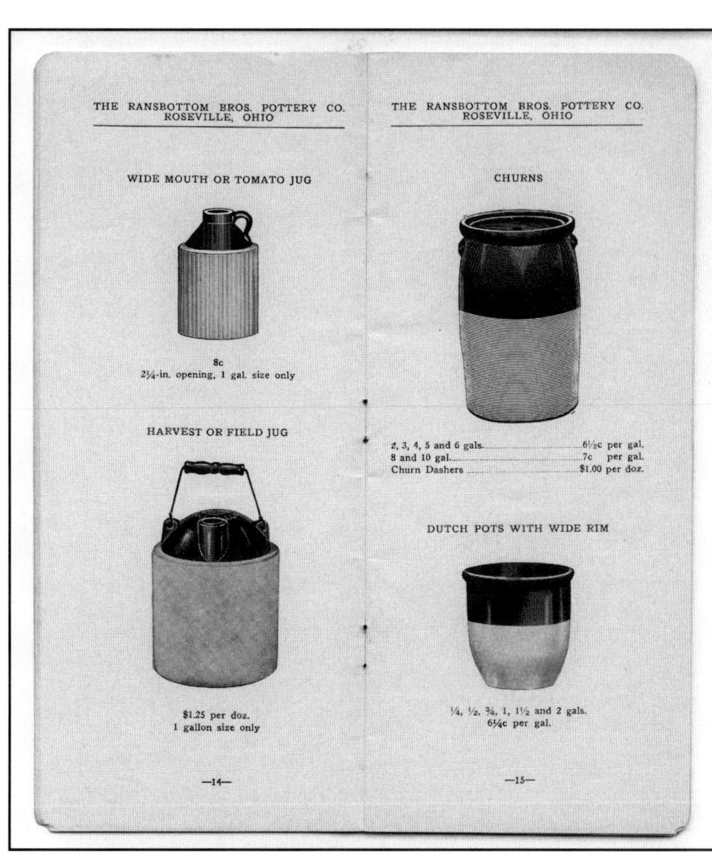

THE RANSBOTTOM BROS. POTTERY CO.
ROSEVILLE, OHIO

WIDE MOUTH OR TOMATO JUG

8c
2¼-in. opening, 1 gal. size only

HARVEST OR FIELD JUG

$1.25 per doz.
1 gallon size only

—14—

THE RANSBOTTOM BROS. POTTERY CO.
ROSEVILLE, OHIO

CHURNS

2, 3, 4, 5 and 6 gals. .... 6½c per gal.
8 and 10 gal. .... 7c per gal.
Churn Dashers .... $1.00 per doz.

DUTCH POTS WITH WIDE RIM

¼, ½, ¾, 1, 1½ and 2 gals.
6¼c per gal.

—15—

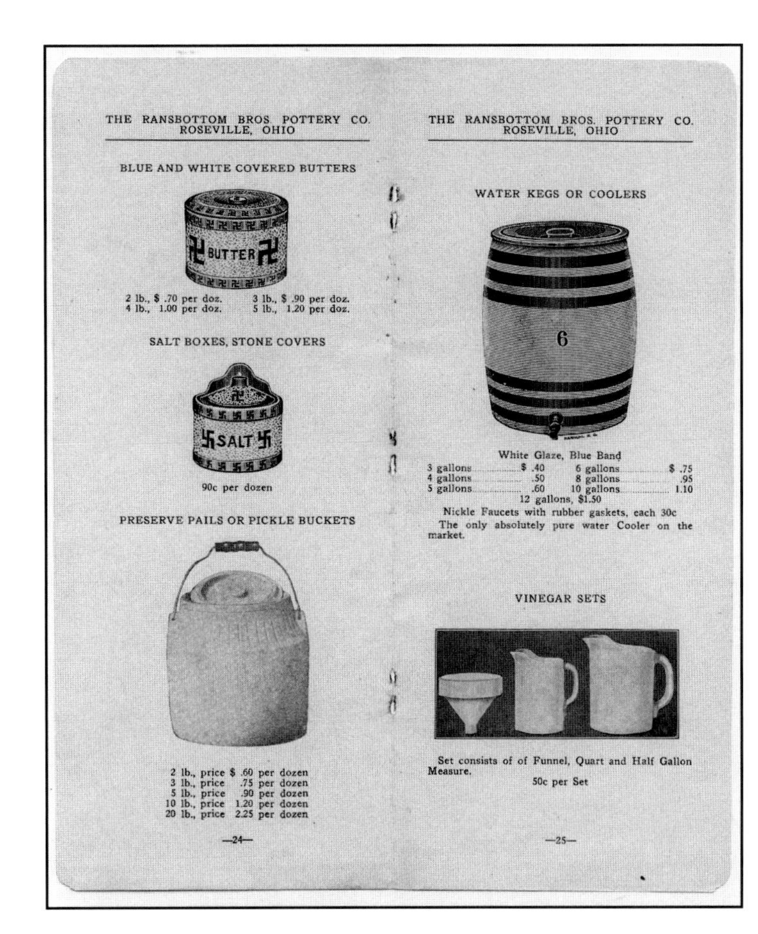

THE RANSBOTTOM BROS. POTTERY CO.
ROSEVILLE, OHIO

BLUE AND WHITE COVERED BUTTERS

2 lb., $ .70 per doz. 3 lb., $ .90 per doz.
4 lb., 1.00 per doz. 5 lb., 1.20 per doz.

SALT BOXES, STONE COVERS

90c per dozen

PRESERVE PAILS OR PICKLE BUCKETS

2 lb., price $ .60 per dozen
3 lb., price .75 per dozen
5 lb., price .90 per dozen
10 lb., price 1.20 per dozen
20 lb., price 2.25 per dozen

—24—

THE RANSBOTTOM BROS. POTTERY CO.
ROSEVILLE, OHIO

WATER KEGS OR COOLERS

White Glaze, Blue Band

3 gallons .... $ .40 6 gallons .... $ .75
4 gallons .... .50 8 gallons .... .95
5 gallons .... .60 10 gallons 1.10
12 gallons, $1.50

Nickle Faucets with rubber gaskets, each 30c

The only absolutely pure water Cooler on the market.

VINEGAR SETS

Set consists of of Funnel, Quart and Half Gallon Measure.

50c per Set

—25—

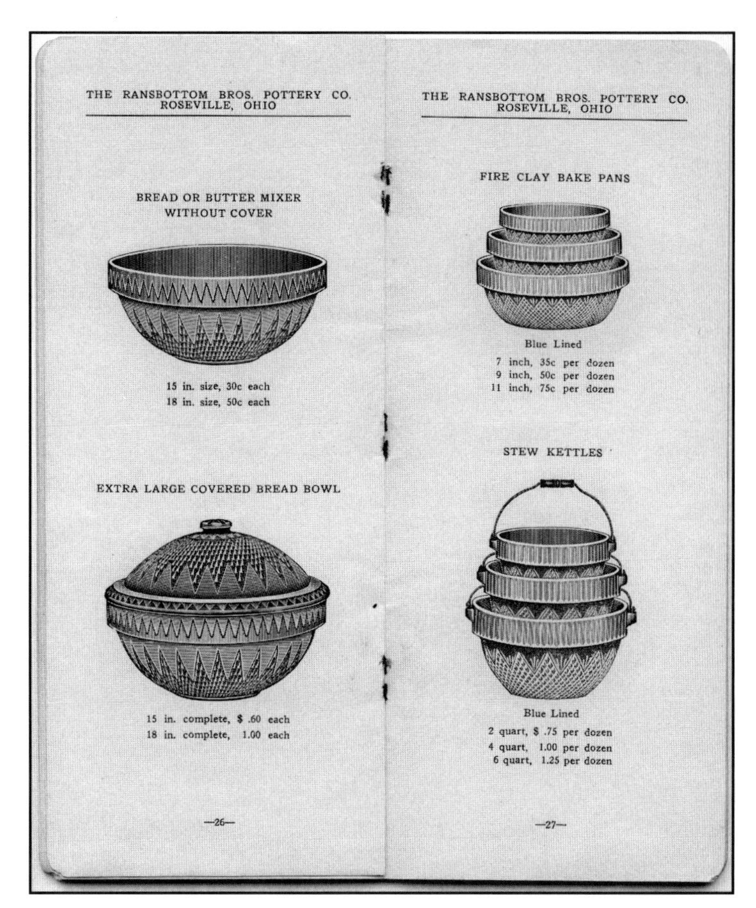

THE RANSBOTTOM BROS. POTTERY CO.
ROSEVILLE, OHIO

BREAD OR BUTTER MIXER
WITHOUT COVER

15 in. size, 30c each
18 in. size, 50c each

EXTRA LARGE COVERED BREAD BOWL

15 in. complete, $ .60 each
18 in. complete, 1.00 each

—26—

THE RANSBOTTOM BROS. POTTERY CO.
ROSEVILLE, OHIO

FIRE CLAY BAKE PANS

Blue Lined
7 inch, 35c per dozen
9 inch, 50c per dozen
11 inch, 75c per dozen

STEW KETTLES

Blue Lined
2 quart, $ .75 per dozen
4 quart, 1.00 per dozen
6 quart, 1.25 per dozen

—27—

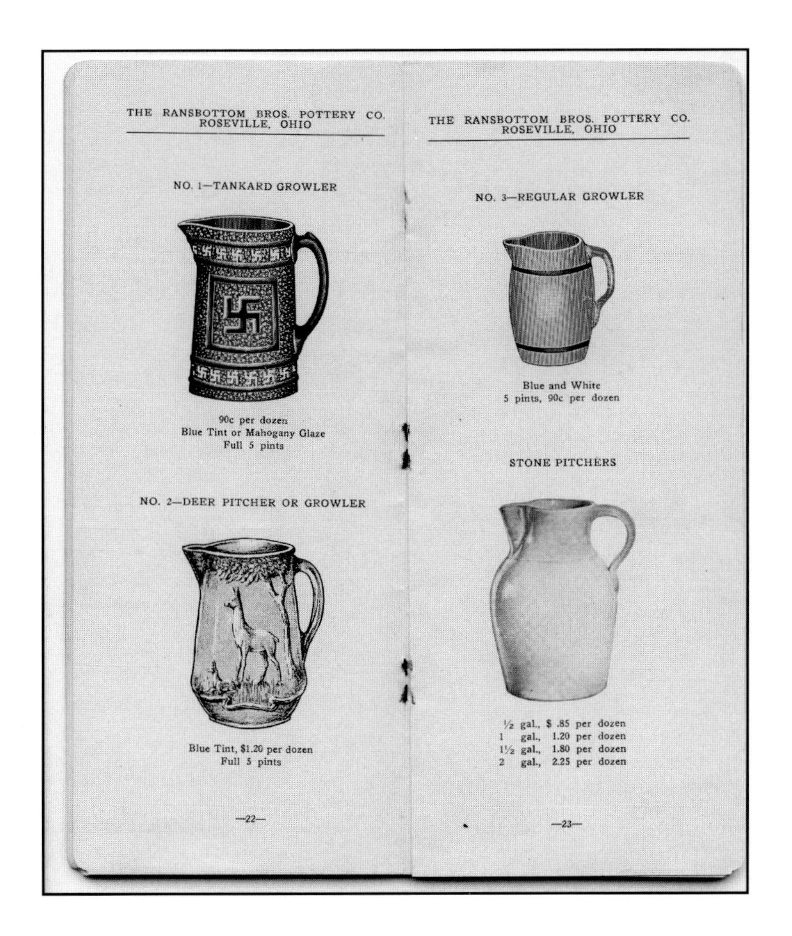

THE RANSBOTTOM BROS. POTTERY CO.
ROSEVILLE, OHIO

NO. 1—TANKARD GROWLER

90c per dozen
Blue Tint or Mahogany Glaze
Full 5 pints

NO. 2—DEER PITCHER OR GROWLER

Blue Tint, $1.20 per dozen
Full 5 pints

—22—

THE RANSBOTTOM BROS. POTTERY CO.
ROSEVILLE, OHIO

NO. 3—REGULAR GROWLER

Blue and White
5 pints, 90c per dozen

STONE PITCHERS

½ gal., $ .85 per dozen
1 gal., 1.20 per dozen
1½ gal., 1.80 per dozen
2 gal., 2.25 per dozen

—23—

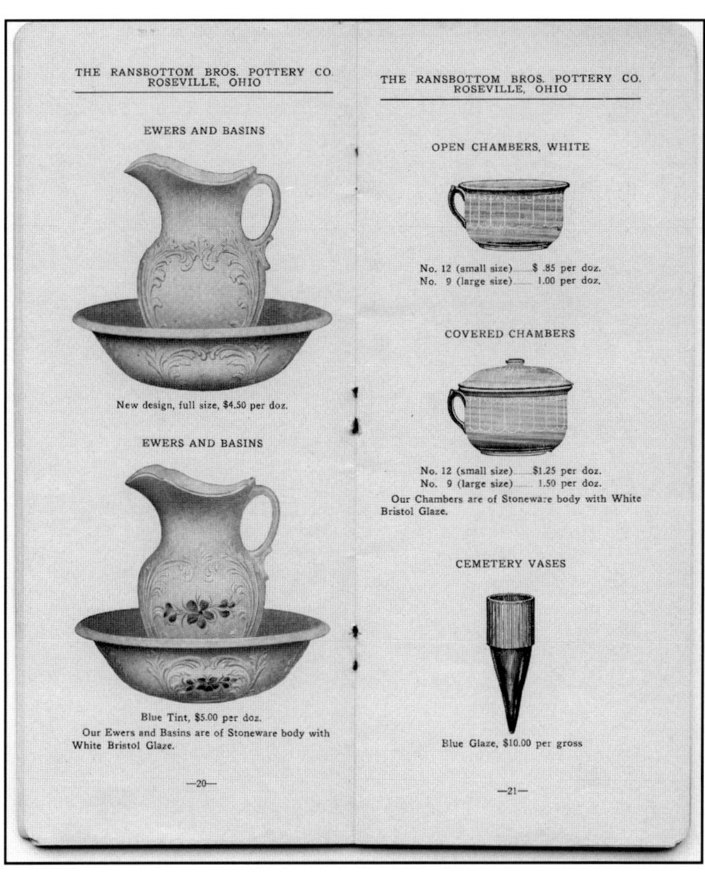

THE RANSBOTTOM BROS. POTTERY CO.
ROSEVILLE, OHIO

EWERS AND BASINS

New design, full size, $4.50 per doz.

EWERS AND BASINS

Blue Tint, $5.00 per doz.
Our Ewers and Basins are of Stoneware body with White Bristol Glaze.

—20—

THE RANSBOTTOM BROS. POTTERY CO.
ROSEVILLE, OHIO

OPEN CHAMBERS, WHITE

No. 12 (small size)......$ .85 per doz.
No. 9 (large size)......1.00 per doz.

COVERED CHAMBERS

No. 12 (small size)......$1.25 per doz.
No. 9 (large size)......1.50 per doz.
Our Chambers are of Stoneware body with White Bristol Glaze.

CEMETERY VASES

Blue Glaze, $10.00 per gross

—21—

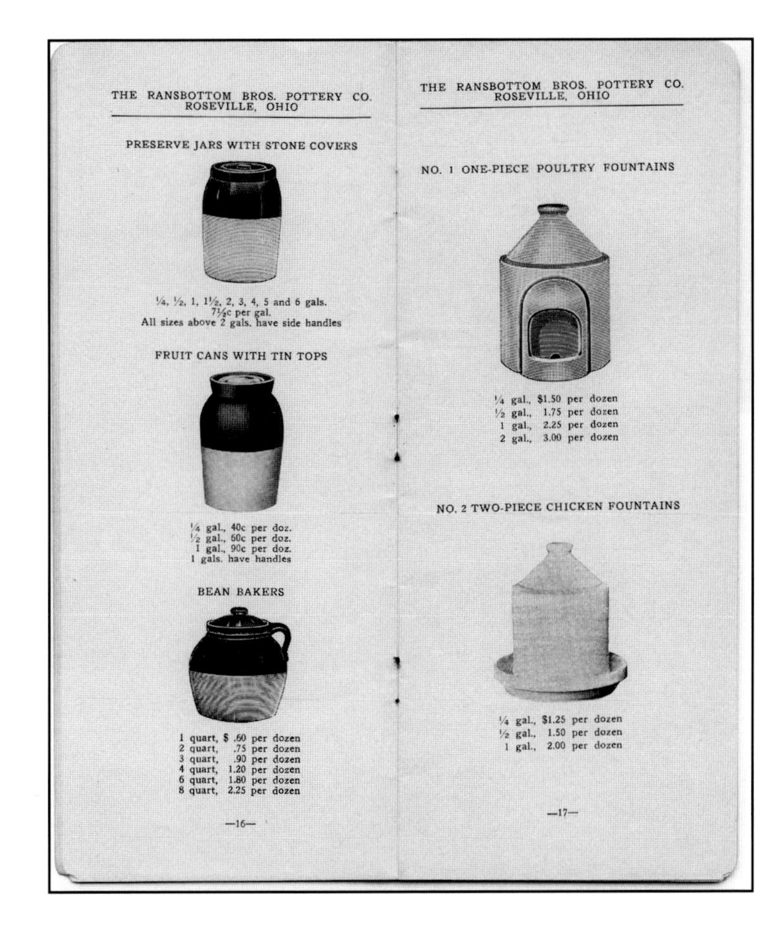

THE RANSBOTTOM BROS. POTTERY CO.
ROSEVILLE, OHIO

PRESERVE JARS WITH STONE COVERS

¼, ½, 1, 1½, 2, 3, 4, 5 and 6 gals.
7½c per gal.
All sizes above 2 gals. have side handles

FRUIT CANS WITH TIN TOPS

¼ gal., 40c per doz.
½ gal., 60c per doz.
1 gal., 90c per doz.
1 gals. have handles

BEAN BAKERS

1 quart, $ .60 per dozen
2 quart, .75 per dozen
3 quart, .90 per dozen
4 quart, 1.20 per dozen
6 quart, 1.80 per dozen
8 quart, 2.25 per dozen

—16—

THE RANSBOTTOM BROS. POTTERY CO.
ROSEVILLE, OHIO

NO. 1 ONE-PIECE POULTRY FOUNTAINS

¼ gal., $1.50 per dozen
½ gal., 1.75 per dozen
1 gal., 2.25 per dozen
2 gal., 3.00 per dozen

NO. 2 TWO-PIECE CHICKEN FOUNTAINS

¼ gal., $1.25 per dozen
½ gal., 1.50 per dozen
1 gal., 2.00 per dozen

—17—

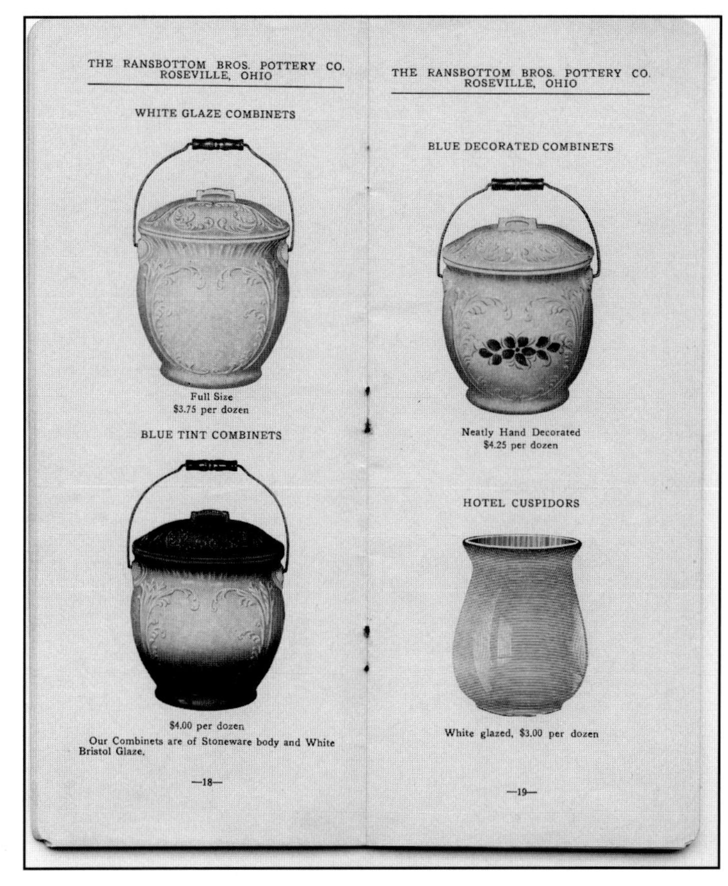

THE RANSBOTTOM BROS. POTTERY CO.
ROSEVILLE, OHIO

WHITE GLAZE COMBINETS

Full Size
$3.75 per dozen

BLUE TINT COMBINETS

$4.00 per dozen
Our Combinets are of Stoneware body and White Bristol Glaze.

—18—

THE RANSBOTTOM BROS. POTTERY CO.
ROSEVILLE, OHIO

BLUE DECORATED COMBINETS

Neatly Hand Decorated
$4.25 per dozen

HOTEL CUSPIDORS

White glazed, $3.00 per dozen

—19—

Catalog 1926

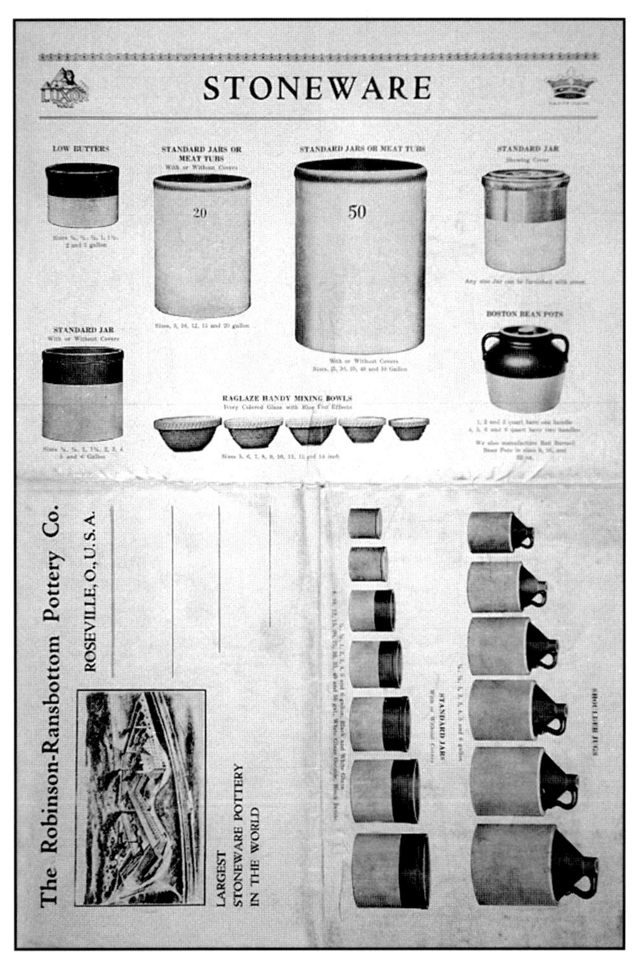

Catalog 1926

The Largest Stoneware Pottery In The World

HOTEL OR FLAT BOTTOM RAGLAZE CUSPIDOR

MOTTLED CUSPIDOR

REGULAR RAGLAZE CUSPIDORS

RAGLAZE BREAD JAR

RAGLAZE REFRIGERATOR PITCHER

GRECIAN BEVERAGE SET

EGYPTIAN BEVERAGE SET

RAGLAZE 5-PIECE COTTAGE TOILET SET

RAGLAZE PLAIN BEVERAGE SET

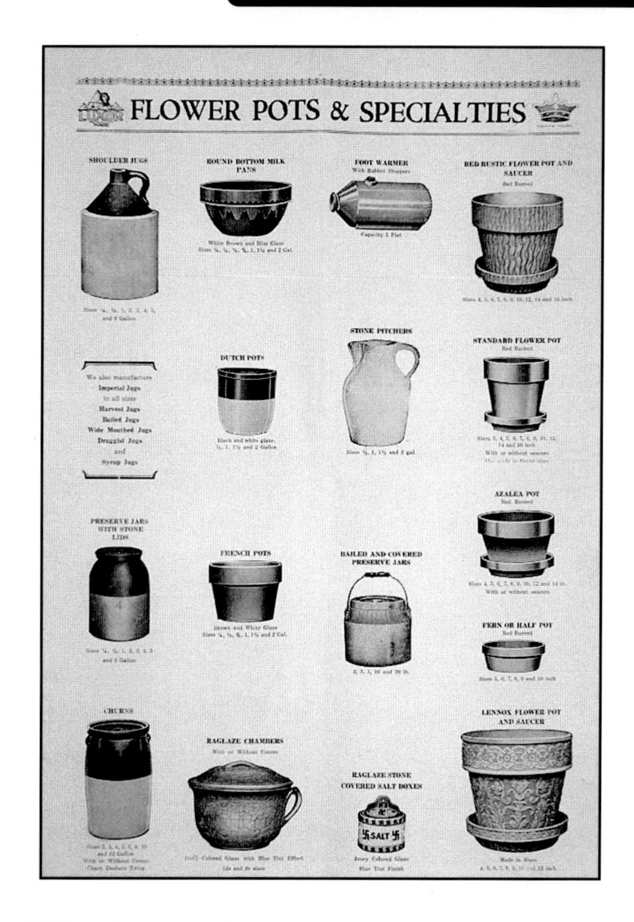

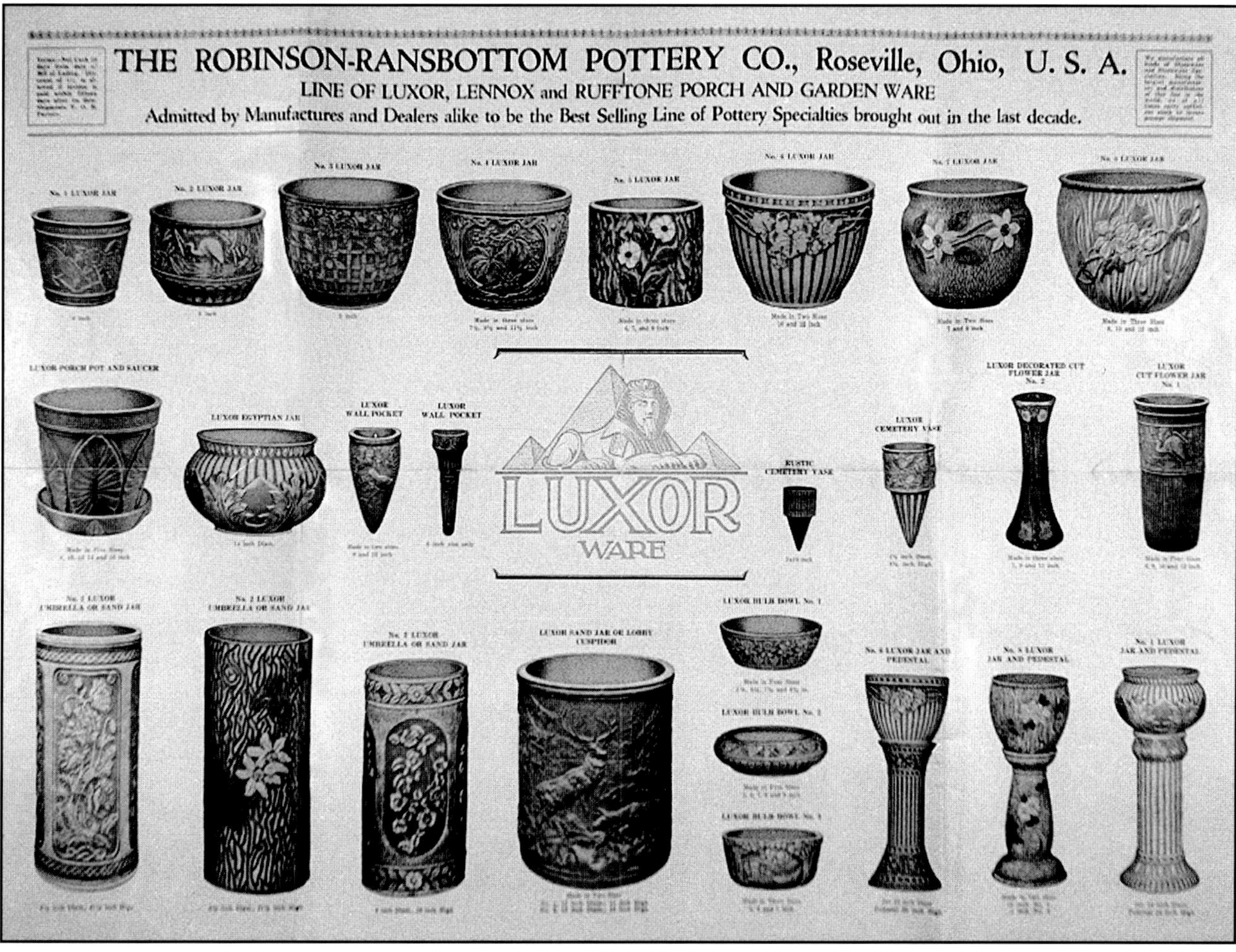

CATALOG 1931

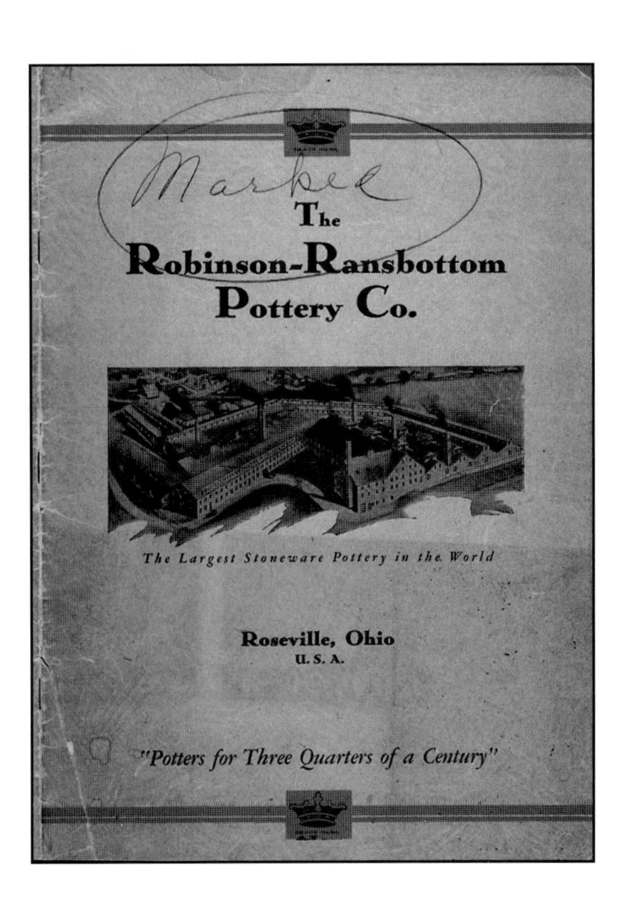

THE ROBINSON-RANSBOTTOM POTTERY COMPANY Roseville, Ohio, U. S. A.

GLAZED PUG DOG
12 in. high
$5.00 each

GLAZED FROG
9½ in. high. Base 10½ x 11½ in.
With and Without Revolving Spray Sprinkler
We also make an Alligator 20 in. long with and without Revolving Spray Sprinkler. Same price as Frog.
Without Sprinkler, each $5.00
With Sprinkler ...... each 8.00

GLAZED RABBIT
7½ in. long .... per dozen $ 9.00
12 in. long .... per dozen 24.00

GLAZED DUCK
9 in. high
$24.00 per dozen

GLAZED EAGLE
11 in. high
$24.00 per dozen

GNOME
Graytone or Green Glaze
11 in. high
$24.00 per dozen

GLAZED BULL DOG
6½ in. high
This sized animal is also made in Airedale, Cat, Dachshund, Pekinese and Frog
$9.00 per dozen

WREN HOUSE
$6.00 per dozen

No. 1 LUXOR CUT FLOWER JAR
6 in. ....per dozen $ 3.60
8 in. ....per dozen 4.80
10 in. ....per dozen 7.20
12 in. ....per dozen 10.80

No. 2 LUXOR CUT FLOWER JAR
7 in. ....per dozen $4.50
9 in. ....per dozen 7.20
11 in. ....per dozen 9.60

No. 8 LUXOR DECORATED CUT FLOWER JAR
12 in. ....each $1.50
15 in. ....each 2.00

No. 9 LUXOR CUT FLOWER JAR
11 in. ......per dozen $8.40

No. 571 CUT FLOWER JAR
Green Glaze on Orchid Glaze or Green Glaze on Blue Glaze
8 in. ....per dozen $ 6.00
10 in. ....per dozen 9.00
12 in. ....per dozen 12.00

No. 1 LUXOR BULB BOWL
5½ in. ....per dozen $1.80
6½ in. ....per dozen 2.40
7½ in. ....per dozen 3.20
8½ in. ....per dozen 4.00

No. 2 LUXOR BULB BOWL
5 in. ....per dozen $2.40
6 in. ....per dozen 3.20
7 in. ....per dozen 4.00
8 in. ....per dozen 5.60
9 in. ....per dozen 7.20

No. 3 LUXOR BULB BOWL
5 in. ....per dozen $2.40
6 in. ....per dozen 3.20
7 in. ....per dozen 4.00

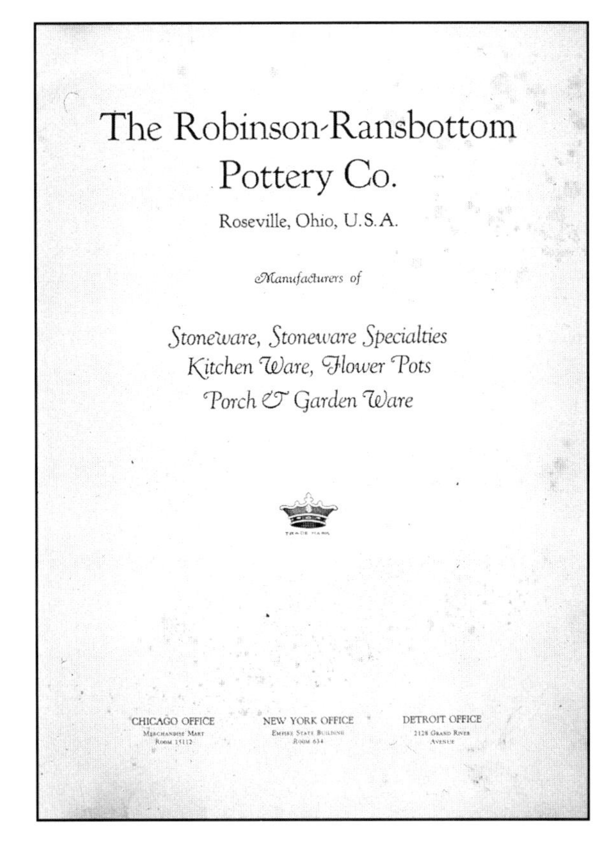

The Robinson-Ransbottom Pottery Co.
Roseville, Ohio, U.S.A.

Manufacturers of

Stoneware, Stoneware Specialties
Kitchen Ware, Flower Pots
Porch & Garden Ware

CHICAGO OFFICE — Merchandise Mart, Room 15112
NEW YORK OFFICE — Empire State Building, Room 614
DETROIT OFFICE — 2128 Grand River Avenue

Foreword

BEING the largest manufacturer and distributor of Stoneware and Stoneware Specialties in the world, we at all times carry sufficient stock to insure prompt shipment. Our immense brick and concrete warehouses have a capacity of six hundred carloads. Our slogan is "Orders shipped within twenty-four hours after they are received." We are located on the Cincinnati Division of the Pennsylvania Railroad.

A WORD OF EXPLANATION

LUXOR
Luxor Ware is made on a Stoneware body, green glazed inside, matt green outside in the low parts, natural Terra Cotta finish on the high parts.

RUFFTONE
Rufftone Ware is made on a Stoneware body, matt green inside, outside finished rough with matt green in the low parts, natural Terra Cotta finish on the high parts.

LENNOX
Lennox Ware is made on a Stoneware body, no glaze on the inside, matt green outside in the low parts, natural Terra Cotta finish on the high parts.

GRAYTONE
Graytone Ware is made on a Stoneware body, the color being similar to concrete.

IRONTONE
Irontone Ware is made on a red body, matt black inside, the outside matt black in the low parts, natural red body on the high parts.

GLAZED WARE
Green on Blue or Green on Orchid.
Green on Blue. The article is glazed Blue with Green Mottling over the Blue. In firing the two colors blend together. The Green on Orchid is the same process, the difference being the article is glazed Orchid with Green Mottling.

DECORATED WARE
The colors are fired in and are guaranteed to stay.

MOTTLED WARE
Three colors are used on our Mottled Ware. In firing they blend together.

SMALL SIZES
Stoneware in smaller sizes than one gallon is figured as follows:
⅛ & ¼ gallon ware counts as ½ gallon
⅜ gallon ware counts as 2/3 gallon
½ gallon ware counts as ¾ gallon
¾ gallon ware counts as one gallon

SPECIAL WORK
For special work the following charges will apply.
Stamping. One cent per gallon, no piece to count less than one gallon. Also cost of stamp.
Faucet holes in Jars or other ware. One cent per gallon, no piece to count less than one gallon.

TERMS
Net cash 30 days from date of invoice, discount of 1% allowed if invoice is paid within 15 days.
All goods are sold f. o. b. factory; no allowance for freight or breakage.
Quotations subject to change without notice. All agreements are contingent upon strikes, accidents and other delays beyond our control.

Catalog 1931

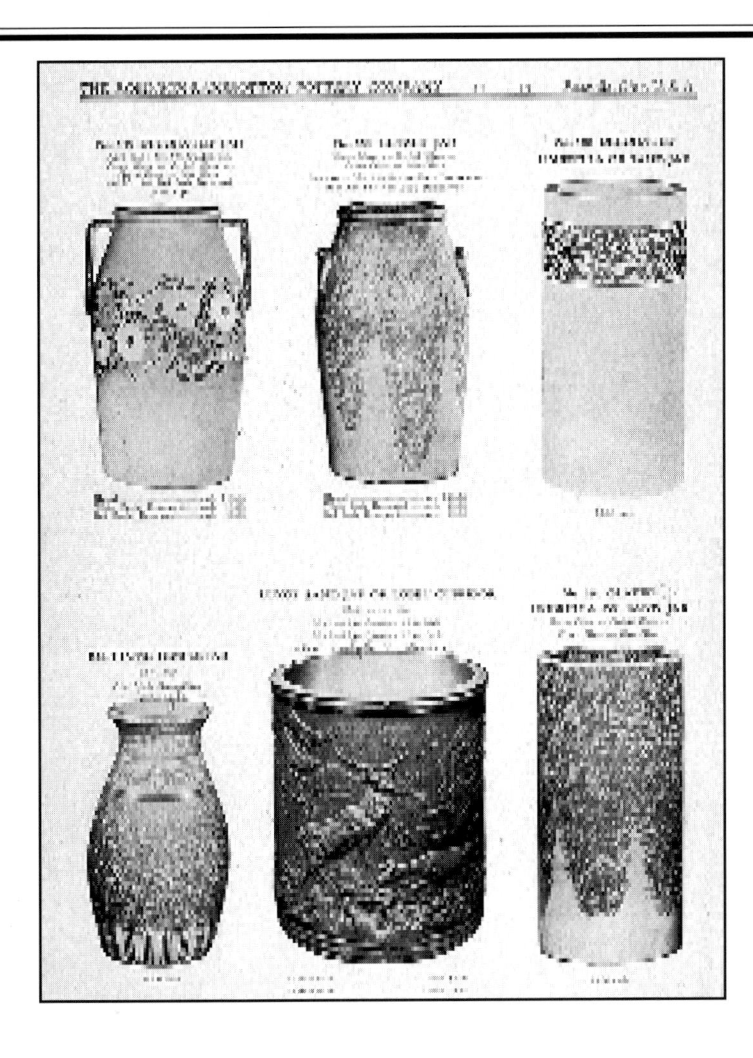

THE ROBINSON-RANSBOTTOM POTTERY COMPANY :: :: Roseville, Ohio, U. S. A.

No. 3 LUXOR JAR

9 in. ....per dozen $9.00

No. 4 LUXOR JAR

7½ in. ......per dozen $ 6.00
9½ in. ......per dozen 9.00
11½ in. ......per dozen 15.60

No. 5 LUXOR JAR
Decorated

6 in. ....per dozen $2.40
7 in. ....per dozen 4.80
9 in. ....per dozen 7.20

No. 6 LUXOR JAR

10 in. ....per dozen $12.00
12 in. ....per dozen 19.20

No. 8 LUXOR JAR
Decorated (per dozen)

8 in. ......$8.00 10 in. ......$14.40 12 in. $24.00

No. 2 LUXOR JAR

8 in. ......per dozen $6.00

No. 9 LUXOR JAR

8 in. ....per dozen $6.00

RUFFTONE EGYPTIAN JAR

14 in. ....each $4.00

LUXOR EGYPTIAN JAR

14 in. ....each $4.00

No. 02 DECORATED GLAZE JAR

8 in. ......per dozen $ 9.00
9 in. ......per dozen 12.00
10 in. ......per dozen 15.60

No. 01 GREEN GLAZE JAR

9 in. ......per dozen $ 9.00
10 in. ......per dozen 12.00
11 in. ......per dozen 15.60

GREEN GLAZED PORCH JAR

8 in. ....per dozen $6.70 10 in. ....per dozen $12.00
12 in., each $1.50 14 in., each $3.20 16 in., each $4.80

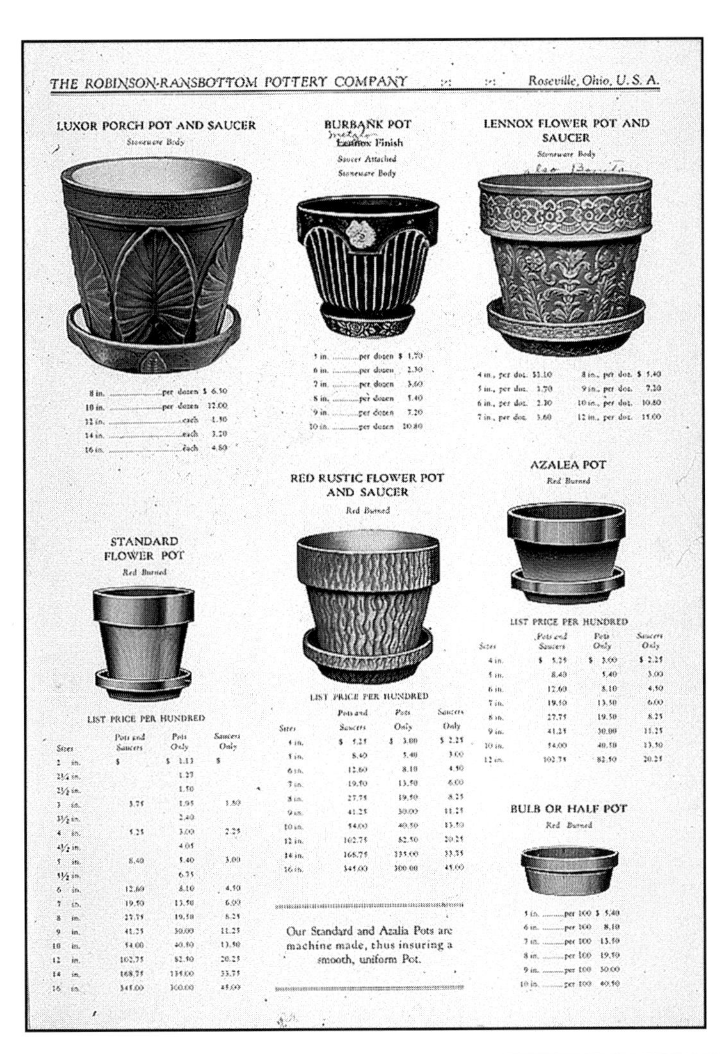

THE ROBINSON-RANSBOTTOM POTTERY COMPANY :: :: Roseville, Ohio, U. S. A.

LUXOR PORCH POT AND SAUCER
Stoneware Body

8 in. ....per dozen $ 6.50
10 in. ....per dozen 12.00
12 in. ....each 1.30
14 in. ....each 3.20
16 in. ....each 4.80

BURBANK POT
Lennox Finish
Saucer Attached
Stoneware Body

5 in. ....per dozen $ 1.70
6 in. ....per dozen 2.30
7 in. ....per dozen 3.60
8 in. ....per dozen 5.40
9 in. ....per dozen 7.20
10 in. ....per dozen 10.80

LENNOX FLOWER POT AND SAUCER
Stoneware Body

4 in., per doz. $1.10 8 in., per doz. $ 5.40
5 in., per doz. 1.70 9 in., per doz. 7.20
6 in., per doz. 2.30 10 in., per doz. 10.80
7 in., per doz. 3.60 12 in., per doz. 15.00

STANDARD FLOWER POT
Red Burned

LIST PRICE PER HUNDRED

Sizes	Pots and Saucers	Pots Only	Saucers Only
2 in.	$	$ 1.13	$
2¼ in.		1.27	
2½ in.		1.50	
3 in.	3.75	1.95	1.80
3½ in.		2.40	
4 in.	5.25	3.00	2.25
4½ in.		4.05	
5 in.	8.40	5.40	3.00
5½ in.		6.75	
6 in.	12.60	8.10	4.50
7 in.	19.50	13.50	6.00
8 in.	27.75	19.50	8.25
9 in.	41.25	30.00	11.25
10 in.	54.00	40.50	13.50
12 in.	102.75	82.50	20.25
14 in.	168.75	135.00	33.75
16 in.	345.00	300.00	45.00

RED RUSTIC FLOWER POT AND SAUCER
Red Burned

LIST PRICE PER HUNDRED

Sizes	Pots and Saucers	Pots Only	Saucers Only
4 in.	$ 5.25	$ 3.00	$ 2.25
5 in.	8.40	5.40	3.00
6 in.	12.60	8.10	4.50
7 in.	19.50	13.50	6.00
8 in.	27.75	19.50	8.25
9 in.	41.25	30.00	11.25
10 in.	54.00	40.50	13.50
12 in.	102.75	82.50	20.25
14 in.	168.75	135.00	33.75
16 in.	345.00	300.00	45.00

Our Standard and Azalia Pots are machine made, thus insuring a smooth, uniform Pot.

AZALEA POT
Red Burned

LIST PRICE PER HUNDRED

Sizes	Pots and Saucers	Pots Only	Saucers Only
4 in.	$ 5.25	$ 3.00	$ 2.25
5 in.	8.40	5.40	3.00
6 in.	12.60	8.10	4.50
7 in.	19.50	13.50	6.00
8 in.	27.75	19.50	8.25
9 in.	41.25	30.00	11.25
10 in.	54.00	40.50	13.50
12 in.	102.75	82.50	20.25

BULB OR HALF POT
Red Burned

5 in. ....per 100 $ 5.40
6 in. ....per 100 8.10
7 in. ....per 100 13.50
8 in. ....per 100 19.50
9 in. ....per 100 30.00
10 in. ....per 100 40.50

THE ROBINSON-RANSBOTTOM POTTERY COMPANY :: :: Roseville, Ohio, U. S. A.

No. 2 LUXOR UMBRELLA JAR
9½ in. diameter, 21½ in. high

$5.00 each

No. 1 LUXOR UMBRELLA JAR
9½ in. diameter, 21½ in. high

$5.00 each

No. 3 LUXOR UMBRELLA JAR
9 in. diameter, 18 in. high

$2.00 each

No. 6 SAND JAR
Green Glaze on Orchid Glaze or Green Glaze on Blue Glaze
10½ in. diameter, 14 in. high

$4.00 each

No. 3 SAND JAR
Green Glazed
12 in. diameter, 20 in. high

$4.00 each

No. 591 GLAZED SAND JAR
Green Glaze on Orchid Glaze or Green Glaze on Blue Glaze
Also made No. 590 Decorated
10 in. diameter, 14 in. high

Glazed ....each $3.00
Decorated ....each 4.00

Catalog 1931

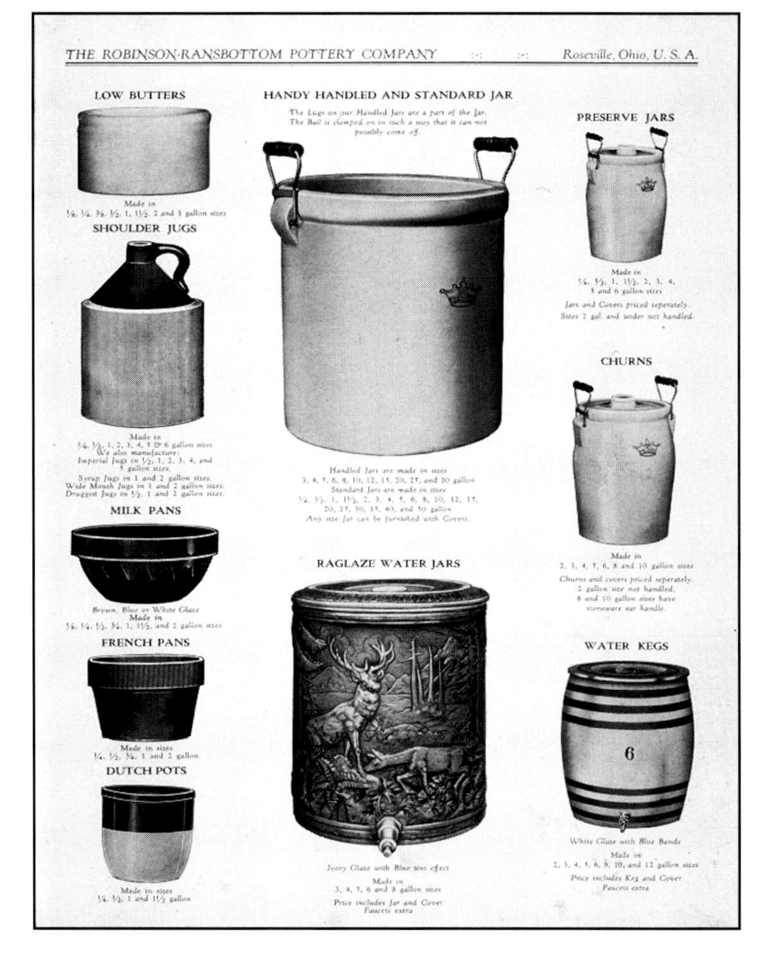

THE ROBINSON-RANSBOTTOM POTTERY COMPANY
Roseville, Ohio, U. S. A.
WHITE BAND SHOULDER MIXING BOWLS
MOTTLED SHOULDER MIXING BOWLS
HAND DECORATED MIXING BOWLS
MOTTLED COVERED REFRIGERATOR SET
HAND DECORATED COOKIE JAR
MOTTLED COOKIE JAR
SPECIAL HAND DECORATED COOKIE JAR
SPECIAL DECORATED COOKIE JAR WITH EARS
HAND DECORATED COVERED UTILITY JAR
HAND DECORATED TEA POT
MOTTLED TEA POT
GLAZE TEA POT

THE ROBINSON-RANSBOTTOM POTTERY COMPANY
Roseville, Ohio, U. S. A.
PEDESTAL with GAZING GLOBE
Luxor or Rufftone
PEDESTAL WITH SUN DIAL
Luxor or Rufftone
DECORATED ROMAN JAR
LENNOX PORCH JAR
LENNOX HANGING BASKET
LENNOX HANGING BASKET SAUCER ATTACHED
GRECIAN JAR
Rufftone, Irontone or Green Glaze
STRAWBERRY JAR
IVY HANGING BASKET
VENETIAN JAR
Rufftone or Irontone

THE ROBINSON-RANSBOTTOM POTTERY COMPANY
Roseville, Ohio, U. S. A.
BREAD JAR
BREAD
REFRIGERATOR JAR
COVERED BUTTER
MILK FEEDER
POULTRY FOUNTAIN
RABBIT FEEDER
RABBIT WATER JAR
REGULAR CUSPIDOR
HOTEL CUSPIDOR
REGULAR BLUE MOTTLED CUSPIDOR
HOTEL MOTTLED CUSPIDOR
FOOT WARMER
MINIATURE JUG

THE ROBINSON-RANSBOTTOM POTTERY COMPANY
Roseville, Ohio, U. S. A.
LUXOR JUMBO BIRD BATH, PEDESTAL AND BASE
BOLIVAR BIRD BATH PEDESTAL AND BASE
No. 3 BIRD BATH AND PEDESTAL
Luxor, Graytone or Green Glazed
No. 1 BIRD BATH AND PEDESTAL
Rufftone or Luxor
No. 4 GRAYTONE BIRD BATH AND PEDESTAL
No. 2 BIRD BATH AND PEDESTAL

1926 Catalog, #1

1931 Catalog, #3

1931 Catalog, #4

1937 Catalog, #7

1926 Catalog, #2

1964 Catalog, #35

1937 Catalog, #8

1938 Catalog, #9

1963 Catalog, #33

1951 Catalog, #18

1941 Catalog, #10

1941 Catalog, #14

1926 Catalog, Luxor Jumbo

1956 Catalog, #24

1958 Catalog, #25

1954 Catalog, #20 Feeder Ring

GRACE AND BEAUTY FOR THE LAWN AND GARDEN

Catalog Details Bird Baths

These dates are the earliest found in catalogs.

1941 Catalog

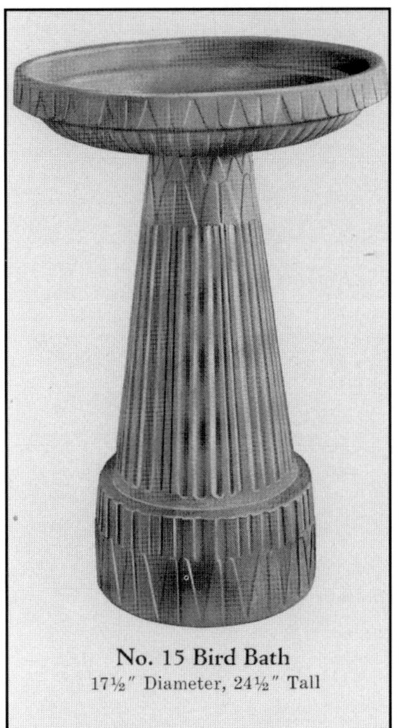

1948 Catalog, #15

No. 12 Bird B
18" diameter, 24

1941 Catalog, #12

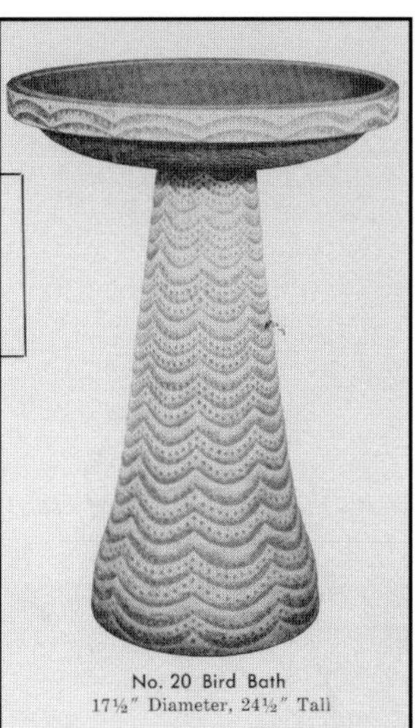

1954 Catalog, #20

1963 Catalog

BOLIVAR BIRD BATH
PEDESTAL AND BASE
Luxor or Graytone
(Luxor shown)
19½ in. diameter, 35 in. high. 3 Pieces

1926 Catalog, Bolivar

Main officers and part of office force: E. M. Ransbottom, M.C. Ransbottom, D. R. Cooper, bookkeeper, Arvilla Scott, clerk and J. Walter Ransbottom, nephew.

Storage clay yard at factory.

Manufacturing large jars on Weaks Machine.

Drying room and glazing department.

Loading ware in cars for shipment

Train load of ware going to market

Workers at rest

Jiggering in the manufacturing department.

Ransbottom Photo Gallery

The Ransbottom and Watt Family Reunion

A Ransbottom family portrait.

Ransbottom salesman on the road.

The family out together.

A Ransbottom family picnic.

A few employees.

Clay washing department.

Jug manufacturing department.

Clay filler presses.

INDEX

A
Advertising, Crock 25, 27
Advertising, Novelties 9
Advertising Jugs 24
Aladdin Jar 108
Alladin Oil Jar 31
Aladdin's Lamp Sand Jar 47
Aladdin's Lamp Vase 100
Ale Mug 65
Anchor Vase 100
Animal Feeders 10-11
Anniversary Pieces 13
Apple Bean Pot 56
Apple Coffee Pot 56
Apple Floor Vase 115
Apple Lamp 82
Apple Vase 115
Art Deco Vase 107
Ash Tray 12, 13, 81
Astroglo 47, 11

B
Baker 53, 73
Bank 18, 76
Barnacle Bill 85
Barrel Churn 84
Barrel Pitcher 57
Barrel Salt and Pepper 74
Basket Planter 93
Bay Area Pottery Show 15
Bean Pot 24, 73, 74, 75
Beau and Belle Planter 94
Beverage Set 57
Bird Bath 15, 30, 31, 35, 136, 137
Bird Bath Insert 32, 33, 34
Blue Band Kitchen Ware 74
Bowl . 48, 49, 50, 51, 53, 55, 67, 68, ... 81, 85
Bread Plate 74
Bread Jar 26, 27
Bread Pan 73
Bronzetone 36
Brown Drip 81
Brown Drip Pitcher 61, 62
Bulb Bowl 48
Butter Crock 26, 51

C
Candlesticks 122
Canister 56
Caramel Cookie Jar 22
Caramel Crock 54, 76
Cardette Set 12
Caramel Ramekin 77
Casserole 26, 49
Catalog ..... 13, 14, 26, 31, 35, 40 41, 43, 45, 46, 50, 51, 52, 53, 54, 55 58, 61, 62, 67, 70, 72, 76, 77, 78, 79, 80 82, 85, 86, 87, 88, 89, 90, 91, 93,94 95, 111, 112, 113, 114, 115, 118, 120, ... 123, 126-127, 128, 129
Cemetary Vase 02
Centennial 14
Cereal Bowl 68, 74
Chamber Pot 85
Chicken Feeder 10
Churn 27
Coasters 12
Coffee Jar 23
Coffee Mug 56
Coffee Pot 98
Commemorative Plate 14
Confetti 48, 52
Console Bowl 120
Cookie Jar ..... 16, 17, 18, 19, 20, 21 ..... 22, 23, 24, 69, 74, 77
Covered Bowl 49, 67, 68, 69
Covered Canister 73
Covered Cassarole ..... 53, 55, 73 ..... 74, 75, 77, 81
Cow Jumped Over the Moon..28, 91
Cream Pitcher 55, 65
Crock..24, 26, 27, 39, 44, 67, 76, 79
Crown Pottery 75
Cup 73, 76
Cuspidor 84
Custard Cup 73
Cut Flower Jar 102

D
Deco Vase 100
Decorated Glaze Jar 42
Decorated Jar 116
Decorator Pot 35-36
DeDonatis ... 16, 17, 21, 51, 63, 75 ..... 104, 105, 106, 109, 116
Deep Bowl 49, 68
Deer and Fawn Pitcher 60
Deer Pitcher 59
Desert Dweller 83
Dessert Plate 74, 77
Dinner Plate 74
Dog 28, 29, 93
Dog Dishes 11
Dorothy Archer 100, 107, 116
Double Boiler 73
Draped Vase 123
Drip 82, 98
Duck 28

E
Eagle 28
Early American Bean Pot 76
Elephant 28
Elmer 85
Ewer 60
Ewer and Basin 65, 69

F
Fan Deco Vase 99
Fan Vase 92
Flared Bowl 89
Flared Crock 73, 74
Floor Jar 116
Floor Pitcher Vase 117
Floor Vase ..... 108, 111, 113, 114 ..... 116,117, 119
Flower Dish / Pot ..... 42, 46, 81, 83, ... 86, 87, 88, 89,121, 122
Foot Warmer 84
Footed Bowl / Planter30, 35, 87, 89
Footed Urn 99
Fountain Top 34
Frog Lawn Sprinkler 33

G
Gala Line 53
Garden Frog 33
Garden Ornament 32, 33, 34
Garden Stump 30
Girl with Watering Can 50
Grass Growing Head 85
Grecian 35, 6, 57, 60

H
Hand Decorated Pieces 63
Hand Painted Jar 108, 116
Hand Painted Tea Pot 71
Hand Painted Vase 104, 105
Handle Planter 93
Hanging Strawberry Pot 46, 47
Hanging Birdbath 14
Hanging Ivy Jar 47
High Jar 69
Hobnail Beater Jar 99
Hobnail Bowl Set 50
Hobnail Cookie Jar 21
Hobnail Pitcher 57, 64
Hootie Owl 32
Hot Caramel Crock 54
House Planter 93

I
Ice holder 74
Ice-Lip Pitcher 53, 60, 61
Iced Tea or Coffee Jar 26
Icicle Bowl 51
Imperial Tub 35
Iris Vase 100
Ivy Jar 47

J
Jardiniere ..... 35, 37, 39, 41, 42 ..... 102, 110, 117, 120, 121
Jardiniere and Pedestal 37, 38, 39, 40, 41
Jocko 85
Jug 14, 25, 76
Juice Jug 61

INDEX

K
Kettle Planter 99
Kitchen Crock 53, 69
Kitchenette Pantry Ware 55

L
Lamp Base 82, 121
Leaf Vase 99
Lennox Window Box 87
Lily Pad 12, 98
Lion 28
Lion Planter 92
Lizard on a Log 83
Love Bird Planter 93
Love Bird Vase 98
Low Bowl 48
Low Crock 79
Low Jar 73
Lucia Jar 107, 112
Luxor 15, 30, 35, 40, 42, 44
.... 46, 47, 48, 98, 102

M
Madonna 34, 92
Mae West Vase 108
Marble Ware 49
Match Holder 84
Meat Tub 27
Medallion Pot 35
Metglo Bowl 48, 49, 98
Milk Pan 51
Milk Pitcher 65
Miniature Jugs 24
Mixing Bowl 50
Modern Apple 20, 56, 82, 115
Morning Glory 16, 75
Mottled Bowl 51
Mottled Glaze 57
Mug 53, 56, 57, 58, 61, 63, 65
.... 69, 77

N
Novelty Planters 90, 91, 92, 93, 94
Nubian Jar 112, 114
Nutone 15

O
Oil Jar 31, 44, 108, 110, 111
.... 112, 113, 115, 116, 123
Old Colony 20, 120, 121
Oscar Cookie Jar 19
Oval Baker 53
Oval Bowl 81
Owl on a Log 83

P
Pace 16, 21, 42, 63, 66, 67, 107
.... 116
Palm Pot 39
Paper Weight 9, 15, 84
Pasta Bowl 66, 73
Personalized Vase 100
Pet Feeders 10, 11
Pie Plate 49, 53, 73, 77
Pillar Vase 65
Pitcher 55, 56, 57, 58, 59, 60
.... 61, 62, 63, 64, 68, 73, 75
.... 77, 106, 123
Pitcher Vase 57, 111, 121
Pizza Plate 73
Plaid Bowl 50
Planter 35, 36, 86, 87, 89, 91
.... 93, 101
Planter Vase 94
Plate 67, 73
Platter 53, 57
Plymouth Colony 20, 65
Porch Jots / Jars 35, 36
Pot 77, 84, 85, 95, 101
Pot Shop 78
Poultry Fountain 10

R
Rabbit 34
Rabbit Planter 91
Ramekin 77
Ransbottom Brothers Pitchers 62
Rectangular Dish 81
Rectangular Vase 106
Red Clay 36, 62, 104, 106, 116
Refrigerator Pitcher 59
Ribbed Planter 88
Ribbon (Bow) Vase 110, 111
Rio Cookie Jar 21
Rio 21, 95, 107
Robinson Clay Products 25
Roman Jar 36
Rope-handled Jar 114
Rose on Trellis 58, 85
Rosella Stein 76
Roseville Anniversary Bowl 49
Ruffled-top Vase 103
Rufftone 31, 36, 40
Rustic J 16, 66, 67, 68, 111

S
Salad Bowl 69
Salad Plate 68
Salt and Pepper 65, 68, 74
Sample Vases 85
Sand glazed Vase 109
Sand Jar 44, 45
Saucer 68
Sayonara Maiden 34
Shell Bowl 43
Shoulder Bowl 48, 50
Shoulder Jug 24
Shy Anne Planter 90
Sleeping Peon 95
Snack Dish 75
Snack Set 77
Snowman 77
Souffle Dish 53
Spaniel Feeder 10
Spatter 49, 50, 64, 86
Spirit Jug 14, 65
Sponge Ware 48, 49, 57, 64
Square Plate 68
Squirrel and Acorn Planter 90
St. Francis 34
Stackable Tea Pot 71
Stained Glass Look 61
Steins 75
Stoneware 10, 60, 65
Strawberry Jar 46, 47
Suburban 69
Suede Vase 103
Sugar Bowl 55, 56, 65
Sundial 34

T
Tantone 35, 89
Tea Pot 71
Terra 72, 88
The Pottery Maker 109
Thistle Refrigerator Pitchers 59
Tionesta Art Ware 103, 122
Tumbler 65
Turtle 32
Tweed 37, 39, 40
Two-handled Vase 103, 105

U
Umbrella Stand / Jar 44, 47, 111
.... 116
Utility Jar 75

V
Vase 57, 63, 81, 95, 98, 99
.... 100, 101, 102,103, 104, 105, 106
... 107, 108, 110, 112, 113, 114, 116
.... 117, 119, 120, 121, 122
Victoria 21, 123
Victorian Vase 108
Villa Pot 35

W
Wall Pocket 58, 91, 102, 103, 107
Water Jar 25, 26, 74
Wheat 22, 48, 73
Wide Vase 99
Williamsburg 74
Window Box 87
Wine Jug Vase 65
Woven Bowl 51
Wren House 31

Z
Zephyrus 58

Bibliography

Huxford, Sharon and Bob "The Collectors Encyclopedia of Weller Pottery" , Paducah, Ky: Collector Books, 1979, 375 pages.

Lehner, Lois, "U.S. Marks On Pottery, Porcelain & Clay", Paducah, Ky: Collector Books, 1988, 634 pages.

Lewis, Thomas W., "Zanesville and Muskingum County, Ohio" (Volume III), Zanesville, Ohio, The S.J. Clarke Publishing Company, 1927.

McDonald, Ann Gilbert "All About Weller ", Marietta, Ohio: Antique Publications, 1989, 220 pages.

Schneider, Norris F. "Y-Bridge City ", Zanesville, Ohio", The World Publishing Co., 1950

OTHER REFERENCES

The Robinson Ransbottom Pottery Company; office records, photos, legal papers and catalogs.

Archer, Rod., Information concerning Dorothy Archer.

Brown, Bill., Information concerning family history and pictures.

DeDonatis, Leo., Information concerning Francesco DeDonatis.

Pace, Dr. Loren. L., Information concerning Willard Pace.

______________. "Ransbottom Brothers Pottery is Growing", Roseville Review, March 26, 1903.

______________. "Robinson Clay Products Company Purchases Part of the Ransbottom Brothers Pottery Co", The Times Recorder, June 28, 1919.

Contributors of Pottery Pieces and Historical Information

Deborah and Keith Allion
Betty and Eugene Archer
Judy Archer
Rod Archer
Judy Bailey
Jean Bonifield
Cindy Carpenter
Leo DeDonatis
Gerald Donaldson
Norm and Barbara Hass
John Henderson
Roy Higgins
Helen Kildow
Jeff Koehler
Nancy McLean
James Murphy
Loren Pace
Donna Ransbottom
Georgiana Ransbottom
John Schwab
Al Sowers
Galen and Connie Thompson
Larry Waltz
Bryce and Cheryl Watt
Bill Brown,
Special thanks to Bill for important historical information

Production
Steve Sanford
Martha Sanford
Vivian Sanford
Maryann Terhune
Diane Senif

History

by

James L. Muphy

One of Roseville, Ohio's least known potteries was the National Pottery Co., predominantly a manufacturer of yellow ware, Rockingham, and unglazed earthenware cooking ware; but this company also sold art ware to some extent and may actually have produced art pottery—sources vary. Certainly it claimed to manufacture art pottery-- the question is whether any of this was actually manufactured by National or whether it was made by Robinson Ransbottom and simply sold with the National stamp applied to it. Available facts are few and it is difficult to relate them together. Whatever the case, it is not true, as some have claimed, that National was simply an outlet for Robinson-Ransbottom. National was an active pottery in Roseville, operating two plants for about twenty years before being virtually destroyed by a disastrous fire.

The National Pottery is shown on the November, 1918, Sanborn Insurance Map of Roseville, on Lots 64 and 65, along the east side of Elkton Place (now called Potters Alley), halfway between First and Second St., and just west of the South Fork of Jonathan Creek, the site later occupied by the Ungemach and Friendship potteries. It was a one-kiln operation, with no watchman and no fire apparatus. This is the earliest available reference to this particular pottery, although as early as 1866 George Lenhart had operated a stoneware pottery on Lot 65.

About a block to the north, on the same side of the street, in 1918, stood the C. W. Lowry Pottery and the Pace Brothers Pottery (closed), on Lots 13 and 14, respectively, both one-kiln operations specializing in cooking ware. The National Pottery is first listed in the Thomas Register for 1922, and seems to have taken the place of the pottery of Pace Brothers & Son, but deed records show a complicated history: George W. Pace (father of Luther C and Leroy Pace) sold parts of Lots 14, 15, and 16 to Luther C. Pace, Jr., et al., in 1904, and this group in turn sold the land to the Continental Pottery Co. October 29, 1919. Earl A. Montgomery was president of the short-lived Continental Pottery, and W. B. Baughman was secretary. The Continental Pottery Co., of which I have found no other record, sold the property to James L. Weaver August 4, 1922 (Muskingum Co. Deeds 196: 3). James L. Weaver, Jr., and wife Josie then sold Lots 14 and 15 to the National Pottery on December 12, 11, 1925, the pottery being owned by Weaver (60%) and J. Burgess Lenhart (40%). In the 1920 census, Burgess Lenhart is listed as the 18 year old nephew of James Weaver, Jr., and book keeper at a pottery (undoubtedly the National Pottery). James Weaver, Jr., aged 31, is listed as salesman, pottery; James, Sr., as foreman, pottery.

So it would seem that by 1925 National was operating two plants in Roseville. By January, 1930, the southern plant had been considerably expanded, with a warehouse extending north to Sioux Place and a large drying room east of the kiln room. The southern factory was mostly engaged in the manufacture of flower pots, while the northern factory presumably made the cooking ware.

In 1931 the company was operating these two plants with two periodic kilns, producing yellow ware and flower pots, with a capacity of 6,000 pieces daily. James L. Weaver was president, and J. Burgess Lenhart was general manager. The pottery was still listed in the 1938 Ceramic Trade Directory, producing art ware and flower pots, but with no mention of cooking ware. Had the northern factory been given over entirely to the production of art ware? Weaver is not mentioned in the 1938 directory, but Lenhart is still listed as general manager. By this time, however, the pottery had been virtually destroyed by a major fire, apparently bringing an end to production at both plants. (Exact date of this fire has yet to be determined but was probably in late 1937; the 1938 Ceramic Trade Directory probably does not reflect this fact, since it still refers to two plants.)

By 1944, Burgess Lenhart had gained control of the Stoin-Lee Pottery of Byesville, Ohio, and moved it to Marietta, Ohio, where it was known as the American Pottery Co. Lenhart also worked as the sales manager for the American Bisque Co., across the Ohio River in Williamstown, West Virginia. He retired from American Bisque in 1961 and died in 1983.

Back in Roseville, the July, 1946, Sanborn fire insurance map shows the southern pottery operated by the Ungemach Pottery, manufacturers of clay novelties, with the Cookson Pottery just to the north, across Sioux Place. Further north, the Lowry and the second National factory are both gone, the sites occupied respectively by a vacant lot and a vacant church. According to Derwich and Latos (1984), Fred Ungemach, a Robinson-Ransbottom employee, began his own pottery in the twelve by twelve foot office remaining after the National fire.

Products and Marks

The most common and the most familiar product of the National Pottery remains its cooking ware marked by the impressed head of an Indian chief wearing a full headdress, covering the entire base of the piece, and the incised word "NATIONAL." The elaborate mark captures the fancy of many collectors, and these pieces have been selling at prices quite out of proportion to the rarity of the pottery. Actually more scarce are cooking ware pieces with the incised "NATIONAL SANITARY COOKING WARE" mark.

National's Indian chief mark aside, it's Rockingham and brown banded yellow ware certainly has more visual appeal than its drab cooking ware but has escaped mention in most of the literature on Rockingham and yellow ware, the single exception being John Gallo (1985), who lists it as an unidentified mark, "possibly Ohio." "NATIONAL" is impressed in large block letters in a semi-circle just inside the basal ring. Except for this mark, National's Rockingham could be easily confused with Brush-McCoy's "Nurock," and the three-banded yellow ware looks much like Weller's yellow ware. The National bowls may be distinguishable from Weller by having two fine raised lines immediately below the rim, but Brush-McCoy bowls also seem to have this feature. Brush-McCoy's yellow ware kitchenware, however, was decorated with white lines instead of brown lines.

As for the artware, many people believe that National Pottery simply purchased their artware from Robinson-Ransbottom and sold it as their own. This may be the case, though it leaves the question of what National was making in its northern plant at the time of the fire in 1937? If cooking ware, why was it not mentioned in the 1938 Ceramic Directory? One possibility is that the fire had completely destroyed the plant and National was trying to stay in business by selling Robinson-Ransbottom's art ware as its own.

Only three available pieces of artware are marked National, and these all have the shield-shaped National black ink stamp on the bottom, undoubtedly applied after firing was finished. These are the olive black, green-mottled jug or pitcher with wire-cut bottom, a bright green frog ash receiver, and a light aqua glazed vase at the Ceramic Center in Crooksville. The mottled glaze of the jug approximates the drip-decorated Blue over Orchid and Green over Orchid glazes of the later Robinson Ransbottom Deodonatis pieces and appears to be identical in shape to a Robinson-Ransbottom jug with floral decoration. And there is a very similarly shaped (though not identical) jug with a granular textured red glaze that closely resembles Robinson-Ransbottom's Suede glaze.

Examining a suite of the "black-" or "ripe olive-glazed" artware with drip glaze initially attributed to National shows gradations from the black or dark gray to a lavender shade, suggesting that there may be complete gradation with the Robinson-Ransbottom orchid glazes, whether the variations are due to accident or deliberate alterations in glaze composition or firing. There are several other shapes—notably one distinguished by angular handles applied on a concave rim-- found with both Robinson-Ransbottom floral decoration or with the "National" drip over olive-black glaze. Likewise, while the one marked National pitcher has a wire cut base, the frog and several unmarked vases indistinguishable in glaze from the National pitcher have a smooth, recessed base. Except for the occasional National mark, no consistent set of characteristics of form or glaze can be used to distinguish the limited examples of National's artware from that of Robinson-Ransbottom. Unless evidence to the contrary is forthcoming, it seems very likely that most if not all of National's art ware was actually manufactured by Robinson-Ransbottom, much as Robinson-Ransbottom now distributes products of Burley Clay.

References Cited

1931 Ceramic Publishing Co.

1938 Ceramic Trade Directory. Newark, N.J
Derwich, Jenny B., and Mary Latos

1984 Dictionary Guide to United States Pottery & Porcelain (19th and 20th Century). Franklin Michigan: Jenstan Research in United States Pottery and Porcelain

1985 Gallo, John; Nineteenth and Twentieth Century Yellow Ware. Oneonta, N.Y.: Gallo.

1918 Sanborn Fire Insurance Maps.

1946 Roseville, Ohio.

1922 Thomas Publishing Co.

1930 Thomas Register of American Manufacturers. New York, N.Y.